A HISTORY OF SDA CHURCH-STATE RELATIONS IN THE UNITED STATES

by Eric Syme

PACIFIC PRESS PUBLISHING ASSOCIATION
Mountain View, California
Omaha, Nebraska   Calgary, Alberta

iv

A HISTORY OF SDA CHURCH-STATE RELATIONS IN THE UNITED STATES

CONTENTS

v

PREFACE

Contemporary thought on church-state relations increasingly concerns itself with the ongoing impact of Government upon the life and work of the church. Practical and social problems in our highly complex era have introduced the Government into virtually every sector of national life. Welfare-state philosophy, American confrontation with global communism, civil rights controversies, antipoverty programs, increasing crime rates, civil disorder, and spiraling education costs involve the increasing participation of Federal Government into both the local and the state scenes.

These zones of Federal activity frequently overlap into areas of church concern, and, in consequence, Christian denominations which formed their church-state views in a much simpler American past now feel compelled to reexamine those views in the light of this changed situation.

Churches differ in their approach to religious freedom and the best way to retain it. They all seem dismayed by the increase of Government influence and the danger it poses to religious liberty. A generation which has lived through the decade of the 30's with its nightmare of emerging totalitarian governments oppressing many religious, racial, and political minorities must be concerned that the extending powers of Government in the 50's, 60's, and 70's may bring even greater perils to the church in the future.

Churches agree more on the problem than on the solution. Separationists believe that to ensure the continuance of religious liberty it is necessary to keep state and church absolutely separate. Transformationists consider separationism as both impossible and undesirable—impossible because the complexity of present civilized life prevents church and state from operating independently; undesirable because separation of church and state might culminate in a totalitarian secularist government capable of dominating both religious and civil affairs. Transformationists believe also that all churches should unite in order to transform the state. Only the combined influence of all churches can direct the Government into policy and legislation which will protect religious and civil minorities and remedy grave social problems.*

The Seventh-day Adventist Church does not accept this transformationist view. It believes that the danger of a union of churches which might dominate the state and procure religious legislation unfavorable to SDA interests is greater than the danger of a strictly secularist state. Since the Seventh-day Adventist denomination holds religious beliefs distinctively different from other Christian groups, the maintenance of religious freedom is very important to it. Yet the denomination in the United States has frequently come into contact with the Government. In the interplay between the Church's separationist belief and its necessary relations with the Government, the denomination has developed a distinctive perspective on the whole problem of church-state relationships. This study is a history of those church-state relations and the forming of a Seventh-day Adventist church-state viewpoint.

---

*A. F. Carillo de Albornoz argues for the transformationist view in his *The Basis of Religious Liberty* (New York: Associated Press, 1963), where he reviews the background of discussions of the subject within the World Council of Churches. Also Thomas G. Sanders, in *Protestant Concepts of Church and State* (Garden City, N.Y.: Doubleday and Co., 1965), discusses various Protestant church-state attitudes, dealing particularly with separationists and transformationists.

Chapter 1

CHURCH-STATE PROBLEMS
AT THE TIME OF CHURCH ORGANIZATION

When the first session of the General Conference of Seventh-day Adventists met at Battle Creek, Michigan, on May 20-23, 1863, its members created a constitution of nine articles, providing for the continuance of the movement as an organized church. This surprisingly harmonious gathering ended a long controversy among these erstwhile Millerites as to whether such formal organization was either necessary or advisable.[1] This meeting crowned 20 years of loose confederacy, a time when these believers remained together, united by common teachings and common hope. But for a long time they saw no need to be formally organized, and their whole experience as Millerites prejudiced them against such a course.

It is not difficult to understand why these Millerites were suspicious of legal church organization. Many of them had been expelled from formal churches because of their Millerite faith, and all of them expected Christ to return very soon. At first they saw no virtue in forming a legal church organization. But those who survived the great Millerite disappointment of 1844, and who became members of the new group of Sabbath-keeping Adventists, no longer looked for a sudden consummation of their spiritual hopes. They believed they had a great work before them, and sheer logic suggested that they legally organize to expedite this work. Yet, much time elapsed before they did organize. One reason for this delay may be found in their Millerite background.

William Miller, an outstanding revivalist of the middle nineteenth century, believed that Christ would return in 1844. His public lectures aroused both interest and opposition. Most of his religious critics did not object to his time calculations,[2] but opposed his teaching that Christ would return in 1844.[3] This and other differences between Miller and opposing groups proved to be quite basic.[4]

William Miller asserted that moral and spiritual conditions in America and the world indicated that human civilization was rapidly nearing its end. He emphasized that mankind's only hope was to repent and prepare to meet Christ when He appeared. Hope based on the idea of world enlightenment, Miller believed, could only lead to frustration and despair.

Miller's opponents, on the other hand, saw no reason for his pessimism, and refused his interpretation of conditions in America. While admitting that the nation had passed through difficult times, they stressed that the second great awakening at the beginning of the nineteenth century had expanded the membership of established churches and had purified and converted the hitherto godless frontiers. This awakening, they reasoned, had prepared the way for the reformatory movement reaching its climax at the very time Miller was publicly presenting his view that total national depravity called for immediate divine intervention.

Miller's opponents insisted that the great reform movements, imperious, ardent, sometimes eccentric, were reaching into every part of the American nation, changing its whole pattern of life and thought. Surely, they argued, under God's guiding hand this process of awakening and reform would continue until the American people became a tool with which God could convert the world.

The controversial statement in Daniel 8:14, "And then shall the sanctuary be cleansed," Miller interpreted as the cleansing of the earth by fire at Christ's second advent. His religious opponents, on the other hand, interpreted this to mean the purification of the church, preparing it for the great task of world evangelism.

This "Christian America" concept was further enhanced by a postmillennial doctrine. Its advocates saw in the advancing foreign-mission movement the continuing growth of the kingdom of God, culminating in the conversion of the entire world. America, they emphasized, was taking the primary role in this work as was demonstrated by a variety of observable evidence.[5] When America finally succeeded in converting the world, they predicted, this would ensure a thousand years of peace at the conclusion of which, Christ would return to the throne of David to rule over the world forever.[6]

The "Christian America" theme was popular in nineteenth-century America. Conservatives—disturbed by egalitarian and radical demands for greater rights, liberties, and privileges—hoped that the churches of America would serve as bulwarks against a developing social radicalism and skeptical secularism. They perceived deistic tendencies in the prevalent emphasis on church-state separation, and they believed these trends could be halted only if the theocratic tradition could be established in America. The French Revolution and the Napoleonic Wars had bred into the conservative mind the conviction that increasing radical demands were causing social turbulence, political anarchy, and religious skepticism. They believed that only a fusion of patriotism, republicanism, and religion could provide an adequate foundation upon which to build an "American Christian nation."[7]

William Miller and his colleagues took strong exception to this "Christian America," postmillennial concept. In their magazine, *The Midnight Cry,* for January 6, 1843, they emphasized that both the German Protestant Reformers and the English Protestants had disavowed the doctrine of a one-thousand-year "golden age" preceding the Second Advent of Christ and the resurrection of the dead. "These official rebukes to the unwholesome doctrine," they stressed, "from the two leading churches of the Reformation placed this blunder among Protestants where it was placed by the church of the fourth century, nearly out of the pale of orthodoxy."

A Unitarian commentator named Daniel Whitby, in 1703, they suggested, first popularized postmillennial views in American Protestantism. Then in the patriotic climate in which American nationalism was shaped, a multitude of Protestant commentators, preachers, and churches fully embraced the doctrine.[8] But, argued the Millerites, although the concept might suit the national *mood* of the time, it was totally unscriptural.

The Bible teaches, said the Millerites, that Christ was about to end this world's history and that upon its ruins He would finally establish His own supernatural, glorious kingdom. Miller presented these arguments well. The urgency of his theme, the religious climate of the time and place, the effective use of charts and illustrations, enabled him to attract increasing audience attention.

When, after 1839, Joshua V. Himes, pastor of the Boston Chardon Street Chapel, promoted and organized Miller's campaign, the movement achieved even greater scope and possibilities. Himes created opportunities for Miller to preach in the larger cities, and by publishing the *Signs of the Times* as the official Millerite paper, he greatly extended Millerite teaching. Camp meetings, in increasing vogue, enabled the Millerites to augment this new interest even further until it peaked when Miller announced that Christ would return in 1844.[9]

This prediction went unfulfilled.

Miller's supporters were devastated. Expelled in many cases from their previous church communion, the few who still remained faithful refused to organize as a separate denomination, considering their common expectation of the imminent return of Jesus Christ as the only necessary basis for unity. Now, isolated, ridiculed, and divided, they became confused and dispirited.

The uncertainty that characterized most of the Millerites at this time did not extend to them all, for a group of Millerites at Port Gibson, New York, discovered what for them proved to be a satisfactory explanation for the 1844 disappointment. The leader of this group, Hiram Edson, a local farmer, attributed Miller's mistake to faulty Bible exegesis.

Miller had assumed that the *earth* was the "sanctuary" referred to in Daniel, and therefore to him the phrase, "then shall the sanctuary be cleansed" had referred to the cleansing of the *earth* by fire at Christ's second advent. But, pointed out Edson, in both the Old and the New Testaments the sanctuary was the place where the priest ministered for the people. Since Christ the High Priest ministered for His church in the heavenly sanctuary, the *cleansing* of the sanctuary must therefore take place in *heaven,* rather than on earth. Edson concluded that the "cleansing of the sanctuary" indicated that a special ministry of Christ had begun in the heavenly sanctuary.

Thus he explained the disappointment. The earth was not at that time being cleansed. The *sanctuary in heaven* was being cleansed. At the same time he provided a logical basis upon which the Millerite movement could be rebuilt—the time of the end had begun (in 1844), and Christ was soon to come.

Edson first published this new explanation in *The Day Dawn,* a small sheet issued at irregular intervals from Canandaigua, New York. In this paper, and in *The Day Star,* Edson and his two supporters, Dr. Francis B. Hahn and Owen R. L. Crosier, tried to convince the scattered Millerites of the validity of the new interpretation. For this purpose they invited Millerites to a study conference at Edson's home in Port Gibson.

Among the group attending was Joseph Bates, a prominent Millerite leader. Bates accepted the Edson interpretation and added to it his own newly developed view that the seventh day was the Sabbath.

This seventh-day Sabbath doctrine was first publicized among the Millerites by Rachel Oaks Preston, a Seventh Day Baptist. But Bates was the first to combine it with Edson's new sanctuary concept and to introduce both to a small group of Millerites, and the combined doctrines assumed great significance.[10]

This synthesis of the sanctuary and the Sabbath teaching laid the foundation for the distinctive Seventh-day Adventist doctrinal position. From this time the two ideas associated themselves in the Adventist mind as twin aspects of a great system of truth. Sunday holiness was now seen as having no greater authority than human tradition.[11] John Nevins Andrews, a pioneer Sabbatarian Adventist, sought to demonstrate this fact in his *History of the Sabbath and the First Day of the Week,* a prodigious work first published in 1861.

The synthesis of the sanctuary and the Sabbath doctrines resulted in a series of Bible Conferences held throughout New York, Connecticut, Maine, and Massachusetts. The early Adventist pioneers wrestled with difficult theological problems and, because of their interpretive disagreements, often made little progress. On these occasions, one member of the group, a young woman named Ellen Gould Harmon, displayed a remarkable ability to guide them through their difficulties.

Her claim to possess the prophetic gift was believed by these men. In view of her age and inexperience they could see no other way to explain her strange and awesome capacity. She married James White, a successful Millerite evangelist, on August 30, 1846, and from this time, she and her husband became an increasingly powerful influence in the developing Adventist movement.

When essential agreement was reached upon doctrine, James White began to edit and publish the new movement's first magazine, *The Present Truth*. The new theological structure rested upon basic Millerite foundations, and it seemed reasonable to White to bring the new concept to the remaining Millerites before he approached the general public.

But the magazine did not convince the vast bulk of the Millerites, and only with the strongest support and counsel from his young wife Ellen could he continue.[12] Finally, however, James decided to broaden his appeal to the general public. He discontinued *The Present Truth* in favor of *The Second Advent Review and Sabbath Herald*.

From its inception this magazine played an enormously important part in the growth of what was to become the Seventh-day Adventist Church. A cluster of able writers gathered about editor White; and, as his editorial staff, these men soon became the unofficial leaders of the seventh-day-Sabbath-keeping Adventists.

This development proved valuable to the group, since at this time there was no recognized church administration and most members were decidedly antipathetic to forming one. Under these circumstances these writers helped to unify the thought of these Adventists around a central doctrinal system. Also, by writing about various activities of the movement, they emerged as leaders in a common cause. Letters written to the *Review* from Adventists in various parts of the eastern United States easily document the importance this church paper achieved in creating a sense of community among Adventists who recognized the seventh day as the Sabbath.[13]

Important as these writers were, they found that they could not satisfactorily substitute for an organized official leadership. Seventh-day Sabbath Adventist families were separated and localized. Unofficial leaders exercised no effective central control. Local groups frequently ordained men who were attracting new members. As these newly ordained ministers gained followings, some of them refused to accept direction from unofficial leaders. Some expounded notions of their own instead of the fundamental doctrinal positions agreed upon during the important Bible conferences of the 1840's.

Insubordination and fanaticism finally became so widespread that James White published a series of editorials in the *Review* on "Gospel Order." The closing article emphasized the considerable public prejudice aroused by these "itinerant preachers."[14] Ellen White also stressed the dangers of hurrying men into the ministry.[15] About fifty years later, Adventist pioneer J. N. Loughborough recalled that the main result of this early organizing attempt was a general agreement that only a minister carrying a signed recommendation or credential from a recognized leader would be accepted by local communities as authorized ministers.[16]

Developments during 1853 further emphasized a need for church organization. Increasing membership resulting from "tent meetings" and other kinds of evangelistic campaigns brought fresh burdens to the church's few credentialed ministers. These few found little time to pastor the new believers. Lacking church funds, they were compelled to earn their own living. Their remaining time they devoted to the evangelistic work. Under multiplying burdens and responsibilities many became ill or otherwise debilitated and thus even less able to deal with the increasing needs of the faithful. Adherents to the movement responded so inadequately to the needs of these men that it became increasingly clear that only a central church organization capable of securing and administering finance could solve the problem.[17]

J. N. Andrews was authorized to form a committee to study into various ways to support the ministry. This committee met at Battle Creek, Michigan, in April, 1858. It proposed a plan of "systematic benevolence." Throughout the early months of 1859, scattered notices in the *Review* indicated that its editor strongly supported this plan, and he fervently urged it upon all readers of the journal.[18]

But with still no official top leadership, church members remained unwilling to contribute, constantly asserting that any legal organization of the church would create a "Babylon," an apostate union of the church with the state. Since even publishing house property was not legally owned by the church, the situation became so intolerable that James White eventually tried to force action by inserting the following notice in the *Review:*

"To those who have so kindly and generously lent money to this office, we wish to say as an individual, we do not wish to be considered in any way responsible for it. We act simply as publishing agent. . . . Those who consider it proper to let their money remain at the office under these circumstances will do so at their own risk."[19]

James White's forthright statements in the *Review* fomented considerable controversy within the church. Arguments used by certain Adventists illustrate how fanatically they opposed legal incorporation. Roswell F. Cottrell, for example, at this time a member of the *Review's* editorial committee, argued that if the church relied upon the state for aid and protection, such a relationship could only constitute what Scripture described as Babylon's spiritual adultery with the kings of the earth. He tried to solve White's problem by appealing to members to hold themselves responsible for one hundred dollar's worth of books. People who wished to lend money to the *Review* must realize that they were lending money to God who would repay them either in this life or in the life to come.[20] The *Review* records many similar reactions from other Adventists.

While the publishing house represented the most crucial aspect, lack of a centralized organization entailed problems for a variety of Adventist churches now beginning to dot various parts of the country. Since there was no official denominational name, individual churches began to take the initiative. The seventh-day Sabbath Adventists of Parkville, Michigan, for example, called themselves the Parkville Church of Christ's Second Advent. Some action had to be taken, asserted Loughborough, commenting:

"Some shrink back as though it were a fearful thing to organize in a legal manner, but I do not thus consider it. . . . Some may be startled at the idea of signing articles. What is in the Bible against organizing as the law requires?"[21]

This deep-seated distrust of government resulted from both eschatological doctrine and interpretation of contemporary events.

In regard to slavery, for example, most seventh-day Sabbath Adventists were abolitionists, and their moral and religious cast of mind did not appreciate Lincoln's temporizing policies. The President's initial emphasis upon saving the Union rather than upon freeing the slaves they interpreted as evidence of a growing national degeneration. Uriah Smith, citing the views of Washington, Jefferson, Madison, Jackson, and Benton, contrasted those men with what he termed "the contemporary views of pro-slavery demagogues."[22]

Despite these factors, however, James White saw clearly that church problems, already acute, would become still more acute as the war mounted and intensified. During August, 1860, he insisted that a new *Review* office must be built and the church must legally own the new plant. James White, supported in this contention by Andrews, Smith, and Waggoner, called for a general meeting at Battle Creek. Representative leaders who met on this occasion followed a plan originally suggested by J. N. Loughborough. Deciding to name the new denomination the Seventh-day Adventist Church, because this title properly represented two of their most distinctive views, they drew up an organizing charter of local conferences operating under the central direction of a General Conference located at Battle Creek, Michigan.[23]

The newly founded church was built squarely on the foundations laid by Millerism. It offered a viable interpretation of Daniel's 2,300-day-year prophecy. It agreed with Miller that only Jesus Christ could establish the kingdom of God on earth at His second Advent.

Postmillennialists, opposing Miller, had stressed that the church should work in concert with the state to create that kingdom. Shortly after this founding in 1863, the new denomination witnessed the rise of a movement bent on securing governmental legislation that would establish a "Christian nation." In the early years, Seventh-day Adventist members faced considerable opposition from this group. These developments form the subject of our next chapter.

REFERENCES AND NOTES

1. "Report of the General Conference of Seventh-day Adventists, John Byington, chairman," Review and Herald, May 26, 1863, pp. 204-206.

2. Leroy E. Froom, The Prophetic Faith of Our Fathers (Washington, D.C.: Review and Herald Publishing Association, 1950), Vol. 4, p. 208.

3. Second Advent Library, No. XLIV, "Reasons for Rejecting Mr. Miller's Views on the Advent," by Rev. George Bush, with "Mr. Miller's Reply," page 11.

4. Joshua V. Himes in "The Advent Herald" of March 20, 1844, p. 53.

5. Arthur E. Ekirch, The Idea of Progress in America 1815-1860 (New York: Columbia University Press, 1944).

6. D. H. Kromminga, The Millennium in the Church (Grand Rapids, Mich.: Wm. Eerdmans Publishing Company, 1945), pages 384-389.

7. James Fulton Maclear, " 'True American Union' of Church and State: The Reconstruction of the Theocratic Tradition," Church History, September, 1966, p. 311. Also John R. Bodo, The Protestant Clergy and Public Issues 1812-1848 (Princeton: Princeton University Press, 1954).

8. Anonymous article "The Millennium," The Midnight Cry, Friday, Jan. 6, 1843, beginning on opening page (unnumbered pages) of this copy of the year's Midnight Cry, now in the Library of Review and Herald Publishing Association, Washington, D.C.

9. Francis D. Nichol, The Midnight Cry (Washington, D.C.: Review and Herald Pub. Assoc., 1944), pages 71-73. Nichol describes the promotional work of Himes which resulted in fuller publicity for the Millerite message.

10. Joseph Bates, The Seventh Day Sabbath: A Perpetual Sign From the Beginning to the Entering in to the Gates of the Holy City According to the Commandments (New Bedford: Press of Benjamin Lindsey, 1846), pages 58, 59.

11. This was partly owing to the work of John Nevins Andrews. Gordon Balharrie gives a full description of his work and influence in "A Study of the Contribution Made to the Seventh-day Adventist Movement by John Nevins Andrews" (Unpublished Master's thesis, The Seventh-day Adventist Theological Seminary, Washington, D.C., 1949) now at the Library of Andrews University, Berrien Springs, Michigan.

12. Ellen G. White, Life Sketches (Mountain View: Pacific Press Publishing Association, 1915), pages 125-128.

13. James White, "Our Present Position," The Advent Review, December, 1850, pp. 15, 16.

14. James White, "Gospel Order," The Second Advent Review and Sabbath Herald, Dec. 6, 1853, p. 173; Dec. 13, 1853, p. 180; Dec. 20, 1853, pp. 188-190.

15. Ellen G. White, Early Writings (Washington, D.C.: Review and Herald Publishing Association, 1938 ed.), page 97.

16. J. N. Loughborough, "Support of the Ministry," Review and Herald, June 18, 1901, p. 397.

17. An excellent general account of this confused situation is provided by J. N. Loughborough, *The Great Second Advent Movement. Its Rise and Progress* (Washington, D.C.: Review and Herald Publishing Association, 1909), pages 194-215.

18. James White, "Systematic Benevolence," *The Second Advent Review and Sabbath Herald,* March 31, 1859, p. 148.

19. J. N. Loughborough, "Legal Organization," *Review and Herald,* March 8, 1860, p. 125.

20. Roswell F. Cottrell, "Making Us a Name," *Review and Herald,* March 22, 1860, p. 140.

21. J. N. Loughborough, "Reply," *Review and Herald,* May 17, 1860, pp. 204, 205.

22. Uriah Smith, "The Degeneracy of the United States," *Review and Herald,* June 17, 1862, p. 22.

23. Carl D. Anderson, "The History and Evolution of Seventh-day Adventist Church Organization" (unpublished doctoral dissertation, The American University, Washington, D.C., 1960), pages 57ff.

Chapter 2

EARLY SUNDAY LEGISLATION AND SEVENTH-DAY ADVENTISTS

The secularizing of America in the 1860's disturbed Protestant Americans who feared that "liberals" were de-Christianizing the country. Their Christian sensitivity and patriotic pride were especially outraged by the lax observance of Sunday by Irish and German Roman Catholics who preferred the greater latitude allowed in Europe, where, provided church or mass was attended, the balance of the day could be spent in nonreligious activities.

To the Puritan mind of nineteenth-century America, these "foreign elements" appeared to occupy most of the "sacred" hours in beer gardens, combining their inexcusably intemperate habits with their abuse of Sunday. Nativist Protestant Americans resolved that they would not allow a "few blatant, beer-drinking foreigners, sustained by lower elements among the citizenry" to corrupt the "Christian" character of the nation.

These same nativist Protestant elements felt that the many Americans who traveled on the "Lord's Day" were equally responsible for the desecration of Sunday. Businesses and corporations who forced workers to labor every day including Sunday further augmented this national problem. They must be checked, decided the reformers, by firm application of American law.[1]

To organize support for such legislation they formed the National Reform Association. At its first convention, held in Xenia, Ohio, on February 4, 1863, a principal speaker, John Alexander, emphasized that slavery and the consequent Civil War grew out of America's original failure to acknowledge God's authority in the national Constitution. The United States had failed to declare itself a "Christian nation," and from this fundamental error the later mistakes and agonies of the American people had come. But

God willed, they vowed, that from the crucible of conflicts would emerge a better citizenry.[2]

The purification of the nation was to be initiated by a constitutional amendment acknowledging and honoring God. A revitalized people would thus rebuild their legislative, cultural, and social activities on God's fundamental law.[3] Delegates at the convention accepted this analysis, and on January 27, 1864, the association organized at Allegheny, Pennsylvania. An excerpt from its constitution indicates its scope of activities:

"Perceiving the subtle and persevering attempts which are made to prohibit the reading of the Bible in our Public Schools, to overthrow our Sabbath laws, to corrupt the family, to abolish the Oath, Prayer in our National and State Legislatures, Days of Fasting, and Thanksgiving, and other Christian features of our institutions and so to divorce the American government from all connection with the Christian religion; Believing that a written Constitution ought to contain explicit evidence of the Christian character and purpose of the nation which frames it, and perceiving that the silence of the Constitution of the United States in this respect is used as an argument against all that is Christian in the usage and administration of our Government;

"We citizens of the United States, do associate ourselves together under the following Articles, and pledge ourselves to God and to one another to labor through wise and all lawful means for the ends herein set forth."[4]

National Reform Association representatives wanted assistance from the state's strong arm but denied that they were attemping to unite church and state. David McAllister, secretary of the association from the time it was founded, argued that membership of the association, drawn from a variety of denominational affiliations and composed of Christians of differing persuasions, would not wish to create a religious establishment. The association believed that the founding fathers had properly rejected any union of throne and altar but considered that calling on the state in this instance would perform a useful service to the American people. While no religious establishment should be tolerated in the United States, the nation should not relapse into total secularism. "General principles of Christianity written into the charter of American government," suggested McAllister, "could best express the life and purpose of its people."[5]

Legal organization of the association at Allegheny, Pennsylvania, enabled the National Reform Association to receive funds and bequests assisting the society to popularize its aims, before bringing to Congress its request for an amendment to the Constitution.

Circulating its memorial throughout America, National Reform Association delegates gained increasing support from lawyers, judges, legislators, and senators, as well as other prominent citizens. By 1871 they numbered among their supporters the governors of Pennsylvania, Vermont, and Kansas; bishops of dioceses such as Massachusetts, Delaware, Ohio, and Missouri; the chaplain of the House of Representatives; and many private citizens.[6] Widespread corruption in civic and governmental affairs persuaded many Americans of the need for change, and when National Reform propagandists linked their campaign with the concept of moral reform they gained increasing support.

Seventh-day Adventists, recognizing the growing scope of the National Reform movement, began to wonder if it constituted the beginning of that repressive religious union anticipated by their eschatology. They disputed the assumption of National Reform writers that strict Sunday observance was fundamental to the nation's morality and asserted that this contention was being used as an excuse to make Sunday violation a criminal act. An article in the official journal of the National Reform Association, *The Christian Statesman,* criticized Vice-president Colfax and several Congressmen for riding trains on Sunday. Arguing that Sunday observance formed the heart of moral law, the *Statesman* stressed that desecrators of Sunday could conceivably commit any crime. Commenting on this, *Review* editor Uriah Smith asserted that National Reform agitation for a religious amendment to the Constitution actually masked the Association's real intent—to enforce Sunday observance.[7]

At the same time, a New York Adventist was saying that the National Reformers were trying to create a union of church and state in order to enforce common religious observances upon all. Although they asked for an "ecclesiastical union based on theological agreement," he pointed out, they really intended to enforce Sunday observance by law and were thus preparing to override the religious liberties of thirty to forty thousand Christians who worshiped on the seventh day. "Ecclesiastical union" could have little meaning if the rights of those who held differing beliefs, however small the minority, were ignored.[8]

In reply, National Reformers said that Seventh-day Adventists and other dissenting groups could expect better treatment from a government that looked to the Bible as its source of authority than from a completely secularized administration.[9]

Jubilant over the progress they had already achieved, National Reform leaders now generated popular support for its petition, now before Congress. Their jubilation was brief, however, for on February 4, 1874, Congress rejected their petition on the grounds that the fathers of the American republic had fully debated the question of the relationship of religion to government and had decided it was not in the interest of the republic to amend the Constitution with any clause promoting any form of religious establishment.[10]

The times also militated against the National Reform Association's major objectives. The year 1875 evoked a considerable public interest in religious liberty. In September, President U.S. Grant, addressing an Army reunion in Iowa, offered three resolutions on public education and stressed the permanent necessity for the nation to defend free thought, free speech, free press, unfettered religious sentiment, and equal rights and privileges for all citizens. He concluded with an exhortation to "keep church and state forever separate."[11] This same year, both major political parties hammered religious liberty planks into their political platforms.[12] As a final blow in December, Congressman James G. Blaine of Maine took advantage of the public enthusiasm aroused by these events to sponsor a Constitutional amendment applying the "establishment clause" to the state as well as to the Federal Government.[13] Had this measure passed Congress it might well have derailed the entire National Reform program. A separationist principle placed on the state level could render unconstitutional every state Sunday law in the nation and could have checked the multiplying Sunday enforcement cases that marked the closing years of the nineteenth century. But the bill failed.[14]

Although the National Reform Association had failed in its attempt to include a religious amendment in the United States Constitution, it had developed sufficient public support to begin a carefully prepared Sunday enforcement drive. Littlejohn, perhaps our best authority on the National Reform movement, dates this Sunday effort from the association's Mansfield, Ohio, convention of 1879.[15] From this time on, regional secretaries of the association used national conventions, planted articles in the press, preached sermons in various denominational pulpits, attempted to persuade eminent citizens, visited seminaries, colleges, summer assemblies, and cooperated with other societies and reform groups to build massive public support in each state.[16]

Pennsylvania was the logical starting point for the NRA's Sunday crusade, since the association's official journal *The Christian Statesman* had already exercised considerable influence from its Pittsburgh base. And the NRA's power was largely concentrated in that state.

This populous and influential state already had a largely unenforced Sunday law which Reform representatives tried to reactivate and to extend its scope and penalties. In January, 1879, while the Pennsylvania legislature was in session at Harrisburg, the National Reform Association convened a major assembly in this city and began to pressure the lawmakers. Presenting a Sunday bill to the legislature, they asked for wider application of the existing Sunday law and the imposition of a $1,000 fine on any business or corporation guilty of violation.[17] The legislators voted the bill into law.

The provisions of the new law were quickly and harshly applied. Seventh Day Baptists in Pennsylvania were particularly harassed by this enforcement, since they observed the seventh day Sabbath and worked on Sunday. They promptly placed a bill before the Pennsylvania legislature to exempt conscientious observers of the seventh day. Since the NRA had previously indicated that it did not wish to persecute minority religious groups, Seventh Day Baptists generally assumed it would favor this exemption clause.

But when the bill reached its second reading, two of the leading NRA representatives in Pennsylvania suggested to the *Pittsburgh Commercial Gazette* that in practice such an exemption could effectively prevent enforcement of the entire Sunday law. They also urged that "numerous and emphatic" protests against the exemption clause should be presented to the Pennsylvania legislature.[18] The Pittsburgh paper published the text of the exemption bill and urged its rejection on the grounds that it was undesirable for the community to observe two different days.[19] The exemption bill lost.[20]

The Seventh Day Baptists now took their case to the people. Renting the Harrisburg Assembly Hall, they stressed that they did not ask for special privileges but for equal rights with other citizens. While it was difficult for them to pay the fines imposed upon them for the exercise of their honest convictions, it was impossible for Pennsylvania, in honor, to impose these fines.[21]

The Seventh-day Adventist *Review and Herald* published various "outside" reactions. One irate "American citizen" described the Pennsylvania Sunday law as unconstitutional, sectarian, unjust, impious, and cruel. This citizen was further aggravated by the actions of Pennsylvania legislators who contrived to be absent when appeals came before them.[22]

Despite these public protests the passage of the Pennsylvania Sunday law precipitated a surge of Sunday law agitation in other parts of the country. During the further course of 1879, Sunday laws also came before Ohio and New Jersey legislatures. The general emphasis amounted to support for Sunday as a civil rest day, based on the "immemorial usage of the American people."[23] This approach to Sunday legislation was particularly true of Northern states, while in the old South attempts to secure Sunday legislation were more openly religious. So was prosecution. In Quitman, Georgia, for example, a Seventh-day Adventist farmer arrested for plowing on Sunday was prosecuted on purely religious grounds. On equally religious grounds he refused to pay his fine and served thirty days in jail.[24]

The tendency of the Northern states to emphasize Sunday as a civil holiday supported by police power, demonstrated a new approach to Sunday legislation. Revealing its dual basis, Sunday observance was seen both as a religious day "consecrated by worship" and as a civil holiday. This distinction was effective. Although the "religious" aspect of forced Sunday observance need not be supported by law, its purely religious partisans could indeed apply the law to enforce Sunday as a civil holiday.

This tack enabled prosecuting groups to strike at businesses and corporations as well as at individuals who ran afoul of the new legislation.[25]

It also enabled them to meet arguments from liberals already denouncing Sunday prosecutions as evidence of incipient union between church and state. In response these liberals appealed to the increasing "European vote," the swarming immigrants of the period whom they saw as susceptible to an appeal to "free liquor" and to oppose Sunday legislation. One meeting of diverse liberals at Baltimore's Patterson Park on October 30, 1879, called on nearly one hundred thousand Germans to vote for a "free Sunday." Again at Newark, New Jersey, the German vote was instrumental in electing its candidate for mayor, a Democrat who stood on a free-Sunday, free-liquor platform. Sunday-and-liquor questions were becoming politically advantageous to Democrats in certain districts; therefore the National Reform Association and similar groups viewed with alarm the new political muscle of these secularist forces.

The differences between the liberal secularists and the several reform groups were epitomized in California. Here two societies had emerged in definite opposition to each other. On one side stood the Home Protection Society, pledged to Sunday law enforcement and similar religious reforms. On the other stood the League of Freedom representing the liberal elements—liquor dealers, saloon owners, and those who disliked religious influence on politics and government.[26] At the Ministerial Union of San Francisco in 1882, clericalists insisted that all public-minded citizens, including publishers and civic organizations, must support Sunday enforcement in California. In this instance, however, the clerical planners defeated themselves. Police courts became so crowded with "religious" violators, and other criminal cases were so neglected, that police officers began refusing to arrest Sunday violators, and police judges began refusing to sign arrest warrants while other cases pended.[27] The Sunday question thus entered the political arena, and the Home Protection Society and the League of Freedom eyed each other for a final struggle.

The Home Protection Society affirmed that it did not wish to disturb conscientious observers of another day if they did not interfere with the peace and quiet Christian people required on the "Lord's day."[28] But when W. C. White, editor of the *Signs of the Times,* was arrested in Oakland for opening the *Signs* office on Sunday, the seventh-day Sabbath people began to realize how little they could depend upon the promises of the Home Protection Society.

Confronted with this prospect, the Seventh-day Adventist Church in California allied with the League of Freedom. Considering this denomination's views on temperance, it seems strange that the teetotaling Adventists should ally with an organization heavily supported by liquor interests, but in this instance they held a common aim—to keep the state out of religious affairs and religion out of state affairs. The League of Freedom had clearly indicated that it intended to fight the Sunday enforcement program and that it was determined to elect a state legislature pledged to repeal the Sunday law. Adventists offered their support.[29]

The Democratic convention that opened at San Jose in June, 1882, declared against a Sunday law.[30] The Republican convention that opened at Sacramento on August 30, 1882, maintained that Sunday should be enforced as a "day of rest and recreation." Thus was the battle joined.

Commenting on the atmosphere of the time, Loughborough says that the Sunday law had become a "bone of contention everywhere."[31] Hoping to gain labor support and votes, Sunday observance enforcement advocates professed their interest in the workingman's right to at least one weekly rest day. [32] When the Adventist camp meeting assembled first at Oakland and later at Healdsburg, California, excitement over the Sunday issue had reached a high level. Adventist leaders distributed a special edition of the *Signs* disseminating the Seventh-day Adventist view to the general public. When the results of the election were published, Adventists rejoiced.

The Republicans had won the previous election by a comfortable majority of 20,319 votes. But the Democrats easily won the 1882 election and immediately set about to repeal the California Sunday law.

Adventist leaders regretted their enforced alliance with the antitemperance liquor interests, but they found themselves unable to avoid this alliance since the temperance cause had been linked with Sunday observance enforcement. Most Adventists normally voted Republican, and only the Sunday law issue had forced them to do otherwise. It was not until 23 years later that the secretary of the International Reform Party, as the National Reform Association then called itself, finally admitted how effective Seventh-day Adventists had been in opposing Sunday laws in California. He lamented that 26,000 Adventists did more petitioning than 26,000,000 "Christians."[33]

Indications of further Sunday prosecutions caused Adventist leadership to try to clarify their position to the general public. Improved public relations became vital, and people needed to understand that although they opposed Sunday legislation, Adventists did believe in temperance. Arrests of Adventists in Arkansas for Sunday violation indicated further troubles to come, for it seemed clear that these Adventists had been singled out for such treatment. Commenting on the evident bias shown at the trial of these men, the *Saint Louis Globe Democrat* spoke of the irony of ministers of the gospel pleading in a court of American justice for liberty to observe God's commandments.[34] Similar arrests were occurring in Tennessee.[35] Such arrests, trials, and convictions goaded Seventh-day Adventist leaders into action.

In addition, the fact that prohibitionist societies were displaying increasing interest in Sunday legislation further hastened action by the Adventist General Conference. They decided to publish a new religious liberty magazine designed to awaken Americans to the growing threat to their religious liberty. Commenting in this new magazine, the *American Sentinel,* editor Uriah Smith stressed the dangers to religious liberty involved in the growing interest in Sunday enforcement by both the Woman's Christian Temperance Union and the Prohibition Party.

When these nationwide organizations united their moral earnestness and promotional skills to the efforts of Sunday propagandists, they greatly augmented the ability of the latter to secure effective Sunday legislation. By 1887, the Woman's Christian Temperance Union had formally associated itself with the National Reform Association and added a Sabbath [Sunday] Observance Department to its own organization. Further developments quickly followed. On November 13, 1887, the Rev. Wilbur Crafts organized the American Sabbath [Sunday] Union Party which soon acquired an important role in Sunday enforcement politics. By 1888 the Prohibition Party had aligned itself with the other three.

At that time Charles Snow, a Seventh-day Adventist, observed that "while in 1883 there was one obscure organization advocating these un-American principles, in 1888 there were four, and each of the three additions was capable of wielding a greater influence among the people at large than the parent organization."[36]

General Conference leaders met to discuss the developing crisis during the 1887 Autumn Council and at that meeting appointed a five-member committee to help local conference groups combat pending Sunday legislation. The move began to score important successes.

One religious liberty worker in Minnesota, Allen Moon, read a newspaper item about a bill designed to eliminate an exemption clause protecting Seventh-day Adventists and other seventh-day Sabbath keepers. When he explained to the judiciary committee studying the bill how the proposed law would adversely affect all who observed the seventh-day as Sabbath, he was successful in blocking the passage of the bill.

A second success came from the combined efforts of religious liberty representatives in Arkansas. These Adventists contacted leading Arkansas citizens who succeeded in showing Arkansas legislators how the repeal of the exemption had brought much suffering to Seventh-day Adventists. When Senator R. H. Crockett called for the passage of a bill to restore the exemption clause and to remove the "foul blot" of persecution from Arkansas, the senators promptly responded to his appeal.[37]

By April 6, 1888, the Sunday issue again reached national dimensions. The Woman's Christian Temperance Union (WCTU) asked Congress for the prohibition of Sunday mails, Sunday trains, and Sunday parades in the Army and the Navy.[38] Mrs. Bateham, superintendent of the newly established Sunday Observance Department of the National WCTU, submitted enormous lists of signatures to the petition. By securing Cardinal Gibbon's signature she felt free to include all the people in his diocese among supporters of the bill. Already sympathetic to the Sunday advocates, Senator Blair, chairman of the Senate Committee on Education and Labor, responded, and sponsored the bill before the Senate.

The Rev. W. F. Crafts aided in this venture by addressing a petition to the General Conference of the Methodist Episcopal Church asking them to form a National Sabbath [Sunday] Committee to work with other religious bodies to influence Congress into passing the bill.[39] Receiving this petition during May, 1888, the Methodist General Conference promptly constituted the requested committee. This committee then contacted other denominations as suggested. When the Baptist Home Missionary Society, the Presbyterian General Assembly, the Synod of the Reformed Church, and several other religious groups responded, their representatives became part of a newly formed National Sabbath [Sunday] Committee.

Recognizing the great threat of the Blair bill and the uselessness of trusting in any kind of "immunity," Adventist Church leaders refused proffered exemption clauses and argued forcefully that just laws do not require exemptions. Religious liberty, they affirmed, is an inalienable right, not an act of government toleration. What one administration bestowed, another could remove. Religious liberty must therefore rest upon a more durable foundation.

To the great relief of Adventists, who felt that they were reaching a momentous phase of their denominational history, the Blair Sunday Bill failed in Congress.

Since 1829 Congress had been undisturbed by such bills. But now the reactivated Sunday movement, supported by upwelling political, social, and religious interests, was attaining unprecedented dimensions and, at least in Adventist eyes, threatening to roll over all opposition. Promoters increasingly associated the needs of the new industrial proletariat for a day of rest with the voices of the traditional religious emphasis. Thus Sunday enforcement was given an idealistic humanitarian guise which brought it support from most reformist and prohibitionist associations. Able to arouse the interest of moral elements in American society, the agitation for Sunday enforcement had gained national scope. By 1888 Ellen G. White was speaking of Sunday agitation as reaching "alarming proportions."[40]

Highly critical of Seventh-day Adventist efforts to defeat pending Sunday enforcement bills, Wilbur F. Crafts, leader of the American Sabbath [Sunday] Union emphasized that 14 million signatures represented the strength of the Sunday proponents. All this public interest, he said, was opposed by liquor dealers, infidels, proprietors of Sunday newspapers, Jews, Seventh Day Baptists, and Seventh-day Adventists. Crafts allowed that he could understand why liberal groups should oppose him, but why should the Seventh-day Adventist journal, *The American Sentinel,* so deliberately misrepresent him? The *Sentinel* replied that Crafts himself was misrepresenting the proposed National Sunday law by calling it a civil ordinance, whereas it was in essence "religious legislation."[41]

The controversy between Crafts and the *Sentinel* pointed up the fact that Adventist attempts to counteract the Sunday promotion movement by publicizing their own opposition program were indeed proving effective. The realization of this fact convinced Adventist leadership that the denomination should form a permanent department to counteract the enforcement activities of the serried array of organizations promoting enforced Sunday observance. Thus the Religious Liberty Association was organized.

REFERENCES AND NOTES

1. This comment appears in *The Christian Woman,* cited by Charles B. Reynolds, "The Sanctity of the Sabbath," *Review and Herald,* July 31, 1879, p. 42.

2. "Proceedings of the National Convention to Secure the Religious Amendment to the Constitution of the United States." Cited by W. A. Littlejohn, *The Coming Conflict* (Battle Creek: Review and Herald Publishing House, 1883), pages xi-xvii.

3. David McAllister, Secretary of the National Reform Association from the time it was founded, reports these events at the Xenia meeting in his later book, *The National Reform Movement* (Philadelphia: Aldine Press Co., 1890), pages 24-26.

4. *Ibid.,* pp. 15, 16.

5. Cited by Uriah Smith, *The Marvel of Nations* (Battle Creek, Mich.: Review and Herald Publishers, 1887), pages 193, 194.

6. Uriah Smith, "The National Reform Convention," *Review and Herald,* Jan. 17, 1871, p. 37.

7. Uriah Smith, "The Constitutional Amendment Question," *Review and Herald,* Dec. 27, 1870, p. 12.

8. E. W. Whitney, "The Sunday Movement," *Review and Herald,* Jan. 8, 1881, p. 36.

9. T. P. Stevenson, "Religious Liberty Under the Proposed Christian Amendment," *Review and Herald,* Feb. 6, 1872, p. 61.

10. "House Reports" I, 43rd Congress, 1st Session Report No. 143. Cited in *American State Papers Bearing on Sunday Legislation,* W. A. Blakely, ed. (Washington, D.C.: Religious Liberty Association, 1911), page 346.

11. Blakely, *American State Papers,* page 326, footnote.

12. *Ibid.,* pp. 168-170.

13. *Ibid.,* pp. 349, 350.

14. McAllister, *op. cit.,* pp. 38, 39.

15. Littlejohn, *op. cit.,* pp. xxi-xxiii.

16. McAllister, *op. cit.,* pp. 32-39.

17. Uriah Smith, "The Religious Amendment," *Review and Herald,* Jan. 16, 1879, p. 20.

18. Littlejohn, *op. cit.,* pp. xxv, xxvi.

19. Uriah Smith, "The Voice of Oppression," *Review and Herald,* March 22, 1881, p. 184.

20. Littlejohn, *op. cit.,* p. xxviii.

21. D. E. Maxson, "Religious Liberty," *Review and Herald,* May 3, 1881, pp. 275, 276; 57:19 (May 10, 1881), pp. 292, 293.

22. "An American Citizen," "Church and State," *Review and Herald,* May 31, 1881, pp. 337ff; June 7, 1881, pp. 353ff.

23. Uriah Smith, "The Sabbath Conflict," *Review and Herald,* May 15, 1879, p. 160; March 6, 1879, p. 79.

24. Blakely, *op. cit.,* pp. 718, 719.

25. George Blagden Bacon, *The Sabbath Question: Sunday Observance and Sunday Laws* (New York: G. P. Putnam's Sons, 1882), pages 34-52.

26. Editorial, "The California Dilemma," *Review and Herald,* March 21, 1882, p. 184.

27. "The State Sunday Law," *San Francisco Chronicle,* April 10, 1882.

28. News item in the *Oakland Times,* Feb. 24, 1882.

29. Editorial, "The California Dilemma," *Review and Herald,* March 21, 1882, p. 184.

30. Editorial, "Sunday in Politics," *Signs of the Times,* July 13, 1882, p. 307. "Democratic Convention," *San Francisco Evening Bulletin,* June 21, 1882.

31. Editorial, "Sunday Demolishing Party Lines," *Review and Herald,* Sept. 26, 1882, p. 616.

32. "California Sunday Law," *San Francisco Evening Post,* March 9, 1882.

33. B. Bassette, General Secretary, in a Letter to Charles D. Stone, Santa Monica, California, July 26, 1906; cited by D. A. Ochs, "A Study of Religious Legislation in California" (Unpublished Master's thesis, University of the Pacific, Stockton, 1934), page 55.

34. Editorial, "The Arkansas Persecution," *Review and Herald,* Dec. 8, 1885, p. 768; citing *Saint Louis Globe Democrat,* Nov. 30, 1885.

35. G. A. King, "Trends in Tennessee," *Review and Herald,* March 9, 1886, p. 150.

36. Charles M. Snow, *Religious Liberty in America* (Washington, D.C.: Review and Herald Publishing Association, 1914), page 283.

37. "Speech of the Hon. Robert H. Crockett in the Arkansas Legislature," *The Sentinel Library* (Oakland, Calif.) No. 2, Feb. 15, 1889, pp. 2-8; citing the *Weekly Arkansas Gazette,* Feb. 10, 1887, p. 8.

38. Alonzo T. Jones, "The Plea for National Sunday Legislation," *Signs of the Times,* June 8, 1888, pp. 343, 344.

39. E. J. Waggoner, "The Blair Sunday Rest Bill," *The Sentinel Library,* page 16.

40. Ellen G. White, *Testimonies to the Church,* Vol. 5, pp. 717-719; also in the *Review and Herald,* Dec. 18, 1888, p. 786.

41. Waggoner and Jones, "Rev. W. F. Crafts Against the Editors of *The American Sentinel,* The Charges, and the Defense, Together With the Report of the Committee of Investigation." *The Sentinel Library,* Oct. 1, 1889, pp. 5-9.

Chapter 3

THE RELIGIOUS LIBERTY ASSOCIATION

Recognizing that the limited coverage they had received from the press had proved a basic weakness in countering the promotional activities of the Sunday enforcement allies, Adventist leaders took steps to gain greater exposure. The denomination thus formed a press committee to publicize the Seventh-day Adventist stand on religious liberty issues. Local conferences also appointed press committees to operate in harmony with this central committee.

The expanded church facilities intensified religious liberty activities on both state and national levels. Agents of these committees contacted local newspapers, secured additional publication opportunities for the denomination, and succeeded in raising considerable new opposition to the proposed Sunday legislation.

This original press committee organization formed the nucleus of the National Religious Liberty Association.[1] In July, 1889, at the Battle Creek Tabernacle, the new national association was formally organized. With an initial membership of 110 persons, it ratified the religious liberty position already established by the Adventist denomination. Its constitution and declaration of principles emphasized the importance of preserving the United States Constitution and opposing the National Reformer Association, which was trying to change or amend it. Specifically pledged to resist religious legislation in the National Congress and in the state legislatures, the Religious Liberty Association accepted responsibility to aid persecuted people of any race, color, or creed. On October 24, 1889, at its first meeting after organization, the National Religious Liberty Association secretary reported that various newspapers throughout America were responding favorably to the association's views and purposes. Its first president, Alonzo T. Jones, declared that the introduction of the Blair Bill in Congress had "plainly indicated to every free man that his liberties were at stake." He pointed out that the National Religious Liberty Association was designed to mount opposition rapidly to counter this threatening type of legislation.

With a president, vice-president, secretary, assistant secretary, an executive committee of seven, and a press committee of five, the central organization could handle all matters referred to it by state conference councils consisting of a vice-president, a secretary, and a press agent appointed by the local conferences. By further appointing acting agents in every church or company within the local conference, any state council could anticipate every challenge to religious liberty occurring within its territory.[2]

The new organization found its resolve quickly tested. On January 6, 1890, Representative W. C. P. Breckenridge of Kentucky introduced a bill designed to prevent anyone from working on Sunday anywhere within the District of Columbia. Sunday law proponents had argued that only in this way could major corporations be prevented from compelling their employees to work on Sunday. The newly organized National Religious Liberty Association saw that religious legislation in the District of Columbia could precipitate similar legislation in any state or even on a national scale. To them, the Breckenridge bill appeared to be an initial step on the pathway of religious legislation. The bill's apparently benevolent nature, its emphasis on protecting the worker, its sheer brevity, all were factors cleverly designed to lure Congress into passing it. In addition, the measure contained an exemption clause, which appeared calculated to disarm anyone who might suspect the element of religious legislation inherent in the proposed law.[3]

Emotions ran high at a well-advertised Sunday Law Convention in Washington, D.C. The large number of Seventh-day Adventists in attendance listened to the Rev. Crafts openly regret the liberal provisions included in the bill for observers of any day other than Sunday, since despite such generous treatment, these Adventists were still ardently fighting passage of the Breckenridge Bill. A second speaker denounced "an insignificant sect of narrow-minded bigots" who joined with atheists, secularists, and socialists to oppose the bill. A third speaker launched a personal attack on Alonzo Jones, a Seventh-day Adventist, for his efforts to defeat the bill.[4] This emotional state of mind continued throughout the bill's initial hearing during February, 1890.

Supporting Crafts and the American Sabbath [Sunday] Union at the Congressional hearing were two other ministers, a member of the Knights of Labor, and a representative from the WCTU. Opposing the measure was a second Knights of Labor representative and three Adventist ministers: Corliss, Jones, and McKee.

Corliss, a successful religious liberty worker from California, who had effectively opposed the Blair Sunday-rest Bill, initiated the Adventist attack on the Breckenridge measure. Insisting that under present law no one in the United States was being compelled to work on Sunday, he averred that the true intent of this legislation was religious. Labor was considered wrong on one day, proper on another. Surely this, he explained, demonstrated the real purpose of the bill—the religious enforcement of Sunday.[5]

Jones pointed out that the Rev. Crafts in his own book, *The Sabbath for Man,* referred to 200 commercial and professional workers who affirmed they had never suffered because of their refusal to work on Sunday.[6] If this was true, asked Jones, what is the need for this legislation?

Following Jones's speech, the representative from the District of Columbia Knights of Labor stated that the appeal by Crafts to the Federation of Labor and to the Knights of Labor had failed because both these organizations had refused to endorse the Breckenridge Bill. While favoring its "rest" feature, they insisted that it should come through means other than religious legislation.[7]

After the subcommittee apparently satisfied itself that the measure was religious and in violation of the First Amendment, the Breckenridge Bill was defeated.

This initial success in the nation's capital, however, was not duplicated in Tennessee. In that state R. M. King, an Obion County farmer, was indicted for working on Sunday. His defense counsel showed, by cross-examination, that the accused was a respected, law-abiding citizen. Only as a practicing member of a Christian denomination which observed the seventh day as Sabbath was he being prosecuted. This evidence, claimed the defense attorney, demonstrated that he was being persecuted on religious grounds. But the presiding judge ruled this and the preceding testimony irrelevent and allowed the prosecuting attorney to attack Seventh-day Adventism. Unsurprisingly, King was found guilty.[8]

The National Religious Liberty Association appealed King's case to the Tennessee Supreme Court which confirmed the verdict of the Obion County Circuit Court. The denomination then appealed by writ of *habeas corpus* to the United States Circuit Court for the Western District of Tennessee. Here the presiding judge admitted that King had been wrongfully convicted, but refused to alter the original judgment, suggesting that the correct arena of appeal was not the court, but the legislature. In effect, the judge was saying that while the law itself was wrong, the method of its administration was correct. The matter was never settled. King's death prevented an appeal to the Supreme Court of the United States.[9]

Seventh-day Adventist president O. A. Olsen, addressing the General Conference Session convening on March 6, 1891, claimed that the Breckenridge Bill, combined with the publicity given to the indictment and trial of King, had broadcast religious liberty principles throughout the country. Officers of the National Religious Liberty Association had used every facility to publicize the King case, and while the legal expenses involved had proved costly, it was felt a justifiable expenditure.[10] Apart from its immediate importance to King and his family, it had succeeded in dramatizing the Adventist position throughout the country, enabling the church to place its religious liberty views before individuals and groups otherwise beyond the reach of Adventist propaganda.

One outstanding lesson learned by Adventists from these Sunday prosecutions was the realization that any community which viewed Adventists in a bad light tended to decide against them. This fact became still more obvious in the rash of Tennessee Sunday prosecutions which followed the King case, and this again highlighted two important ideas. The denomination must first achieve better public relations, and then it must increase its efforts to educate backward communities in those religious liberties properly belonging to any American citizen. The Association noted that in better-informed sections of the nation, the press tended to defend and sympathize with those it considered victims of local religious prejudice.[11]

By the last decade of the nineteenth century, Sunday legislation proponents concentrated their efforts on a national scale. The projected World Exposition at Chicago offered a major opportunity to enact such a measure. So on January 2, 1892, a bill was introduced into the House of Representatives requiring that "no exposition or exhibition for which appropriation is made by Congress shall be opened on Sunday."[12] A further clause requiring Sunday closing of the Fair as a prerequisite to any New York support of appropriations was later added. This created a situation in which the committee, in order to gain the necessary appropriations in time, might be compelled to enforce such a closure.[13] When the Senate committee arranged its hearing for the bill on March 24, 1892, National Reform members and American Sabbath Unionists crowded the hearing to exert "public" pressure.

A Supreme Court decision of February 29, 1892, had provided Sunday advocates with new and potent arguments supporting their concepts of the "Christian state" and its role in society. In the *Church of the Holy Trinity* v. *United States*, Mr. Justice David J. Brewer ruled that a Federal law which banned alien labor contracts did not nullify the right of a Christian church to pay a pastor from a foreign nation.

America, he added, was a "Christian" nation. Precedents in Ferdinand and Isabella's commission to Columbus, in the first colonial grant to Sir Walter Raleigh, James I's first charter to Virginia, and in the charters granted to later colonies, said Justice Brewer, all demonstrated the Christian basis on which the United States was founded.[14] No legislation, either state or national, could be interpreted as permitting acts against religious interests.

The theocratic concept so disliked by the Millerites had now been underwritten by a Supreme Court ruling. A "Christian nation" would logically pass "Christian laws," and these would include enforced observance of a "Christian Sabbath."[15]

Alarmed, Seventh-day Adventist leaders recognized that Justice

Brewer's ruling virtually established a legal religion in the United States. Their alarm was increased when on July 14, 1892, the Senate accepted a proposal that appropriations to the World's Fair should be made only if that exposition were closed to the public on Sunday. When, four days later, the House accepted this ruling and the President signed it into law,[16] it seemed that all three branches of American Government were cooperating to create an American religious establishment.

Following the counsel of A. T. Jones, the National Religious Liberty Association circulated a petition against Sunday closing of the exposition. Jones was permitted to state the Adventist viewpoint to the Select Committee on the Chicago Exposition. But the majority of the committee, including its chairman, showed little interest in Jones's constitutional arguments. Taking the view that Congress had already passed the law which closed the Fair on Sundays, the committee members were not interested in reopening this question. They explained that the question which concerned them now was whether the fair should remain closed on Sundays or whether it could be reopened on that day for religious demonstrations.

Jones concluded that whether the fair was open or closed on Sunday was now beside the point. The point, he felt, was that Congress had formed a religious establishment and was unwilling to review the issue on constitutional grounds. The Constitution had been the basis for Adventist arguments and appeals against Sunday laws. As Jones viewed the situation, this constitutional basis was now lost and the situation completely altered.[17]

Jones's disquiet was to be deepened by events which lay in the immediate future.

As president of the National Religious Liberty Association, Jones related his constitutional arguments to the activities of the association within the framework of the Seventh-day Adventist world field. The now worldwide Seventh-day Adventist denomination decided to change the name of the National Religious Liberty Association to the International Religious Liberty Association, thus reflecting its larger world responsibilities.

It has become significant now, however, that Jones apparently gave no consideration to varying conditions in countries other than the United States. The newly international society still sturdily emphasized total separation of church and state even in countries where Adventist churches were strongly established and where actual church-state separation was impossible.[18]

These varying conditions came forcefully to the attention of Adventist leaders as the result of a controversy developing between the editors of *The American Sentinel* and Seventh-day Adventist missionaries in Matabeleland and Mashonaland (now Rhodesia).

The conflict arose when the South Africa Land Company offered free land to any denomination entering the area for missionary purposes. At the General Conference council of February 15, 1893, missionaries emphasized the growing needs in their fields. When the delegation from South Africa stated their case, Peter Wessels, a missionary who had invested a large part of his personal fortune in the Adventist work in Africa, urged the denomination to accept the donation of free land.

Such a gift, he said, would bring pronounced advantages to the church. Gold and diamonds had been found in South Africa. In fact, Wessels himself had become wealthy from the discovery of diamonds on his own farm. But on February 28, 1893, the committee on resolutions proposed two new resolutions which, when accepted by the General Conference, ruled against proceeding further with the suggestion of Peter Wessels. These were:

"Whereas: In view of the separation which we believe should exist between the Church and the State, it is inconsistent for the Church to receive from the State pecuniary gifts, favors, or exemptions, on religious grounds; therefore

"36 *Resolved:* That we repudiate the doctrine that Church or other ecclesiastical property should be exempt from taxation; and therefore, further,

"37 *Resolved:* that henceforth we decline to accept such exemption on our own behalf."[19]

Peter Wessels did not abandon his plan. During the afternoon session of March 5, 1893, he argued that since a private company, and not a government, had offered the land, Resolution No. 36 did not prohibit acceptance.[20] He persuaded the General Conference officers to resume negotiations, and A. T. Robinson, a Seventh-day Adventist missionary in South Africa, secured an interview with Cecil Rhodes, prime minister of Cape Colony and chairman of the South Africa Land Company. Rhodes gave him a sealed letter for Dr. Jameson, secretary of the company, and Jameson allowed Adventists to select 12,000 acres upon which to establish a mission which became known as the Solusi Mission project.[21]

A. T. Jones now believed that his promotion of church-state separation and religious liberty was as effectively countered by his own church's action as by the decisions of the United States Supreme Court and Congress. If the principle of church-state separation was worth anything, he insisted, it was as valid in the African wilds as in the American West or in the streets of Washington. The claim that the gift was donated by a private company, Jones dismissed as "subterfuge." He could demonstrate that the "company" was merely a facade for British colonial rule.[22]

In the columns of *The American Sentinel,* Jones continued his attack, inquiring how the South African missionaries proposed to serve both church and state. The gospel of force, he said, was being carried into the newly opened parts of Africa by missionaries coming in the wake of troops of the British South African Land Company. Mashonaland and Matabeleland were conquered, and the natives were to receive benefits in the form of civilizing influence. How, he asked, will these missionaries who have sold themselves for "a mess of African pottage" serve two masters?[23]

Jones's attitude is understandable. He had served in the forefront of Adventist battles for religious liberty throughout the tense period of Sunday prosecutions. In 1894 he could not foresee what problems lay in the future. His whole program was based upon his firm belief in complete and absolute separation of church and state. Now he believed his own church had undermined this program by its acceptance of land from a government bent upon an imperialistic program. He felt that by this decision his church had bartered away its own future and safety.

The Seventh-day Adventist Foreign Mission Board was concerned that Jones's reaction might torpedo a valuable acquisition. But after continued deliberations, the General Conference president informed Robinson in South Africa that a general consensus of opinion among denominational officials in Battle Creek now favored buying the land. Disturbed by this sudden change of front, S. N. Haskell, now heading the Solusi project, spoke out. While admitting that from the American point of view, the position of the South African missionaries might seem wrong, he felt obliged to point out some practical factors which needed to be considered. The land had already been stolen from the natives. The grant had been made on the understanding that the natives should remain on the land and should be educated by the church. The clock could not be turned back, and nothing would be gained by the church in refusing to take advantage of a situation that would benefit the people who owned the land by right of occupation.

When Jones continued to publish adverse statements in *The American Sentinel,* Haskell complained in a letter to the General Conference president. He sent a copy of this letter to Ellen White, who at this time was living in Australia. She responded with a 14-page letter to Haskell, sending a copy to the General Conference leaders, then holding their spring council of 1895 in Battle Creek.

During the course of this spring council the chairman of the committee on resolutions had submitted a report suggesting that the denomination should refuse gifts from any civil government. It also suggested that in harmony with this resolution, the General Conference should pay the equivalent value of the land secured in Africa.[24] A. T. Jones now believed that it was essential that he should reinforce what he considered to be the vital principle of church-state separation. At the eighth meeting of the General Conference held Sunday morning, February 24, 1895, he again stressed the fundamental "principle" of complete separation of church and state.[25] It was shortly after this that the General Conference representatives received their copy of Ellen G. White's letter to Haskell stressing that since the world belongs to God, church leaders should contact men in high office, men whom God could in turn influence to help the church. Many opportunities, she emphasized, had been lost through the church's failure to do this. It required no sacrifice of principle or truth, she asserted, to establish contact with important individuals in state office. Cyrus of Persia had ordered that Jerusalem be rebuilt,

Darius had implemented that rebuilding, and Nehemiah had readily accepted aid from Artaxerxes of Persia. Then referring specifically to the Solusi land grant question, she argued that God still prompts men to assist the cause of Christ.[26]

This was a considerable modification of Jones's rather doctrinaire position, and it represented a change of direction which was not confined to the question of mission land grants. It also helped to determine General Conference policy on paying taxes on denominational medical institutions and church structures for Ellen White's letter also stated: "Our brethren . . . are not looking at everything in the right light. The movements they have made to pay taxes on the Sanitarium and Tabernacle have manifested a zeal and conscientiousness that in all respects is not wise and correct. Their ideas of religious liberty are being woven with suggestions that do not come from the Holy Spirit, and the religious liberty cause is sickening; its sickness can only be healed by the grace and gentleness of Christ."[27]

Under these circumstances the original controversy of the Solusi land grant and the tax exemption resolutions were settled by General Conference action. But the philosophy of complete separation of church and state or of a modified separationism conditioned by issues of time and place has been discussed frequently by Seventh-day Adventists since that time. Inevitably the issues have been greatly sharpened by the financial support which the United States Government has so generously offered hard-pressed institutions of education. As far as that immediate time was concerned, the original Solusi incident marked only a temporary rift between the International Religious Liberty Association and other departments of the General Conference. The Association had often demonstrated its usefulness and had operated harmoniously within the denominational polity. After 1895 the Association again turned its attention to cases of Sunday prosecutions of Seventh-day Adventists. In his 1897 report the association president detailed a list of Sunday infringement prosecution cases which had affected a number of American states since March 4, 1895.[28] Such a listing could not but demonstrate the value of the association.

However by the spring session of the General Conference in

1898, reactions to this year's report showed that some delegates were questioning the continued value of the association.[29]

The association report at the session a year later showed that others had accepted this idea. The corresponding secretary reported to the General Conference in session on February 19, 1899, that the association president had so many other responsibilities that his services were all but lost to the association. The same problem existed with many members of the general board. Council sessions had not been held.

As the threat to religious liberty began to ebb, efforts to fight that receding threat became less necessary. International Religious Liberty Association officers noted a significant softening of attitude on the part of major temperance societies toward enforced Sunday observance.[30] The national convention of the Prohibitionist Party held at Pittsburgh, Pennsylvania, in 1896 aired a demand from within the membership to the effect that while advocating protection for a day of rest, the party did not support harassment of those observing a day different from Sunday.[31] A group of delegates at the national convention of the WCTU at Seattle in 1899 protested against temperance work being used to support those who, because of their ignorance and religious prejudice were persecuting others.[32] This attitude of religious toleration developed so markedly in the WCTU particularly that during its national convention in 1900 notice was given that an important amendment to the society's constitution would be offered at the next annual convention. This amendment would require that nothing should be accepted by the WCTU which could interfere with perfect liberty of conscience concerning days of rest and the manner of their observance.[33]

Adventists wrongly believed that, because of the temperance movement's association of Sunday enforcement with its temperance goals, public interest in both temperance reform and Sunday legislation was waning. By 1899 they decided that temperance was ceasing to be an important factor in political campaigns.[34] In fact, as subsequent events would show, whereas public interest in Sunday observance legislation was declining, public interest in temperance was increasing. While they regretted what they considered declining public interest in temperance ideals, they rejoiced at the concomitant declining public interest in Sunday legislation. Furthermore, the change of attitude affecting the temperance societies was beginning to remove from Seventh-day Adventists the stigma of being classed with the liquor interests. With agitation for Sunday observance apparently separated from the efforts of temperance groups, Adventists could see the possibility of cooperation with such organizations in advocating antiliquor legislation. A united front might even strengthen an effective prohibition program. Thus, a shift of national mood away from Sunday enforcement toward temperance goals might seriously sap the strength of the movement to secure Sunday legislation.

Leaders in the Sunday enforcement movement were beginning to recognize their mistake in attempting to curtail the Seventh-day Adventist Church by prosecuting its members for Sunday violation. This realization may explain the notable decrease in such prosecutions by the end of the century.[35] It may also account for the changing attitudes of the temperance parties. Public sentiment was emerging that opposed infringements on personal liberty. Those supporting the Sunday movement saw this development and backed away from strident attacks.

This turn of events underscored the new importance of public relations and public education, both to the Seventh-day Adventists and to Sunday law supporters. At the 1901 General Conference spring session, the International Religious Liberty Association reported that few Adventists had been prosecuted during the past two years, leaving the bulk of the association's funds to be invested in public education by lectures and literature on principles of religious liberty.[36] Adventists moved to unite their efforts and utilize every church agency in a comprehensive promotional educational program.

By the close of the century, each of the denomination's various agencies had become virtually independent. Organization had come slowly and with great difficulty in the early phases of the church's development. The form that it now had was that of a small group of individuals directing each church agency within the general denominational program, each group largely independent of the General Conference and of each other agency. Tending toward arbitrary use of authority derived from their office, they effectively removed from local representatives, and from ministers, the individual initiative needed to make wise decisions and to broaden the scope of action. Instead of cohesion and resultant harmony, overlapping and rivalry developed, resulting in dissatisfaction on the part of many church members. Unhappy members in turn withheld funds until they could develop more confidence in the administration, an action which tended to paralyze the activity of the church.

By 1901 the General Conference leaders had determined to reorganize conference affairs completely.

The plan they envisioned returned greater responsibility and initiative to the individual minister and clarified the relationship between church agencies and the central administration and the inter-relationship between agencies. The new streamlined organization would encompass local conferences, union conferences, divisions, and finally the centralized General Conference with the somewhat maverick agencies becoming its departments.

As a part of this complete reorganization, religious liberty also came under the General Conference as a regular department.[37] Thus began a new phase of denominational church-state activity.

Although Adventists would be prosecuted again for Sunday "violation," the intensive campaigns of the late nineteenth century were not repeated. The first two decades of the twentieth century witnessed new Adventist promotional and educational campaigns, including religious liberty activity, and cooperation with other churches to achieve a national prohibition law. This program culminated in the passing of the Eighteenth Amendment in 1919.

This great "triumph" of educational, promotional, and legislative activity was not won easily, nor was its advantage permanent. The activity of the Adventist Church in these first two decades of the twentieth century forms the subject of the next chapter.

REFERENCES AND NOTES

1. "Report of the Secretary of the Press Committee," General Conference Proceedings, Seventh Meeting, *Daily Bulletin* of the General Conference, Friday, Oct. 25, 1889, pp. 75, 76.

2. *Ibid.*, pp. 77, 78.

3. L. A. Smith, "The Breckenridge Bill for the District of Columbia," *Review and Herald,* Jan. 21, 1890, p. 40.

4. J. O. Corliss, "Sunday Law Convention in Washington," *Review and Herald,* Feb. 11, 1890, p. 90.

5. Introduced in First Session of Fifty-first Congress, H.R. 3854: "To prevent persons from being forced to labor on Sunday" (in the District of Columbia), W. C. P. Breckenridge, of Kentucky, Jan. 6, 1890; to Committee on District of Columbia; hearing on bill before subcommittee Feb. 18, 1890; not reported. Congressional Record 21:403. Also W. H. McKee, "Arguments on the Breckenridge Sunday Bill: The Object and the Price of Exemption Clauses," *The Sentinel Library,* April, 1890.

6. Wilbur F. Crafts, *The Sabbath for Man,* pages 428-435.

7. McKee, "The Breckenridge Sunday Bill," pages 26-28.

8. Dan T. Jones, "Religious Intolerance," *Review and Herald,* March 18, 1890, pp. 172, 173.

9. W. A. Blakely, ed., *American State Papers Bearing on Sunday Legislation* (Washington, D.C.: Religious Liberty Association, 1911), pages 455-457.

10. "Address of Elder O. A. Olsen, President of the General Conference," General Conference *Daily Bulletin,* March 6, 1891, p. 5.

11. This inference is drawn from the results obtained in Tennessee in 1892 in contrast with the successes in 1890 as reported by C. Eldridge, "Report of Religious Liberty Work for the Year 1890," General Conference *Daily Bulletin* March 15, 1891, p. 112.

12. H.R. 7520, Sunday Civil Bill, lending $5,000,000 to Chicago's World's Fair, conditioned on Sunday closing. Approved August 5, 1892. Congressional Record 23:7040.

13. H.R. 9710: "To aid in carrying out an act of Congress to provide for celebrating the discovery of America" (with proviso for closing Columbian Exposition on Sundays). Reilly of Pennsylvania, August 4, 1892; W. H. McKee, "Legislative Religion in Washington," *The American Sentinel,* April 14, 1892, pp. 116, 117.

14. *Church of the Holy Trinity* v. *United States,* 143 U.S. 226 (1892).

15. W. H. McKee, "The Establishment of Religion by Colonial Grant and Charter," *The American Sentinel,* May 26, 1892, p. 163.

16. H.R. 9710: "To aid in carrying out an act of Congress to provide for celebrating the discovery of America" (with proviso for closing Columbian Exposition on Sundays). Reilly, of Pennsylvania, August 4, 1892; to Committee of Whole House; passed House and Senate and received President Harrison's signature on Aug. 5, 1892. Congressional Record 23: 7064-7, 7086, 7102.

17. A. T. Jones, "The Third Angel's Message," General Conference *Daily Bulletin,* Jan. 27, 28, 1893, pp. 39-41.

18. "Proceedings of the National Religious Liberty Association, Second Meeting," General Conference *Daily Bulletin,* Feb. 28, 1893, p. 423.

19. "Council Meeting #12: Needy Mission Fields," General Conference *Daily Bulletin,* Feb. 15-19, 1893, pp. 268, 269; "General Conference Proceedings: 13th Meeting," General Conference *Daily Bulletin,* March 1, 1893, p. 437.

20. "General Conference Proceedings: 18th Meeting," General Conference *Daily Bulletin,* March 6, 1893, p. 486.

21. *Spirit of Prophecy Counsels Relating to Church-State Relationships.* Assembled for the study of the Committee on Church-State Relationships (Ellen G. White Estate: General Conference, Washington, D.C., 1964), pages 146, 147 (Mimeographed).

22. Editorial, *The American Sentinel,* Nov. 1, 1894, p. 344.

23. Editorial, *The American Sentinel,* Nov. 22, 1894, p. 368.

24. "Mission Property," General Conference *Daily Bulletin,* extra, Feb. 21, 1895, p. 283.

25. "General Conference Proceedings," General Conference *Daily Bulletin,* extra, Feb. 23, 1895, pp. 340, 341.

26. *Spirit of Prophecy Counsels,* pages 163-176.

27. "Tax Exemption and Grants," *Spirit of Prophecy Counsels,* page 169.

28. Allen Moon, "Religious Liberty Association President's Report," General Conference *Daily Bulletin,* Feb. 26, 1897, pp. 161, 162.

29. "Report of the Proceedings of the International Religious Liberty Association Board," General Conference *Daily Bulletin,* March 14-20, 1898, pp. 203, 204.

30. "Report from the Corresponding Secretary of the International Religious Liberty Association," General Conference *Daily Bulletin,* Feb. 19, 1899, p. 47.

31. Editorial, "Prohibitionists and Their Platforms," *The American Sentinel,* June 11, 1896, p. 190.

32. A. T. Jones, "The National WCTU on Record," *The American Sentinel,* Nov. 30, 1899, pp. 739, 740.

33. A. T. Jones, "The WCTU and Sunday Laws," *The American Sentinel,* Jan. 4, 1900, pp. 3, 4.

34. Editorial, "Temperance Retrogression," *The American Sentinel,* July 20, 1899, p. 435.

35. "Report of the Corresponding Secretary," General Conference *Daily Bulletin,* April 16, 1901, p. 25.

36. "Biennial Report of the International Religious Liberty Association," *Ibid.,* p. 224.

37. "General Conference Proceedings: 21st Meeting," *Ibid.,* April 18, 1901, p. 312.

Chapter 4

PROBLEMS
DURING THE PROHIBITION STRUGGLE

The power of the liquor industry had grown prodigiously since the Civil War. Strong in wealth and economic affiliations, it was buttressed by alliances with corrupt political machines. Financial interests dominated the major political parties. The flood of new immigrants found a chief recreational recourse in beer halls and saloons.[1] But with the twentieth century came reform, which began to change the political life of the nation.

Hesitantly, despite considerable frustration, the progressive reform movement began to grapple with the social and economic ills of the nation. Since the liquor traffic was associated with many other social ills, temperance reform took a vital place in the reform program. Shedding its apathy, the Puritan heritage began to interest itself once more in the temperance question.[2]

Appreciating this reform climate and recognizing that temperance societies were no longer supporting the Sunday legislation that had threatened their religious liberty, Adventists revived their temperance work as an integral part of their evangelism. Temperance reform assumed even greater importance to Seventh-day Adventists, because of their insistence that alcohol and drugs enslave their users "in a bondage" to their own appetites. So the denomination wholeheartedly accepted prohibition. They believed that liquor dealers had no right to expose individuals to constant temptation by their advertisements, enticing both those who already drank to increase consumption, as well as those who had never drunk alcoholic beverages to begin. Effective governmental prohibition was the only useful way to end the evil. This, Adventists emphasized, constituted no violation of proper church-state relations.

During the closing decades of the nineteenth century, Seventh-day Adventists had not joined other evangelical Protestant churches in promoting the temperance cause. The Prohibition Party and the WCTU had worked with the churches to achieve Sunday legislation. The efforts of prohibitionists to close saloons on Sunday were interpreted by Adventists as subordination of the prohibition cause to enforcement of Sunday observance. To protect themselves, Adventists had joined liquor interests to oppose the legislation and thereby endured the opprobrium of being associated with the liquor forces. This division among Protestant forces, a general Protestant apathy, and the strength of the liquor interests combined to defeat reform efforts in the late decades of the nineteenth century.

The denominational reorganization of 1901 had incorporated physicians, printers, and businessmen into an expanded General Conference committee. This diversity of talent, together with that of the ordained ministers, laid a foundation for increased evangelical activity along many lines.[3] The physicians on the committee stressed the need for renewed Adventist emphasis on temperance. Believing that God communicates with man through his physical senses, Adventists thought of "temperance" as more than mere abstinence from alcohol. To them it indicated an altogether different way of life based on health principles. To them prohibition of liquor and drugs was only the legislative side of the issue— treating the symptoms rather than the disease. Temperance as a way of life could not be maintained either in the church or in the nation without a corresponding educative effort. Unless church members and the general public were informed on the importance of temperance principles, the legislative effort to eliminate the liquor traffic would end in failure.[4]

In August, 1903, therefore, the General Conference launched an educational campaign to educate first its own church members. These health principles should be understood, not as an expertise practiced by specialists within the denomination, but as the natural heritage of each church member. If Adventists could be persuaded to practice these principles and to teach others to do so, they would set an excellent foundation for a future promotion of temperance on a wider scale.[5]

The church conceived this temperance program as an essential part of its Christian witness. At home as well as in the mission fields, the medical organization became the right hand of the church. People who sensed no spiritual need could appreciate a program designed to recover and maintain physical health.[6] If Adventists could develop such a health-oriented witness, it could do more, perhaps, to create favorable public relations than anything else. Such was their concept.

As an important part of this new thrust, the denomination planned to establish small sanitariums—medical institutions designed to minister to each patient's body, mind, and spirit. Provided with their own chaplains, these sanitariums would be equipped to show the importance of temperance principles.[7] They would demonstrate the advantages of the health principles urged by the Seventh-day Adventist Church. Controlled by the denomination but motivated by unselfish rather than commercial aims, they would acquaint the public with the signal importance of temperance, and provide a positive expression of the principle to bulwark the negative effort to close saloons.[8]

Small sanitariums as medical-evangelistic agencies seemed even more attractive to the denominational leaders because of the ill fate of the Battle Creek Sanitarium. The first sanitarium constructed by Adventists, this institution ministered to its patients according to Adventist health principles under the guidance of John Harvey Kellogg, M.D., its superintendent. It developed rapidly. But Kellogg gradually grew away from the Adventist leadership. Denominational leaders felt that to lose control of the hospital would eventually mean losing the very purpose for which it was founded. After the sanitarium was destroyed by fire on February 18, 1902, Kellogg and the Battle Creek Sanitarium Board came out in open opposition to General Conference policies. This conflict came to a head at the 1903 General Conference spring session. At this time, Kellogg informed General Conference officers that in his view their desire to direct personally all church-affiliated institutions was "communistic." The tension between Kellogg and the sanitarium directors mounted. After a second disaster on December 20, 1902, when the Review and Herald Publishing House burned to the ground, the General Conference leaders moved the central administration and the new publishing house to Washington, D.C.

They purchased two tracts of land in Takoma Park, a suburb about seven miles north of the center of the city. On one five-acre tract they constructed the buildings to house the Review and Herald Publishing Association and the General Conference headquarters. The other, a fifty-acre tract, was to accommodate the Washington Sanitarium and Washington Missionary College.

J. S. Washburn, the financial secretary of the new relocation plan, eulogized the splendid view overlooking the magnificent Capitol building with the Statue of Freedom on its lofty dome. But, he said, across from the Capitol and the Library of Congress grounds was the building used as headquarters by the International Reform Bureau and its secretary, W. F. Crafts. To him the close proximity of opposing forces near the center of the nation's government represented a dramatic confrontation. On the one hand was the promise of freedom as represented by the Statue of Freedom—freedom from drugs, liquor, vice, as well as from political and religious tyranny. These were the objectives for which Seventh-day Adventists were struggling. On the other hand, the International Reform Bureau, offspring of the National Reform Association, at this very time engaged in promoting a new Sunday-rest bill,[10] promised tyranny.

In 1903 the House of Representatives was, in fact, considering two Sunday-rest bills. One was sponsored by the International Reform Bureau; the other resulted from efforts of local butchers and grocers in Washington to secure by law Sunday closing to avoid any loss in trade from competing merchants.[11] Both bills emphasized Sunday rest in the District of Columbia, which could serve as a stepping-stone toward a national Sunday law.

In face of the new danger, Adventists had the advantage of the presence of the relocated central denominational organization in Washington. Not only did this provide opportunity for their Religious Liberty Department to use all of its resources in opposing the two bills, but other Adventist activities in the city began to create a favorable impression both on the major newspapers and on the general public, who could now see a true rather than a distorted view of Adventists.

When the Sunday-rest bill sponsored by the butchers and grocers passed the House and was recommended to the Senate, the Seventh-day Adventist Religious Liberty Department was in an excellent position to oppose the measure. Assisted by the major Washington newspapers, it circulated a protest petition.[12] The *Washington Post,* in particular, regretted that though many people recognized that there was no actual basis for observing Sunday as a sacred day, few were as consistent as the Seventh-day Adventists in keeping any day of the week. The main force of this particular editorial, however, served to assert that since Sunday was for most people merely a holiday, there was no point in stirring up intolerant feelings by enforcing its observance.[13]

Congress adjourned without passing the Sunday-closing bill, although it was recommended by the Commissioners of the District of Columbia. But the Adventist Church was sufficiently alarmed by the resurgence of activity on legislation to renew publication of a journal committed to religious liberty. The editorial of the new *Liberty* magazine, first published in 1906, announced that it was succeeding the *American Sentinel,* and the *Sentinel of Christian Liberty,* both of which had been published at a time when the denomination had felt itself threatened by the increasing advocacy of religious legislation.[14]

In this same issue of *Liberty* a writer took sharp exception to the assertion of those Sunday advocates who claimed that California had suffered the 1906 San Francisco earthquake because it had no Sunday law on its statute books. If this were the case, he argued, why was Lisbon destroyed on November 1, 1775? Certainly no one would suggest that Lisbon lacked a Sunday law![15]

Writing some months after the earthquake, Ellen White deplored the fact that, although for some time after the earthquake, the San Francisco authorities closed all saloons, they had allowed them to reopen even though the strictly enforced ordinance for a time had helped to reduce crime in the city.[16] Concerned with this apparent correlation between drunkenness and crime, Ellen White, writing in *The Bible Student's Library,* used the example of San Francisco to illustrate the role of alcohol in crime in the early years of the twentieth century.[17]

Her point of view was important to temperance reformers in

the progressive era. For example, on the basis of the records of several convicts, the Committee of fifty, a group of scholars and businessmen interested in temperance, sponsored studies on the social and psychological effects of alcohol. The committee concluded that alcohol was a significant factor in almost 50 percent of the cases.[18] Many progressive reformers, considering liquor an important causitive factor in crime, social disease, accident, and death began to join the prohibitionist movement.[19] Ellen White contended that all through human history, liquor had been responsible for the downfall of individuals and nations. Alcoholic beverages, she said, often "dethroned" reason and caused evil which was later regretted and expiated on the gallows. Was not the liquor dealer responsible? she queried. Were not houses of prostitution, dens of vice, prisons, insane asylums, and hospitals filled indirectly by dealers dispensing alcohol? And if the liquor dealer was responsible, so also was the government which allowed him to pursue his vile trade. Liquor saloons must be abolished, and the people must be aroused to the evils of intemperance. So urged Ellen G. White.[20]

Confronted with a growing need to dramatize the evils of intemperance before the American public, Seventh-day Adventists used various methods to urge the necessity of prohibition by legislation. One writer in *Signs of the Times* emphasized "the awful curse of intemperance" by suggesting that America in 1906 consumed 20 gallons of liquor for every man, woman, and child in the nation. Since many drank no alcohol at all, other individuals must have drunk far more than the 20-gallon average. Given the dangerous effects of alcohol on the human system, it was not difficult, the writer suggested, to understand the reasons for the prevalent squalor, misery, and crime. Perhaps the underlying cause of this large consumption of liquor was the inadequate diet of the average American. His system consequently craved alcohol as a kind of pseudorelief. The temperance reformer who succeeded in closing the saloon must also teach the individual to live in such a way that he would no longer crave the stimulating effect of strong liquor.[21]

The author appealed to *Signs* readers to support the temperance cause. First, they must accept its principles for themselves, then persuade the family, and finally the community. They must organize temperance societies in their own neighborhoods, whose members would sign the pledge to temperance. Temperance rallies at proper intervals where suitable literature was distributed could rally many to the cause. From such activity national prohibition could become a possibility.

In October, 1907, when this article was published, temperance advocates had little hope of effective temperance control even if a national law should be enacted. Another *Signs* article in the same issue pointed out that Maine, for example, had had a prohibition law for nearly half a century, but in practice it had been little more than form. To outward appearance the saloons were closed, but in reality intoxicating liquor could be procured almost anywhere. New Hampshire also had had statutory prohibition for 50 years, but there the saloon business was conducted openly in many cities. In Kansas also, much the same situation prevailed. In spite of these inconsistencies, however, the author concluded that prohibition was worthwhile. Difficulties of enforcement urged against prohibition, he claimed, were equally applicable to the enforcement of any law.[22]

Differences among its advocates and strong resistance from its opponents made national prohibition still more difficult. Many among the principal religious groups were still trying to secure Sunday closing of saloons while others considered that intemperance was equally wrong on any day and that intolerance was a crime to rival intemperance. Recognizing that Sunday-closing would lose the Irish and the German patronage, saloon owners strongly resisted such legislation.[23] In this struggle they found an unexpected, albeit welcome, ally in the Adventists, who, although not relishing the companionship, still opposed the major prohibitionist parties who were only tardily moving away from the Sunday-saloon-closing policy. During a meeting of the Seventh-day Adventist Religious Liberty Department at the 1909 General Conference spring session, delegates discussed the question, "What should our attitude be toward the Sunday closing of saloons?" They decided they must continue to oppose the aims and objectives of the strong temperance parties. They thus remained, in this one area, the unwilling allies of the liquor interests.[24]

But, after 1907, a more widespread interest in temperance reform was developing rapidly in the United States. Early in 1908, Will Irwin and Arthur Gleason published a series of articles in *Collier's Weekly* exposing the corrupt alliance between liquor interests, commercialized vice, business, and politics.[25] From this time public interest in the question gathered momentum.

Adventists believed that previous public interest in temperance had prepared the way for the great resurgence now taking place. These temperance successes had come largely through local option, and Adventists viewed them as the upwelling of the people, long oppressed by the tyrant Liquor.[26] Buoyed by this new wave of temperance reform, the General Conference Committee moved to shape a new policy. They passed this resolution:

"Whereas: The liquor traffic is a great social evil, a menace to the home, the city, the state, and the nation; and

"Whereas: There is a great movement in this country to stay the tide of this iniquitous traffic; therefore,

"Resolved: That we put forth every laudable and consistent effort in opposing the liquor traffic by our example, our pen, our voice, and our vote."[27]

Adventist leaders strongly encouraged their members to vote for temperance candidates. There was nothing radical in this. As early as 1855 Ellen White's diary mentioned a discussion between her husband and other Adventists on whether to vote in the coming elections. They soon decided to do so, since a failure to vote might elect "intemperate" men into positions of power and influence.[28] Fifty years later, in 1905, Mrs. White wrote that "those who by their votes sanction the liquor traffic will be held responsible for the wickedness that is done by those who are under the influence of strong drink."[29]

Still, Adventists must do more than just vote. They had always opposed the liquor interests, but had so feared the Sunday-closing policy advocated by the churches and temperance societies that they had been forced to join the liquor interests in defeating Sunday-closing legislation. Now the General Conference recommended temperance rallies at Adventist camp meetings throughout the country. Every effort, they realized, must be made to attract the public.[30] Doctors should lecture on temperance and demonstrate proper habits of healthful living.[31] Adventists should give temperance literature to the public.

Two tracts were published. One, "Prohibition and the Liquor Traffic," was a compilation of temperance addresses by Adventist leaders delivered at prohibition hearings before the House District Committee in Washington, D.C., on April 1, 1908. The tract demonstrated the falsity of charges that Adventists were allied with liquor interests.[32]

The other tract, "Prohibition and Sunday Legislation," had a double purpose. The first section of the tract explained why Adventists believed in temperance legislation. Arguing that intemperance attacked the well-being of the nation, society, the home, and particularly the individual citizen, the writers suggested that obligation to check this disorder came within the proper scope of civil government. It must pass laws forbidding the sale of intoxicating liquor. But the issue for Sunday legislation was entirely different. In the second section of the tract the authors protested both the state interference in the religious rights of the individual and the movement toward a union of church and state. Sunday laws interfered with a citizen's right to work, thus robbing him of his basic liberties as an American and contradicting the *laissez faire* principle of government upon which America's prosperity had been established.[33]

The General Conference *Bulletin* of spring, 1909, printed the resolution passed by the council of the previous year. After this was read during the spring council, delegates urged implementation of this resolution to counter comments in some Washington papers that Adventists were opposed to prohibition. One General Conference delegate, George I. Butler, listening to this information, commented that although this was a serious slur on Adventists, who had always opposed the liquor interests, it was an attitude probably attributable to the fact that most Adventists tended to remain aloof from politics. But now, he said, the widespread public interest in prohibition rendered it essential that every church member should campaign and vote for prohibition.[34]

The Religious Liberty Department's report of May 31, 1909, attacked the problem of the church's stand on prohibition legislation. In the past, suggested chairman A. G. Daniells, individuals such as W. F. Crafts, leader of the International Reform Bureau in Washington, D.C., had charged that Adventists, who had canvassed the public to prevent passage of Sunday laws, were not equally zealous in campaigning for prohibition legislation.[35] Now that the church was throwing its energies into the prohibition cause, said the chairman, the liquor interests, who by cooperating with Seventh-day Adventists in defeating Sunday-closing legislation had greatly embarrassed the church, would now be taking a very different view. Their cooperation had sprung from their own cynically selfish motives, and certainly they deserved no credit for this. On the other hand, temperance reform advocates were sincerely idealistic in trying to procure Sunday legislation. Their motives, though misguided, were better than those of the liquor interests. The Adventist Church needed to break down the walls of prejudice between itself and other temperance groups, he continued, so that it could convince its new friends that Sunday laws violate religious liberty. This, concluded Daniells, was the supreme task of the denomination at that time.

Adventists thus tried to establish a working relationship with other temperance reformers. Some limited results appeared at the temperance convention held in Washington during December 12-17, 1909. Temperance and other social issues were first discussed; then the delegates considered Sunday legislation.

The Secretary of the International Reform Bureau in California, Dr. G. L. Tufts, addressed himself to this subject, emphasizing that the two major enemies to Sunday laws worked, one from within, and the other from without, the church. Saloon owners and liquor dealers were the external enemies. But the internal enemy was the Seventh-day Adventist Church. The combination of two such dissimilar groups against reform parties was amazing, the secretary concluded. Rebuttal came from Dr. D. H. Kress, the superintendent of the Adventist Sanitarium in Washington, the next speaker.

He began by reminding the delegates that Adventists did indeed favor prohibition. To suggest that they fostered liquor interests, he pointed out, was palpably false. Adventists opposed the sale of liquor on all days of the week, including Sunday. If prohibition parties would omit the Sunday legislation issue from their platform, abandoning this segment of their reform crusade, Adventists would work unitedly with other temperance groups to obtain prohibition.

Support for this contention came from none other than W. F. Crafts, speaking from his conversations with Adventist officials and from personal experience with Adventist sanitariums. The important issue, he said, was to secure temperance legislation. Sunday closing should be considered only because the abundant leisure of the working class on that day inclined toward drunkenness and vice. Since Adventists agreed with other temperance advocates on eleven out of twelve issues, he said, surely this should enable all to work harmoniously for reform.

Yet even for the sake of harmony, Adventists would not agree to closing saloons on Sunday only. To them, Sunday laws provided opportunity for idleness on that day. The excessive drinking and drunkenness on Sunday was thus a by-product of Sunday agitation. Adventists, then, could not be held responsible.[36]

Clearly, Adventists considered themselves to be more consistent supporters of prohibition than any other reform group. They wished to close the saloons every day of the week. To liquor apologists who argued that since the brewer and the liquor dealer paid a large amount of tax revenue they should receive better treatment, Adventists replied that these revenue taxes for the government came from the people in any case. If the liquor trade were abolished, taxes would accrue from better sources.

One Adventist writer pointed out that the future of the liquor traffic depended on creating an appetite for liquor among American youth. This made it impossible merely to regulate the traffic, for closing saloons on Sunday would not solve this problem. Liquor must be forbidden because every dollar returned in revenue cost the government two additional dollars to support the jails, courts, and poorhouses.[37]

Fear that the nation's youth would be seduced by the liquor interests loomed large in all temperance thinking. Adventists attempted to reach the youth by publishing special temperance issues of their *Youth's Instructor*.[38] Partly because of public interest and partly because of ardent denominational promotion of the magazine, the circulation of the paper jumped. A 1911 temperance issue pointed up the importance of the youth factor by showing that the vast majority of child cruelty or neglect cases could be attributed to liquor. The paper suggested that if the United States Government would cease to look at the liquor tax and consider the American boy or girl, it would end the liquor traffic.[39]

In 1909 Adventists, in common with other temperance advocates, were disturbed by a hiatus in the onward march of the prohibition cause. Although temperance forces had gained considerable grassroots support, Congress refused to pass a law empowering the states to forbid the passage of liquor into or through their territories. This made it difficult for the dry states to enforce prohibition since liquor dealers could import liquor, reselling it in defiance of state prohibition. Furthermore, liquor advertisements and traveling liquor salesmen could create an appetite for alcohol which they could immediately exploit if the public mood should change. Congress had refused to grant these powers on the Constitutional basis that only Congress had the power to regulate interstate commerce. It could not delegate this right to the states.[40]

Reasoning that this emphasis on constitutional rights ignored more vital questions, Adventists included in their youth paper a prize oration of the Inter-Collegiate Prohibition Association, at Valparaiso, Indiana. The author of this article, Lewis M. Simes, advanced the argument that many state court decisions had swept away the liquor industry's constitutional defenses. Most important of all, he asked, what constitutional rights could be claimed ethically for an industry that violates the freedom of others? If liberty did not include the right to injure or interfere with welfare of others, the liquor traffic had no right to exist.

The *Youth's Instructor* referred to liquor advertisements which emphasized that if statewide restrictions on liquor should be imposed, they would sell even greater quantities.[41] The *Instructor* argued that, even if liquor interests should sell imported liquor from "wet" states, they could not defeat the prohibition cause. To demonstrate this, the journal published an article written by Robert B. Glenn, an ex-governor of North Carolina. He stated that while the statewide prohibition of alcohol in his state had not prevented some violation of the ordinance, because of shipments allowed by interstate commerce law, yet the evil was 50 percent less under state prohibition than previously. If each state should adopt prohibition when public sympathy was sufficiently aroused, Congress would then, he urged, be forced to legislate against the importation of liquor into a dry state. Glenn stated that with prohibition, dry states would be so much more prosperous than others, that their example would soon be followed. This, he concluded, would render national legislation certain.[42]

By 1910 brewers, recognizing the dangers threatening their industry, renewed their efforts to defeat prohibition. *Liberty* reported that in the Kentucky prohibition fight, brewers paid $30 per vote to defeat temperance legislation.[43] The liquor interests were generally supported by the urban masses, many of whose voters were newly enfranchised. In 1911 in Maine, for example, when the issue of whether to retain the prohibition clause in the state constitution came before the citizenry, the rural population voted for its retention, while the urban "alien" population joined liquor interests in voting against.

Reporting this contest, one correspondent, G. B. Starr, referred to the "alien" element who came to this peaceful and prosperous state and insisted on retaining their drinking habits. Maine, he emphasized, would not be so degraded, even in her cities, if she would stand by her principles.[44] The conflict between city and country, suggested the author, revealed the old-stock middle class engaged in a struggle with city corruption, a corruption which certainly included the liquor dealer—who acted as one of its chief instigators.[45]

For a variety of reasons Adventists had tended to neglect urban evangelism. Urgent messages from Mrs. White brought a new emphasis on big-city evangelistic campaigns. Adventists decided to use a health approach. In 1912, at a Washington evangelistic council, several Seventh-day Adventist spokesmen advocated that urban opposition to Adventist preaching could be offset by stressing medical and temperance work.[46] As Adventists tried to evangelize American cities, their efforts harmonized with those of other Christian conservatives then involved in a rebirth of fundamentalism. This wave of fundamentalist furor helped prepare the way for the last phase of the prohibitionist drive.

Adventists began to use the press to promote urban evangelism. On January 1, 1912, Walter L. Burgan, an Adventist ex-journalist, persuaded the denomination to establish a press bureau as a General Conference department. The new department endeavored to secure wider publicity for Adventist teachings and assisted in the big-city evangelistic crusades.[47] By 1913 the foreign-born population of the United States numbered up to 40 million, and church leaders suggested that this enormous influx transformed the large cities of North America into the church's most important mission field.[48] Because the vast majority of these immigrants were Roman Catholic, and because of Adventist fears of the growing power of Rome,[49] this evangelistic task was the more important. They regarded this large foreign-born element, oriented to Roman Catholicism, as providing an ominous base for Roman Catholic expansion in America.

Equipped with new evangelistic facilities and techniques, Adventists played a significant part in the great final prohibition drive. On December 13, 1913, temperance forces organized a major rally at Washington, D.C. Headed by the Anti-Saloon League and the WCTU, the prohibitionist representatives marched to the Capitol to present petitions to both houses of Congress. The petitions argued medical, moral, economic, and social reasons for prohibition and stressed liquor's responsibility for degeneracy in children, for placing an economic burden on the citizenry, for lowering the nation's moral standards, and for causing crime and pauperism.[50]

Prohibitionists suggested an amendment which forbade the sale but not the consumption of alcohol. This distinction enabled the Anti-Saloon League and other prohibitionist organizations to gain wider public support. Even some drinkers might be won to support a blow against the liquor traffic, yet would resist any interference with their own consumer rights.[51] The resolution won a two-thirds majority in the House when presented by Representative Richard P. Hobson, but failed in the Senate.[52]

Commenting on this defeat, C. S. Longacre, at the time (1915) Secretary of the Religious Liberty Department, cited William Jennings Bryan's statement in the *Commoner* that even though the prohibition forces could not achieve the requisite two-thirds majority, the liquor business could be regarded as a fugitive from justice soon to be defeated. The vote on the amendment demonstrated that the prohibitionist wave sweeping America would succeed.[53] Longacre believed it vitally essential for the resources of the denomination to support the great effort mounted by the Anti-Saloon League.

By the time the 64th Congress opened on December 6, 1915, the league had reintroduced the Hobson Bill and had begun an intense prohibitionist drive. All temperance groups were to cooperate to make this effort a success.[54] Longacre lectured at temperance conventions and worked through the Instructor Temperance Leagues, whose members aimed to place the Temperance edition of the *Youth's Instructor* in every home. The temperance forces hoped to create a public sentiment for temperance capable of winning local and state prohibitionist elections. In this way increased pressure could be brought to bear on recalcitrant legislators. Nineteen states had already decided for prohibition. Seven more would decide during the next two years. Longacre intended to show that this constituted the main opportunity for the temperance forces.[55]

But delays developed. Cardinal Gibbons of Baltimore opposed any state-wide prohibition bill on the basis that such a law would encourage hypocrisy and interfere with personal liberty. Adventists regarded his attitude as additional proof that the Roman Catholic Church was willing to perpetuate the drink traffic for its own reasons. If Roman Catholicism demanded complete abstinence of its members, reasoned one writer, it would not be difficult for any state to enforce a prohibition law.[56]

Certain Adventist contributors to *Liberty* were equally irritated by one congressman who, at the annual Massachusetts Brewers Association banquet, stressed the damaging effects of prohibition on the country's economy. *Liberty's* correspondent pointed out the need to elect men who "would enforce the law and defend the public weal."[57]

On January 8, 1917, the United States Supreme Court upheld the constitutionality of the Webb-Kenyon law, which prohibited liquor from being shipped from "wet" to "dry" states, thus aiding dry states to enforce their prohibition laws.[58] The next month,

Congress passed a bill banning the sale of liquor in the District of Columbia.[59] Complete success appeared to be just ahead.

America's entry into World War I hastened national prohibition. At a time when the country was suffering from shortages caused by the war, the Government began to look askance at the use of grain by liquor interests. The Anti-Saloon League and its allies recognized this as an ideal opportunity to strike. By associating prohibition with patriotic war restrictions they made liquor interests look even more comical and vicious. Seventh-day Adventist leaders advised their fellow members to write their representatives in Congress protesting the manufacture of liquor from grain.[60] The result was that on August 10, 1917, Congress banned the use of foodstuffs for the manufacture of distilled spirits. Food administrator Herbert Hoover also secured legislation limiting the proportion of foodstuffs allowed for the manufacture of beer.

The 1917 elections greatly encouraged the temperance forces. New Mexico and New Jersey prohibitionists scored outstanding victories. The enfranchisement of women in New York increased the prospects of the "drys" in that state. National prohibition was now almost achieved.

Adventists, however, worried whether the tremendous forces mobilized by the Anti-Saloon League would disintegrate once its immediate objectives were obtained. Or would the society, in a moralistic tone, turn toward the enactment of a national Sunday law? This question weighed heavily in the minds of Religious Liberty Department officers and helped to shaped their later policy.

Earlier Seventh-day Adventist differences with major temperance organizations had almost entirely disappeared in their common campaign to secure a prohibition amendment. As this objective was now being accomplished, the Adventist leadership looked for ways to maintain the friendly association which had paved the path to reform. An opportunity presented itself when the National Dry Federation held its first annual executive meeting on December 17, 1918, in the Continental Hotel, Washington, D.C., presided over by William Jennings Bryan.

This federation combined virtually all the temperance organizations with the intention of reorganizing into an international body aiming for world prohibition. Longacre pledged Adventist cooperation and offered the use of denominational world mission stations to forward this plan. Temperance leaders complimented Adventists on their activity in the prohibition cause, and Longacre concluded that as a result of the church temperance efforts, its public image was better than ever.[61]

REFERENCES AND NOTES

1. James H. Timberlake, *Prohibition and the Progressive Movement 1900-1920* (Cambridge: Harvard University Press, 1963), pages 102, 103, 112, 113.

2. Critical of the prohibitionist movement as a whole, Andrew Sinclair remarked on the strongly Protestant nature of the gathering temperance drive. He emphasized that while the Anti-Saloon League was ostensibly a political and educational organization, it eventually gained the support of so many churches that it led to much unpleasantness.—Andrew Sinclair, *Prohibition: The Era of Excess* (Boston: Little, Brown and Company, 1962), pages 63-83.

3. "Chairman's Address," General Conference *Daily Bulletin*, March 31, 1903, p. 18.

4. Adventists consider that the failure of the prohibitionist movement was largely due to insufficient emphasis on education to accompany legislation.

5. E. G. White, "Importance of Health and Temperance Publications," *Review and Herald*, June 23, 1903, p. 20.

6. E. G. White, *Evangelism as Set Forth in the Writings of Ellen G. White* (Washington, D.C.: Review and Herald Publishing Association, 1946), page 514.

7. E. G. White, "Manuscript 14, 1901," *Temperance as Set Forth in the Writings of Ellen G. White* (Mountain View: Pacific Press Publishing Association, 1949), pages 247, 248.

8. E. G. White, "Lessons From Josiah's Reign," General Conference *Daily Bulletin*, April 1, 1903, pp. 32, 33.

9. E. G. White, "Our Duty to Leave Battle Creek," *Ibid.*, April 3, 1903, pp. 84-88; A. G. Daniells, "The Removal to Washington," *Review and Herald*, Aug. 11, 1903, pp. 5, 6 and *Ibid.*, Aug. 20, 1903, pp. 3-5.

10. J. S. Washburn, "A Glorious Opportunity," *Review and Herald*, March 10, 1904, pp. 6, 7.

11. W. A. Spicer, "More Sunday Bills Before Congress," *Review and Herald*, March 3, 1904, pp. 4, 5.

12. W. A. Colcord, "Petition Against Religious Legislation," *Review and Herald*, April 28, 1904, pp. 23, 24.

13. Editorial in the *Washington Post*, Dec. 28, 1904; cited in editorial, *Review and Herald*, Jan. 5, 1905, pp. 3, 4.

14. W. A. Colcord, "Editorial—Liberty," *Liberty*, April, 1906.

15. J. O. Corliss, "The Lesson of the California Earthquake," *Liberty*, *Ibid.*, pp. 23, 24.

16. Ellen G. White, "Drunkenness and Crime," *Review and Herald,* Oct. 25, 1906, pp. 8, 9.

17. Ellen G. White, "Drunkenness and Crime: Their Significance," *The Bible Student's Library,* No. 196 (Mountain View: Pacific Press Publishing Association). This particular tract is undated.

18. John Koren, *Economic Aspects of the Liquor Problem,* a report published by the Committee of Fifty of the results of its investigations into alcohol as a factor in poverty and crime in the District of Columbia. Koren was the editor and a member of the committee; cited by Timberlake, *Prohibition and the Progressive Movement 1900-1920,* page 57.

19. Timberlake, *op. cit.,* pages 57, 58.

20. E. G. White, "Drunkenness and Crime," pages 4-15. This, of course, was a common contention among temperance advocates during the period. Compare Andrew Sinclair, *Prohibition: The Era of Excess* (Boston: Little, Brown and Company, 1962), pages 36-62. Sinclair emphasized the "frenzy" of the prohibitionists in their use of this kind of propaganda.

21. David Paulsen, M.D., Superintendent, Hinsdale Sanitarium, "The Awful Curse of Intemperance," *Signs of the Times,* Oct. 2, 1907, pp. 2, 3.

22. Professor George Rine, "The Outlook for Prohibition," *Signs of the Times,* Oct. 2, 1907, pp. 6, 7.

23. Arthur Gleason, "The Saloon in New York," *Collier's Weekly,* May 2, 1908; cited by Timberlake, pages 110, 111.

24. "Departmental Meetings: The Religious Liberty Department." General Conference *Daily Bulletin,* June 6, 1909, p. 323.

25. Timberlake, *op. cit.,* p. 156.

26. C. M. Smith, "The Temperance Crusade," *Review and Herald,* April 23, 1908, pp. 4, 5.

27. K. C. Russell, "Resolutions Relating to Religious Liberty Work and Temperance," *Review and Herald,* May 14, 1908, p. 20.

28. "Excerpt From Ellen G. White Diary," March 6, 1859, *Spirit of Prophecy Counsels on Church and State,* pages 97-103.

29. "Letter 243a, 1905," *Temperance,* page 255.

30. K. C. Russell, "Camp-Meeting Temperance Rallies: A New Departure," *Review and Herald,* July 16, 1908, pp. 5, 6.

31. L. J. Otis, "A Revival of Temperance Work," *Review and Herald,* Aug. 6, 1908, p. 12.

32. Editor, "A New Tract: Prohibition and the Liquor Traffic," *Review and Herald,* Aug. 6, 1908, p. 30.

33. "Prohibition and Sunday Legislation." *Words of Truth Series,* No. 49 (Washington, D.C.: Review and Herald Publishing Association, no date). A series of tracts has been issued at intervals, when judged necessary. This particular tract has been bound with other miscellaneous tracts of the period under the title *Selected Tracts,* Volume 2, by the Pacific Union College Library, Angwin, California.

34. "The Liquor Traffic: Report from Committee on Plans and Finance," General Conference *Daily Bulletin,* May 24, 1909, pp. 130, 131.

35. W. F. Crafts in Washington *Post* of April 5, 1906; cited by K. C. Russell, "Report of the Religious Liberty Department," General Conference *Daily Bulletin,* May 31, 1909, p. 248.

36. K. C. Russell, "A Reformers' Conclave," *Liberty,* first quarter, 1910, pp. 11-14.

37. Matilda Erickson, "Should the Liquor Traffic Be Abolished?" *Liberty,* second quarter, 1909, pp. 42-45.

38. The *Youth's Instructor* was founded by James White in August, 1852, to "teach the young the commandments of God and the faith of Jesus." Published by the Review and Herald Publishing Association, at this time it was a weekly.

39. M. E. Kern, "Past Records," *Youth's Instructor,* Feb. 28, 1911, p. 16; "What the Societies Seeking to Protect Children Say," *Youth's Instructor* (Special), 1912.

40. Timberlake, *op. cit.,* pp. 161, 162. Deets Pickett, *The Truth About Prohibition and Repeal* (Columbus School and College Service, n.d. but after 1950), pages 8, 9. Strongly slanted toward prohibition, the book provides statistical data showing the gradual development of prohibitionist sentiment on the state scene.

41. Lewis M. Simes, "Prohibition and Personal Liberty," *Youth's Instructor,* March 7, 1911, pp. 17, 18.

42. R. B. Glenn, "Statewide Prohibition," *Youth's Instructor,* March 7, 1911, p. 26.

43. "Brewers Aiding State Prohibition," *Liberty,* third quarter, 1910, p. 46.

44. G. B. Starr, "The Prohibition Battle in Maine," *Liberty,* fourth quarter, 1911, p. 44.

45. Timberlake, *op. cit.,* p. 151.

46. *Review and Herald,* July 11, 1912, p. 20.

47. W. L. Burgan, "The Press Bureau," General Conference *Daily Bulletin,* May 21, 1913, pp. 79, 80.

48. O. A. Olsen, "Report of the North American Foreign Department," *Ibid.,* pp. 52, 53.

49. W. W. Prescott, "Report of the Secretary of the Religious Liberty Department," *Ibid.,* May 21, 1913, p. 68.

50. "Petition to Congress," *Liberty,* first quarter, 1914, p. 45.

51. Timberlake, *op. cit.,* p. 171.

52. *Congressional Record* 63rd Congress, 2nd Session SJR 88, pp. 736-745.

53. C. S. Longacre, "The Liquor Business a Fugitive From Justice," *Liberty,* second quarter, 1915, p. 945.

54. Peter H. Odegard, *Pressure Politics: The Story of the Anti-Saloon League* (New York: Octagon Books, Inc., 1966), pages 149ff. gives an excellent description of the increasing political pressures exerted by this powerful League.

55. C. S. Longacre, "A Call to the Instructor Temperance League," *Review and Herald,* Feb. 10, 1916, p. 17.

56. Editorial, "Cardinal Opposed to State-wide Prohibition," *Liberty,* third quarter, 1916, pp. 93, 94.

57. W. E. Gerald, "Starvation and Anarchy Will Follow National Prohibition," *Liberty,* third quarter, 1916, pp. 98, 99.

58. The Webb-Kenyon bill passed successfully; *Congressional Record* 62nd Congress, 3rd Session, p. 2806, but was vetoed by President Taft;

p. 4203; the Senate then passed the measure over the President's veto by 264 votes to 95; pp. 4297-4299. When on January 8, 1917, four years later, the law came under review by the United States Supreme Court, its constitutionality was completely sustained, *Clark Distilling Co.* v. *Western Maryland Railroad,* 242 U.S. 311 (1917). The act is discussed from a legal standpoint in *Columbia Law Review,* 1916, XVI, pp. 1-17.

59. "Make Way for Prohibition," *Review and Herald,* July 12, 1917, p. 2.

60. C. S. Longacre, "Prohibition and the Fall Elections," *Liberty,* first quarter, 1918, pp. 22, 23.

61. "National Prohibition a Fact," *Liberty,* first quarter, 1919, p. 23.

Chapter 5

PROBLEMS IN WARTIME

Seventh-day Adventists have long discussed their responsibility to government in time of war. Does the Old Testament justify military action? Since Christ's kingdom is not of this world, should Christ's servants participate in any human war effort?

Before the formally organized Seventh-day Adventist Church was a year old, the Civil War forced Adventists to clarify their convictions. Unlike the Quakers, most Seventh-day Adventists had no objection to alternative service such as working in hospitals or caring for freed slaves. Most of them sought to avoid only actual combatancy. Many simply avoided military service by paying the $300 commutation fee. But when the conscription act of March, 1863, was adopted, a whole new situation developed.

From his editorial office James White realized that the denomination faced a dangerous situation. Determined to obtain a consensus of Adventist opinion, he solicited letters from *Review* readers. Replies covered a wide spectrum of opinion. Most respondents agreed with him that the best policy was to support the Government but to avoid actual combatancy.[1] Nearly four years passed before the denomination officially formulated this view. But as early as August 3, 1864, it stressed that Adventist teachings contradicted the spirit and practice of war. The sixth commandment forbade the taking of human life. And the fourth with equal emphasis required abstinence from labor on the seventh day of the week, a virtual impossibility for a man performing ordinary military duties.[2]

Adventist leaders first approached several state governors and then Army headquarters. In response to their request for Federal recognition of their particular conscientious scruples, the provost general agreed that men objecting to active military service for religious reasons could discharge their obligations to their country by either working in hospitals or by caring for the newly liberated freedmen. This noncombatant arrangement was satisfactory to both sides. Adventists continued thereafter to take this position in time of war.[3]

With the close of the Civil War, the issue ebbed. But after the turn of the twentieth century, developments in Australia and New Zealand again brought the issue to the fore. In 1909 the Australian government passed a defense act which included compulsory military training. A similar situation confronted Adventists in New Zealand. When the religious liberty committee of the Australasian Union Conference of Seventh-day Adventists petitioned the two governments, its prompt and logical presentation resulted in favorable action.

The decisiveness and verve of Australian Seventh-day Adventists in meeting this difficulty contrasted with the procrastination of the British Union Conference which delayed petitioning the British prime minister until the lengthening casualty lists and the ravenous demands of the war machine had greatly exacerbated the situation. English Seventh-day Adventists consequently experienced continual hardships throughout the First World War.[4]

When the tempo of conflict accelerated in Europe and the international crisis became increasingly serious, the United States prepared for war. Because American Adventism had forged its noncombatant principles during the Civil War, the church in the United States was able to concentrate on determining what constituted acceptable noncombatant forms of service. Initial concern involved the noncombatant medic and his training. To prepare their young men, Adventists established Red Cross Training Schools in several denominational colleges and sanitariums. In these, students received battlefield medical instruction. As with the cooperation of the surgeon-general's office, these institutions ensured the War Department that the training was satisfactory.[5]

Graduates entering military service, however, discovered that they could seldom attend any Seventh-day Adventist church services. To meet their spiritual needs the General Conference, therefore, developed a camp pastor system. Employed and financed by the denomination, these camp pastors ministered to large numbers of young Adventists who had entered military service. The camp pastor's work soon developed into a specialized form of ministry; and since they were employed by the church, Adventists sensed no harm to church-state separation.

Realizing that Adventist draftees—when refusing to carry a weapon or to accept unnecessary duties on their Sabbath—would face disciplinary action anyway, the General Conference appointed Carlyle B. Haynes, prominent Adventist minister and writer, as secretary of a War Service Commission designed to care for these and other military problems which might affect Seventh-day Adventist servicemen. Camp pastors would report such difficulties to this commission, and where necessary the commission could utilize denominational resources in remedial action.[6]

When World War I ended and the church felt no further immediate need of these wartime organizations, the medical training program fell into disuse. But the changing political climate of the "thirties" soon reawakened Adventists to the importance of preparation for the possibility of another war.

By 1934 Adventists showed increasing concern over the rapidly deteriorating international situation. The world teetered on the brink of disaster. Explosive materials appeared everywhere and needed only a spark to set them off. Many Adventists at this time could see that current conditions made war inevitable.[7] Revival of the training program, now called the Medical Cadet Corps, seemed essential.

To stimulate Seventh-day Adventist thought on the subject, the Ministerial and Youth Departments of the General Conference published *Seventh-day Adventists in Time of War,* by Francis McClellan Wilcox, an Adventist editor and scholar. Adventist leaders urgently recommended it for reading by their respective groups.

Described as the outstanding Seventh-day Adventist book published in 1936, this volume popularized the revived medical-military training by describing the church's attitudes and activities during both the Civil War and World War I.[8]

At the same time Dr. E. D. Dick, professor and historian at Union College in Nebraska, and Major Cyril B. Courville of the United States Medical Reserve Corps, inaugurated an advanced

Medical Cadet Corps Training program. This training program, however, made little real headway until the outbreak of the second world war in Europe threatened American involvement.[9]

Renewed military trouble struck Seventh-day Adventists first in the British Isles. Unfortunately no denominational preparation for noncombatant service existed in the United Kingdom. After the fall of France, Adventist draftees in Britain, with little counsel from their church leaders, were confused and divided about what to do.

Some volunteered for active service, believing that by so doing they could select their own form of participation. This writer, for example, served in a London Civil Defense Unit during the period of the London air raids, later volunteering for medical service in the Royal Navy. It was possible in this way to serve as a noncombatant on various ships and in different theaters of war "for the duration." Others volunteered for the Royal Air Force and the Army. Still other Seventh-day Adventist young men registered as conscientious objectors and served their country by working on farms and raising critically needed food. On the whole, the British government followed a basically tolerant policy and generally recognized the rights of conscience.

American Seventh-day Adventists continued in the denominational pattern already developed during World War I. Adequate medical and educational facilities gave the denominational training program a rapid development as the United States braced itself for war. Regular Army officers directed and supervised each phase of Medical Cadet organization and thus ensured a total program harmonious with Army standards and methods and expectations.[10]

Some Adventist draftees found that their local draft boards refused to supply them with the requisite Form 47. But Carlyle B. Haynes, again the appointed chairman of the General Conference office of military affairs, renamed the National Service Commission, was usually able to smooth out these wrinkles at Selective Service Headquarters in Washington. Still other inductees faced hostile attitudes of uninformed or unsympathetic individual officers or from their own failure to follow established Governmental procedures. In these situations, also, Haynes and his associates consulted the proper authorities and almost always succeeded in resolving the difficulties.[11]

When the first District of Columbia contingent of the Medical Cadet Corps was graduated, Seventh-day Adventist leaders enjoyed the unstinted praise of the representative from the surgeon-general's office who delivered the graduation address and inspected the corps. He complimented the church's farsightedness in providing this training for its youth, and he expressed the interest of Army authorities in this training program. Adventists were further honored when Washington units of the Medical Cadet Corps were selected to man first-aid stations along the route of the Inaugural Day ceremonies of January 20, 1941. Medical Cadet Corps groups training in the Southwest were not only commended by visiting Army officers but were congratulated by the *Fort Worth Star Telegram,* which also commended the denomination for its policy of wartime cooperation. In Grand Ledge, Michigan, where a national MCC training camp was conducted, the local Chamber of Commerce congratulated the church on its public spirit and good citizenship.

This favorable public and official reception of the Medical Cadet Corps encouraged the General Conference to recommend that all Seventh-day Adventist conferences and institutions promote similar corps within their respective territories.[12]

The ready acceptance of the Medical Cadet Corps program by Governmental and military authorities caused some Seventh-day Adventists to criticize the total concept. In forwarding this non-combatant plan, the critics reasoned, the denomination had become a part of the national war machine and was therefore guilty of actively assisting men to make war.[13]

Seventh-day Adventist leaders replied that it is not the business of the church to judge the reasons behind the nation's decision to wage war. Its church members are responsible to their governments, and the only concern of such Christians should be limited to not violating their own consciences. By training thousands of Adventist youth as medical cadets, the leaders asserted, the church simply continued its essential work of Christian healing and witness. Any service rendered to the state came in addition to this primary benefit.[14]

Other church apologists suggested that since God's church on earth transcends all nationalities, and since Seventh-day Adventists cannot kill other Christians simply because they are citizens of another nation, they can and should cooperate actively in saving lives irrespective of national allegiance. Adventists took the position that noncombatancy is essentially an expedient, for it enables the denomination to practice reverence for life and obedience to God, while also "rendering unto Caesar" in effective and legitimate ways.[15]

Inevitably Seventh-day Adventist servicemen on occasion were ordered to carry weapons. In order to minimize such clashes, Carlyle B. Haynes, head of the War Service Commission, stressed that even for drill or ceremonial purposes no Seventh-day Adventist soldier should ever carry any weapon.[16]

Though opposed to bearing arms, Haynes still found no objection to church members buying Government savings bonds or engaging in civil service duties. In reply to the criticism that to buy Government bonds was to support the war, he argued that the Government used this public investment to supply food, shelter, clothing, and medical supplies as well as for weapons and munitions.[17] To further demonstrate the denomination's contribution to the Government, F. D. Nichol, editor of the *Review and Herald,* published a series of articles detailing the Seventh-day Adventist position on missions, health practices, moral emphasis, temperance advocacy, and stress on religious liberty as examples of the benefits the church rendered to the state.[18] One outstanding example of Adventist contributions during wartime was illustrated by a letter, dated 25th May, 1944, received by the Secretary of the General Conference from a Marine major concerning the Seventh-day Adventist mission-trained nationals of New Guinea and the South Pacific Islands:

"Having recently returned from _____, I should like to be able to express the gratitude which I feel, and I know that my men feel, toward your native missionary there, Robert Salau.

"Salau is a remarkable man. He is extremely intelligent, dignified, and had the respect of every one of us. He contrived to hold his people with him and to hold them as Christians throughout two arduous years of Jap occupation. . . .

"I hope that you soon will be able to contact Salau and help him carry on."[19]

Salau was but representative of various nationals who saved the lives of Allied military personnel, frequently at great risk to their own.

Although the denomination handled the noncombatancy problem so as to ease problems for native-born American GI's, its position imposed great difficulty upon would-be immigrants. The United States Immigration Service denied citizenship rights to aliens who refused to take an oath to bear arms in defense of the United States. Several test cases came before the United States Supreme Court, and in all of these instances the highest court of the nation upheld the decisions of the Immigration Service.[20] But after hostilities ceased in 1946, the James Louis Girouard case reversed the previous judicial trend. Girouard, a Seventh-day Adventist, pleaded that his devotion to his country was as truly demonstrated by noncombatant service as by combatant. The Supreme Court accepted his argument and reversed the earlier Schwimmer, Macintosh, and Bland rulings.[21] The *Christian Century* commented that the successful outcome of this case removed a shadow which had long darkened the fair tradition of American law and government.[22] Important as it was, however, the Girouard decision did not terminate the problems facing Seventh-day Adventist aliens applying for United States citizenship. Legislation introduced by Senator Patrick A. McCarran of Nevada would have debarred from citizenship any alien refusing to bear arms in defense of the United States. Fortunately for Adventists, this clause was deleted and the McCarran-Walter Immigration and Nationality bill became law with a provision that an alien for conscientious reasons could refuse to bear arms.[23]

The outbreak of the Korean War resulted in new conscriptions of Seventh-day Adventist young men. Three hundred and fifty Seventh-day Adventists were engaged in overseas service by the end of 1951. Deeply concerned over their spiritual welfare, the General Conference authorized the appointment of military chaplains. This decision marked a significant departure from the church's previous interpretation of the principle of separation.

Church leaders reasoned that chaplains were all volunteers

and, although paid by the military, were still basically in denominational employ. By October, 1952, the church had four chaplains in the Army, and two months later another chaplain had volunteered for service in Korea.[24]

Viewed as a way to provide a ministry to its church members, the appointment of chaplains emerged as a practical decision. Although some considered such appointments to violate the principle of church-state separation, others viewed them as implementation of the free-exercise clause. Chaplains could maintain closer relationships with servicemen than the earlier "camp pastors," and since they were officers, they could better represent their men to the military leadership.

In a sense, ministers as chaplains might be considered the capstone of Seventh-day Adventist labor to create an effective, harmonious working relationship with the Government in time of war. While Adventist servicemen made their wartime contribution to their country, the church provided a pastoral service for the spiritual needs of its men in uniform.[25]

REFERENCES AND NOTES

1. D. T. Bourdeau, "The Present War"; B. F. Snook, "The War and Our Duty"; James White, "The War Question," *Review and Herald*, Oct. 14, 1862, pp. 154-159. The opinions of the church members in response to the editorial request were printed in this and succeeding issues of the journal.

2. Francis McClellan Wilcox, *Seventh-day Adventists in Time of War* (Washington, D.C.: Review and Herald Publishing Association, 1936), page 37.

3. *Ibid.,* pp. 57, 65.

4. *Ibid.,* pp. 262, 263.

5. I. H. Evans, "Our Late Council," *Review and Herald*, Aug. 16, 1917, pp. 2, 6.

6. W. A. Spicer, Secretary, "Midsummer Council of the General Conference Committee," *Review and Herald*, Aug. 1, 1918, pp. 723-726.

7. Gwynne Dalrymple, "Looking Back at the Year 1933," *Ibid.*, pp. 6, 7.

8. Wilcox claimed that he was fulfilling three objectives: (1) providing a history of Adventist wartime relationship with government; (2) explaining Adventist noncombatant attitudes; and (3) helping Adventist men who would be called to serve their country.

9. Carl D. Anderson, "The History and Evolution of Seventh-day Adventist Church Organization" (Unpublished doctoral dissertation, The American University, Washington, D.C., 1960), p. 304.

10. "Preface to the First Edition," *Medical Cadet Corps Training Manual,* second ed., Cyril B. Courville and Elmer W. Gilbert, eds. (Washington, D.C.: Review and Herald Publishing Association, 1950), page 5.

11. Carlyle B. Haynes, "Report on the Commission in National Service and Medical Cadet Corps Training," *Review and Herald,* June 8, 1941, pp. 197-201.

12. A. W. Cormack, "The 1941 Autumn Council," *Review and Herald,* Dec. 4, 1941, p. 14.

13. The writer has quite often heard this opinion expressed by college teachers and students.

14. F. D. Nichol, *The Wartime Contribution of Seventh-day Adventists* (Washington, D.C.: Review and Herald Publishing Association, 1943), pages 6-8.

15. Clark Smith, "Noncombatancy and Governmental Relationships," *Character Guidance Studies for the Seventh-day Adventist Medical Cadet Corps* (Washington, D.C.: Seventh-day Adventist War Service Department of the General Conference, no date (mimeographed).

16. Haynes, "Noncombatants and Rifle Drill," *Review and Herald,* Jan. 8, 1942, p. 16.

17. Editorial, "Honoring the Flag," *Review and Herald* 119:20 (Feb. 5, 1942), p. 16.

18. F. D. Nichol wrote a series, "Our Wartime Contribution to Government," weekly in the *Review and Herald,* commencing with Aug. 26, 1943, and concluding with Nov. 25, 1943.

19. W. G. Turner, "From Cannibalism to Christianity, Allied Troops Testify That Foreign Missions Are Worthwhile," *Watchman Magazine,* January, 1945, pp. 8, 9, 14.

20. Notably the following cases: *United States* v. *Schwimmer,* 279 U.S. 646, (1929); see Anson Phelps Stokes, *Church and State in the United States* (New York: Harper and Brothers, 1950), Vol. 3, pp. 269-271; *United States* v. *Macintosh,* 238 U.S. 605, (1931); see Joseph Tussman, ed. *The Supreme Court in the United States* (New York: Oxford University Press, 1962), pages 51-64; *United States* v. *Marie Averil Bland,* 238 U.S. 636, (1931), see A. W. Johnson and F. H. Yost, *Separation of Church and State in the United States* (Minneapolis: University of Minnesota Press, 1948), pages 193, 194. Although these cases varied somewhat in individual details, in each case the aliens were excluded from American citizenship because of their refusal to swear to bear arms in defense of the United States as part of their oath of allegiance.

21. *United States* v. *Girouard* 328 U.S. 61, (1946). See Johnson and Yost, *Separation of Church and State,* pages 195-198.

22. Charles C. Morrison, editorial, "Dr. Macintosh—Apply Again," *Christian Century,* May 8, 1946, pp. 583, 584.

23. Carlyle B. Haynes, "Naturalization in the United States and Bearing Arms," *Review and Herald,* Oct. 30, 1952, p. 6.

24. W. H. Bergherm, "Prayers for Servicemen," *Review and Herald,* Dec. 13, 1951, p. 24.

25. The original view of Adventists on military chaplains might be illustrated by the action of A. T. Jones, as editor of *The American Sentinel,* when he reported in that journal a sermon by a Baptist minister who argued

that the appointment of chaplains to the Army and Navy struck at "the very first principle of free government."—*The American Sentinel,* Sept. 18, 1890, pp. 290, 291. The present secretary of the War Service Department of the General Conference, Clark Smith, expressed his opinion in a conversation with this writer, at Washington, that although some Adventists were disturbed when Seventh-day Adventist chaplains were first appointed, he did not consider that this action violated church-state separation, since the denomination retained its jurisdiction over its chaplains. If the church withdrew its ministerial credentials, the Armed Services would terminate their services.

The following statement shows that these facts as stated by Clark Smith are correct: "Each chaplain must be endorsed as duly ordained or licensed and qualified as a clergyman by a recognized civilian ecclesiastical agency, before he receives his commission, and such ecclesiastical commission is regularly reviewed by the civilian agency."—*The Military Chaplaincy: A Report to the President by the President's Committee on Religion and Welfare in the Armed Forces,* Oct. 1, 1950, p. 1.

At the same time it is important to note that: "The military chaplaincy program is an integral and vitally important phase of the varied program of our Armed Forces to meet the responsibilities of the Government to promote the general welfare of the men and women of the Armed Forces. The religious programs and services of the Armed Forces, in addition to their primary spiritual values, are an essential part of the attempt to make available an environment and services which will improve the general morale, promote military efficiency, and enhance national preparedness and security." *Ibid.,* p. 2.

It seems that the best justification of the practice is on the basis of "free exercise of religion." Notice this statement: "Our traditional faith in freedom of worship makes it important for the Armed Forces to make appropriate provision for religious opportunities. Were there no provisions for a religious program in the Armed Forces, military restrictions in the Armed Forces could seriously hamper the individual serviceman's opportunity to worship and, indeed, might completely nullify it." *Ibid.*

Chapter 6

POSTWAR FEARS OF
BIG GOVERNMENT AND A SUPERCHURCH

Social changes which concerned Seventh-day Adventists before the second world war assumed paramount importance after it ended. The decade of the "troubled thirties" with its labor conflicts, changing concepts of the role of government, decline of traditional Christianity, and rejection of prohibition, Adventists interpreted as national degeneration of those qualities essential for maintaining a democratic system.

Government propaganda used in the early phases of World War II to coordinate national resources seemed to further undermine individualism and personal probity. Certainly nations would be less able to cope with inevitable postwar problems. Overwhelming national debt faced all countries. Adventists looking at this fact, and at the apparent inability of humanity to solve its problems, considered the possibility of resultant dictatorship. To Adventists this threat to religious liberty was aggravated by the growing power of the Roman Catholic Church.[1]

Adventist eschatological interpretation anticipated Roman Catholic world dominance. Now they cited evidences to show its near approach. Roman Catholic influence was increasing in American urban centers because of the influx of European immigrants who came from Catholic-dominated regions of Europe. The population was shifting from Protestant to Catholic. The population shift was reflected in the labor force, which showed strengthened Catholic influence within the trade unions. Believing that influences adverse to personal and religious liberty would eventually flow from concentrations of this labor strength, Adventists distrusted the trade union movement. This distrust is clearly evident in some of the denomination's most prominent writers.[2]

Further augmenting Adventist fears concerning the developing strength of Catholicism was President Roosevelt's appointment of Myron C. Taylor as his personal representative to the Vatican. In common with other Protestant groups, Adventists considered this a breach of church-state separation which would lead to further encroachments, presaging virtual union of church and state in America.[3] With traditional standards toppling everywhere, and with communism and secularism apparently undermining religion, morals, home, and society, Americans were anticipating a new religious voice. Would this provide the papacy with its great opportunity?

Its power and influence were increasing everywhere. Would it capitalize on a widespread yearning for authority? Consistent supporter of the holiness of Sunday throughout early Christian history,[4] could it designate Sunday observance as the symbol of a national religious revival to counter the "new paganism" undermining Christian society?[5] In a "holy war" with "communism," could Sunday observance become the convenient rallying point of Roman Catholic leadership of the "Christian" forces? These issues vitally concerned Adventists at this time.

In protesting the appointment of an "ambassador" to the Vatican, Seventh-day Adventists acted in accord with other Protestant groups. *Liberty* published an editorial by Charles Clayton Morrison of the *Christian Century,* in which he emphasized President Roosevelt's political intuition in appointing Mr. Taylor to this post at this time when a majority of Americans were so vitally concerned with the progress of war in the European theater that they would probably overlook the implications of such an action. Secular newspapers, said Morrison, were too highly sensitive to Roman Catholic frowns to protest. Simultaneously extending invitations to Dr. George Buttrick of the Federal Council of Churches, and to a leading rabbi, Cyrus Adler, the President made it seem as if he were simply discovering each religious leader's views on problems of peace and world reconstruction. In this way, suggested Morrison, he disguised his real intention of establishing permanent diplomatic relationships with the pope.[6]

At the 1940 General Conference, spring session, delegates decided to publicize the significance of President Roosevelt's action. They commissioned the Religious Liberty Department to produce about two million copies of a small tract on the Vatican appointment. In addition, they urged Adventist church members to canvass their friends and neighbors on the threat to religious liberty implicit in this appointment.[7]

When published, the tract affirmed that this sudden reversal of attitude by the United States had caused amazement everywhere. The tract pointed out that as far away as Australia and New Zealand, people were surprised that the United States, which had advocated separation of church and state, should now grant special recognition to the Roman Catholic Church.

Roman Catholic representatives, on the other hand, rejoiced at the new status accorded their church. Few seemed to accept President Roosevelt's explanation that the ambassadorial arrangement was merely a personal affair. Most realized that representatives of a great nation and a great world church should never be "personal" in matters of this kind. They could not divest themselves of their representative character, the tract concluded.[8]

The Seventh-day Adventist denomination persisted in its agitation for a time, calling for every lover of liberty to protest the President's action. But the combined Protestant publicity had little permanent effect. By 1943 Americans, who at first strongly opposed Taylor's appointment, had become relatively apathetic on the matter.

Roman Catholics, declared one Adventist writer, interpreted this uncritical public attitude as evidence that Americans realized complete separation of church and state to be impossible and even undesirable.[9] Some Catholic apologists went so far as to advocate that the pope should be asked to mediate at the peace table. (Adventist eyes saw the Roman Catholic Church already too elevated before the world.) Diplomatic activity focused on the Vatican's interests. Trade union leaders gave unremitting attention to papal social and economic encyclicals. And the President of the United States maintained ambassadorial relationships with the church.[10] To Adventists the fact that the papacy was both recognized and provided with a world role by the United States, a nation dedicated to church-state separation, clearly showed an ominous increase in the Roman Catholic threat.

As the close Presidential liaison with the Vatican entered its fifth year, Seventh-day Adventists noted with some perturbation that President Roosevelt was continuing his secret negotiations with Pope Pius XII and that such important Allied personalities as British Prime Minister Winston Churchill had openly visited the pope. Did these negotiations presage a developing collaboration between the Allies and the Vatican which, extending beyond the second world war might endanger the peace by producing in the United States a virtual union of church and state? If so, was not the vital principle of religious liberty greatly endangered?[11] Seventh-day Adventist *Watchman* editor, Robert Leo Odom, reasoned that it was, since this United States-British-Vatican relationship suggested that papal collaboration would be involved in the reconstructing of Germany, Italy, and possibly the whole of Western Europe.[12]

To most Seventh-day Adventists the end of the war did not indicate that they should change their views about the new and dangerous role of the Roman Catholic Church in Europe. Adventist writer and editor W. L. Emmerson, for example, suggested that Western European nations obviously depended upon the potential influence of the Roman Catholic Church to provide them a viable bulwark against the onward sweep of both communist ideology and power. Catholic-oriented leaders in France, Austria, and Italy all looked to the Vatican for ideological support. Similar political parties were rising in Belgium, Holland, and Western Germany. Even Protestant England was sending her statesmen and service chiefs to enter into discussions with the pope and his representatives.[13] Meanwhile, *Signs* Editor Maxwell wrote: "Pius XI cultivates America as his finest ally in the holy war with the Kremlin." "With the Black International facing the Red International," the editor continued, "lovers of freedom should reflect on the ideology and performance records of both of these organizations. Liberty could not flourish if associated with either of the two systems."[14]

Review Editor F. D. Nichol questioned the propriety of criticizing another religious denomination. Adventists, he argued, were not anti-Catholic, *per se,* but they did oppose the Roman Catholic Church in its refusal to grant liberty of conscience to others. Roman Catholic history indicated that this church did not readily grant religious tolerance to peoples of other faiths. Even in America, the Vatican consistently opposed the principle of church-state separation. And now her crusade against communism was poisoning relationships between the United States and the Soviet Union and rendering any intelligent diplomatic relationship between these two superpowers virtually impossible. The Roman Catholic crusading motif against communism was sowing seeds of danger for the future. In building its own imperialistic hierarchy within the United States, the Vatican utilized propaganda, education, trade unions, and diplomacy. While it was considered bad taste to criticize another religion, loyal citizens did need to guard against the threat posed by Roman Catholic postwar activities, stressed Nichol.[15]

Nor were Nichol and his denomination alone in this opinion. Their strongest statements were matched by those of the POAU, a new society recently and expressly founded to guard against the developing threat to religious liberty in America. Calling itself "Protestants and Other Americans United for the Separation of Church and State," this association pledged itself to resist attempts to break down the historic "wall." If it could prevent Roman Catholic depredations on state resources, reasoned F. D. Nichol, POAU would render a great contribution to American freedom. He regretted only that so far the society had failed to recognize legally forced Sunday closing of all businesses as equally threatening to religious freedom.[16]

Roman Catholic reaction to these criticisms assumed a faintly derisive air. Commenting on the formation of POAU, the leading Jesuit weekly, *America,* expressed relief that present-day anti-Catholic concern no longer conjured up fiery visions of the Apocalypse or lurid disclosures of the "Maria Monk" variety. Present criticism of Roman Catholic activities employed the "pale metaphor of the camel's nose." *America* then suggested that the best Catholic answer to Protestant criticisms might be to discuss candidly the whole problem of religious liberty, particularly such complex issues as Spain's political tradition and the materialistic secularism now developing in all countries.[17]

F. D. Nichol replied that POAU's reaction to Roman Catholic

intrusions was certainly a valid one. The Supreme Court also had noted the problem of the "camel's nose." A whole history of its judicial decisions concerning church-state issues involving the activities of the Roman Catholic Church was the best evidence of that. As for the intolerant conditions in South America and Spain, preventing Protestant ministers from preaching, it was not sufficient to blame national tradition. Was it not the Roman Catholic Church itself which had created that tradition? If Roman Catholic aims and objectives concerning American education should be realized, a similar tradition might develop in the United States.[18] Historical Roman Catholic theories on church-state relations, urged Nichol, still included the doctrine that where the salvation of the soul was imperiled, the church could supersede the state. This dogma provided a "bridge" over which popes and prelates could walk whenever they wished to exercise church power over the state.[19]

Other Adventists commented variously on Roman Catholic views on church-state relations during this period. Frank H. Yost, Religious Liberty Department secretary and veteran teacher of church history, criticized John Courtney Murray's[20] argument that the First Amendment involved only a political principle. Yost contended that it still implied a religious corollary by its constitutional stress that no religious test should be imposed as a prerequisite for holding Federal office. Dr. Murray's argument, said Yost, failed to note that where Roman Catholics composed a large majority in a state, the First Amendment could not operate effectively as a political expedient. The consciences of the Roman Catholic majority might cause them to influence the state into passing legislation affecting religious concerns, thus violating the rights of religious minorities.[21]

The increasing national and international prominence of the Roman Catholic Church, including its repeated endeavors to gain Government subsidies for its educational system,[22] caused the Seventh-day Adventist General Conference to take important decisions on church-state attitudes during 1948. At its spring session in May, 1948, it heard several reports on ways in which the denomination could relate to the Government in "these significantly changing times."[23] Presenting the report of the subcommittee on religious liberty problems, its chairman, J. I. Robinson, while accepting traditional denominational views on religious liberty, declared that church-state separation was a policy rather than a principle.[24] Few Adventists agreed with this contention, including a number of his own committee members, but it sparked an extended discussion of religious liberty issues in the following General Conference autumn council of 1948.

Delegates at this meeting discussed rather fully the principle of "soul liberty." Scripture, they stressed, indicated very clearly that God desired individuals to approach Him on the basis of faith and love. Since God does not employ His power to force people to follow certain religious practices, it was clear that human institutions and churches must allow all men freedom of choice. Both the church and the state must leave man free to believe in and respond to God's love. Love rather than force underlies both the law and the gospel.[25] From these conclusions, delegates tried to shape the ideal relationship between church and state in the changed situation of the late forties. The discussion finally resulted in a careful reaffirmation of traditional Seventh-day Adventist separationist views.

Some delegates argued, however, that in countries where different forms of church-state relationship prevailed, overseas divisions should apply the principle of separationism only where possible. They must adapt to existing conditions.

A similar compromise was accepted on tax exemption. The denomination accepted tax exemption for its properties on the grounds that where one church was exempted, all should be.

Concerning the threat of Sunday laws, it resolved to defeat these laws whenever and wherever possible. It urged that neither religious legislation nor religion was the business of the state.

While state-supported schools might teach morality and ethics, they should not teach religion. This Council decided that Adventist schools not use textbooks supplied by public funds or accept Government grants for teacher salaries or school maintenance. Government-provided public health services could be accepted in the denomination's schools.[26]

Thus 1948 autumn council clarified the Seventh-day Adventist official position on religious liberty. As far as the United States was concerned, it took strong positions on church-state separationism, accepting only tax exemption on its properties.

A similarly uncompromising attitude actuated Frank H. Yost when, as representative of the Religious Liberty Department of the General Conference, he attended the 1948 Amsterdam meeting of the World Council of Churches. Although he regarded its four declarations on religious liberty as admirable, he considered them nullified because they lacked a definite commitment to church-state separation. To assert the right of each individual to determine his own faith and creed; to express his religious beliefs in worship, teachings, and practice; to associate with others for religious purposes; and to operate through a chosen religious organization to form religious policies and practices was all splendid, said Yost; but such resolutions would accomplish little unless the church and the state were kept separate.

Yost thought church-state separation was the only thoroughly effective way to preserve religious liberty. Collaborating with Alvin W. Johnson, another religious liberty leader, in the revision of Johnson's book on church-state separation, Yost set forth strong views on this separationism ideal and greatly influenced SDA denominational policy.[27]

After his attendance at the Amsterdam meeting, Yost concluded that the churches of America were moving to the "left." Although free churches of America were still much freer than state-controlled churches in Europe, Yost noted the presence of paternalistic trends. American churches were increasingly relying on the state, he believed, and if this trend continued, a World Council of Churches could bring on an unmitigated disaster to liberty of conscience.[28]

Other Seventh-day Adventist writers saw this "leftist" trend as more clearly evident in the social record of the Roman Catholic Church. Carlyle B. Haynes remarked that much was heard in the United States of communist infiltration into American trade unions, but little was stated concerning the labor schools that trained Roman Catholic trade unionists. Within the scope of modern American social history, the Roman Catholic Church had gradually passed from its initial hostility to labor organization, to an attitude of patronage and support of unionism. The Roman Catholic Church, Haynes argued, now used its educational institutions to gain control of organized labor and thus secure the best and highest positions for priests and Roman Catholic agents.[29]

Although these social aspects of Roman Catholic development caused concern to Seventh-day Adventists, President Truman's appointment of General Mark Clark as the first United States plenipotentiary to Vatican City caused shock.

President Roosevelt had assaulted Protestant sensibilities by appointing Myron C. Taylor as his personal representative to the Vatican. But Roosevelt had assured Protestants that Mr. Taylor would never become an accredited ambassador. They were unconvinced; but, at least, Roosevelt kept his word. Now President Truman had sent General Mark Clark as an official American plenipotentiary to the pope. At their 1951 Autumn Council Session, held in Cleveland, Ohio, Seventh-day Adventist leaders passed the following resolution: *"Whereas:* In the appointment of an ambassador to the Vatican by the President of the United States, we see a deplorable disregard of Protestant and democratic sentiment and a further departure from and weakening of the constitutional principle of the separation of church and state, also an inevitable deepening of religious rivalries, and controversies; *Voted:* That our official protest against this appointment, voted October 21, be implemented by: 1. Asking our conferences, churches, societies, institutions, and church members in the United States to write letters to their senators, urging that confirmation of any ambassador to the Vatican be withheld."[30]

The *Signs of the Times* contributed to the general chorus of Adventist dissent by publishing an article written by Glenn L. Archer, executive secretary of POAU. Editor A. S. Maxwell urged his readers to discover from Archer's article why America must not send an official representative to the Vatican.[31] The article followed the usual course of Protestant dissent, drawing the conclusion that the appointment assisted the pope rather than the United States.

Archer then asked whether the Vatican deserved this recognition, answering his own question by recounting the role of the Roman Catholic Church in relation to totalitarian forms of government. He pointed out that the Holy See had signed concordats with Mussolini and Hitler and maintained these agreements until their regimes ceased to respect Roman Catholic prerogatives. Only as allied troops neared Berlin did the papacy shift to the democratic cause. At the same time, 1952, the Roman Catholic Church favored and supported Franco, Salazar, Peron, and other dictators.[32]

Liberty took a somewhat different tack. It published a number of magazine and newspaper articles on President Truman's ambassadorial appointment, but the editorial pointed out that the journal did not handle political matters, since it was interested only in preserving complete separation of church and state in America. It was not an anti-Catholic journal. It did not criticize the Roman Catholic Church except for its concepts of church-state relationship. *Liberty* evidently wished to ensure its effectiveness as a defender of American and human liberties while trying to avoid unnecessary antagonism.[33]

Regarding President Truman's argument that the pope could assist in coordinating world efforts against the communist threat, Adventists urged that the "communist threat was used as an excuse for everything dubious in the public life." Adventists further pointed out that the strongly Roman Catholic countries most easily succumbed to communism. In the showdown, Protestantism, with its essential individualism, proved the more resistant. The Roman Catholic Church had held sway for centuries in Italy, and here communism was making tremendous inroads. How unfortunate, suggested Adventist Editor Rodney E. Finney in his magazine *These Times,* that the President should risk religious division at home for such doubtful advantage abroad. The Roman Catholic Church needed America, not the reverse.[34]

Although many other Protestants expressed concern over the "Catholic threat," there was little agreement on ways to meet it. Charles Clayton Morrison, former editor of *The Christian Century,* argued that because of its disunity Protestantism was unable to compete with a successfully united Roman Catholicism. Only as Protestantism united, urged Morrison, would it be able to challenge Roman Catholicism for the soul of America and the world. Morrison was, of course, expressing his convinced ecumenism, and he felt that the splintered Protestant Christendom belied the name and title of the church of Jesus Christ. The Christian church, he asserted, came into being from the mind of Christ, and He certainly did not accept its fragmentation into self-assertive and quarreling sects.[35]

Adventists disagreed. The recently popularized concept of unity in adversity, said Frederick Lee, an Adventist editor, held little appeal for those who believed in the intrinsic importance of truth. Unless a unanimity of doctrinal belief existed, he argued, real unity could not be achieved.

The Roman Catholic threat to religious freedom was sufficiently alarming, but a contrived unity of the Protestant churches could also lead to intolerance and persecution. It would be easy for such a group to appeal to the state to enforce a common religious view upon all who dissented from it. While every credit for good intentions could be given to the leaders of the present ecumenical movement, they could not be sure that new leaders would have the same regard for religious freedom.

The Amsterdam meeting of 1948, and the Cleveland, Ohio, gathering of 1950, had successfully promoted the formation of the World Council of Churches and of the United States National Council of Churches. But these great conferences had done little toward solving the problems of denominational doctrinal disagreements. Adventists believed that observance of the seventh day of the week was necessary to the proper keeping of the Ten Commandments. But this was obviously a view held by only a tiny minority of Christian churches. How would Adventists fare in any union of Christian churches?[36]

In 1954 *Signs* Editor Maxwell attended the Evanston meeting of the World Council of Churches, where he was deeply impressed by the quality of Christian devotion manifested by leaders of theological thought at the gathering of this second general asssembly. However, he shed the usual Adventist pessimism about such meetings. The hope of the second advent of Jesus, he said, was vividly discussed, and the delegates had emphasized the need for religious liberty. Speakers referred to dangers threatening Protestant liberty in Italy and Spain, voicing the opinion that even in the United States great battles for human freedom were still to be fought and won.[37]

He complimented the patience, tact, and kindliness of the leaders of the World Council. "To suggest," he said, "that these good men have in mind the establishment of a superchurch with a Protestant pope is to libel their intentions. They have no such thought in mind. Nor have they any plan to coerce the smaller religious bodies nor to persecute those who may disagree with them. They would be shocked at the very suggestion. At the present time any church which joins the World Council may withdraw from it at any time."

These men, Maxwell insisted, were searching for truth. There was no reason why everyone, including Episcopalians, Methodists, Presbyterians, Baptists, and Seventh-day Adventists should not welcome the opportunity to compare views in a common quest for truth.[38]

This was, of course, a reasonable, charitable viewpoint. Sincerity is a common coin for all men of good faith. But while *Signs* Editor Maxwell stressed the importance of a united search for truth as the basis for true spiritual unity, *Review* Editor Nichol, also an observer at the Evanston Conference, noted that the various religious bodies at Evanston were so preoccupied with adjusting their doctrines and government to produce a superficial harmony that they were unable to arrive at any fundamental unity. While he admitted, as Maxwell did, the evident sincerity and irenicism of of the ecumenical leaders and cautioned against manipulating prophetic portions of Scripture to denounce them, he nonetheless called attention to the fact that prophecy did indeed foresee a time when an autocratic church-state union would suppress religious freedom and persecute dissenters.

All Seventh-day Adventists, affirmed Nichol, have the right and the responsibility to guard against such an occurrence.[39]

REFERENCES AND NOTES

1. "Setting the Stage for Revelation 13," editorials in *Review and Herald* beginning Feb. 29, 1940, and continuing weekly through April 4, 1940.

2. John D. Hicks has pointed out that in the 1928 Presidential election Hoover consistently stressed what he termed "the American system" while Alfred E. Smith, who was both a Roman Catholic and a product of the cities, made his appeal to the urban population. The results of the election

demonstrated the new importance of the urban masses. John D. Hicks, *Republican Ascendancy 1921-1933* (New York: Harper & Row, 1960), pages 204-212. Probably these facts have a bearing on the rather consistently Republican flavor of Adventist "politics" in America. Certainly this was a continuing phenomenon in American political life. A notable example of this point of view regarding unions can be seen in Ellen G. White, *Testimonies,* Vol. 7, p. 84.

3. J. L. McElhany, "The United States and the Vatican," *Review and Herald,* Jan. 11, 1940, pp. 4, 5. Robert A. Graham, a Jesuit writer admits that while on Dec. 23, 1939, President Roosevelt announced his intention to send Myron C. Taylor as his "personal representative," reactions at the Vatican indicated that from the beginning of his mission, Taylor was regarded as the diplomatic representative of the United States Government. Robert A. Graham, *Vatican Diplomacy* (Princeton: Princeton University Press, 1959), pages 326-330.

4. Adventists have always emphasized that as successor to the Old Catholic Church, Rome is the prime supporter of Sunday as the "Sabbath" of the Christian world.

5. F. D. Nichol, "Wanted—A Voice of Authority," *Review and Herald,* March 28, 1940, pp. 9, 10.

6. Charles Clayton Morrison, "An Un-American Appointment," *The Christian Century,* Jan. 10, 1940.

7. E. D. Dick, "Principles of Protestantism and Separation of Church and State," *Review and Herald,* May 16, 1940, p. 13.

8. W. A. Spicer, "President Sends Ambassador to Pope," *The Present Truth,* June 1, 1940, pp. 1-3.

9. H. H. Votaw, "Are Americans Indifferent?" *Liberty,* first quarter, 1943, p. 28.

10. F. D. Nichol, "The Catholic Church and Religious Liberty," *Review and Herald,* July 22, 1943, p. 7; Nichol, "The Pope as Mediator," *Ibid.,* Sept. 3, 1943, p. 10; Nichol, "Shall the Church Dictate the Peace?" *Ibid.,* Oct. 28, 1943, p. 16.

11. Robert Leo Odom, "These Diplomatic Relations With the Vatican," *Watchman Magazine,* March, 1945, pp. 4, 5, 13.

12. *Ibid.,* p. 5.

13. W. L. Emmerson, "Will Europe Return to Rome?" *Signs of the Times,* June 11, 1946, pp. 8, 9; extremely anti-Roman Catholic, Avro Manhattan, *Vatican Imperialism in the Twentieth Century* (Grand Rapids: Zondervan Publishing Company, 1965), deals with the work of these Catholic parties. He fails to distinguish between the differences of relationship between these parties and the hierarchy in various countries, nor does he recognize the divergences of outlook in the Roman Catholic Church —divergences which made Vatican II a possibility. Note particularly pages 385ff. A quite contrary approach which emphasizes America's "exploitation" of the Vatican for her own diplomatic reasons is given by Robert A. Graham, *Vatican Diplomacy,* pages 347ff.

14. A. S. Maxwell, "Coming Struggle," *Signs of the Times,* Oct. 29, 1946, p. 3.

15. F. D. Nichol, "Voices Raised Against Rome," *Review and Herald,* March 4, 1948, pp. 4, 5.

16. F. D. Nichol, "Protestants Organize Against Catholic Legislative Campaign," *Review and Herald,* April 1, 1948, pp. 3, 4.

17. F. D. Nichol, "Catholic Reaction to Protestants United," *Review and Herald,* April 8, 1948, p. 4, responding to editorial, "Religious Liberty the Concern of All," *America,* Feb. 7, 1948. For POAU concepts of its own mission, see C. Stanley Lowell, *Embattled Wall—Americans United: An Idea and a Man* (Washington: POAU, 1966); also C. Stanley Lowell and Herbert C. Southgate, "POAU Position on Church-State Relations," *A Journal of Church and State,* May, 1963, p. 41.

18. F. D. Nichol, "Catholic Authorities on Church-State Relations," *Review and Herald,* May 13, 1948, pp. 3, 4.

19. F. D. Nichol, "The Catholic Bridge Between Church and State," *Review and Herald,* May 20, 1948, pp. 5, 6. Nichol indicates no recognition of John Courtney Murray's central contention that the Roman Catholic Church's spiritual power is limited to spiritual matters and can only reach the temporal power through the consciences of Roman Catholic citizens. This point is dealt with more fully by Frank H. Yost.

20. Father John Courtney Murray is the notable Jesuit theologian, principal architect of the Roman Catholic Declaration on Religious Liberty, and apologist for the idea that the emerging world consciousness of the importance of religious liberty is the chief factor enabling its achievement at the present time.

21. Frank H. Yost, "Confused Thinking on the Separation of Church and State," *Liberty,* second quarter, 1947, pp. 27-29. Apart from Murray's own works, for excellent comments on his ideas see Thomas T. Love, *John Courtney Murray: Contemporary Church-State Theory* (New York: Doubleday and Co., 1956); and Donald Wolfe, "The Uniting Theory of Church-State Relations," *A Journal of Church and State,* May, 1962, pp. 42ff. Both deal with Murray's ideas, finally emphasizing that the First Amendment, because it is simply a good legal enactment, is subject to development and interpretation, and must be differently applied under changing circumstances.

22. These issues will be considered in chapter 10, which deals with the subject of education.

23. E. E. Roenfelt, Associate Secretary of the General Conference, "Spring Meeting of the General Conference Committee," *Review and Herald,* May 27, 1948, p. 7.

24. J. I. Robinson, "Religious Liberty versus Separation of Church and State," Personal position paper mimeographed Sept. 8, 1949, p. 10; William A. Loveless, "Federal Aid and the Church-operated College" (unpublished doctoral dissertation, University of Maryland, 1964), pages 73, 74.

25. W. B. Ochs, vice-president of the General Conference, "Soul Liberty: A Glance at Biblical Authority," *Liberty,* first quarter, 1948, pp. 16, 17.

26. Norman W. Dunn, Associate Secretary of the General Conference, "Autumn Council Proceedings," *Review and Herald,* Dec. 2, 1948, pp. 6-8.

27. Alvin W. Johnson and Frank H. Yost, *Separation of Church and State in the United States* (Minneapolis: University of Minnesota Press,

1948); originally Johnson, *Legal Status of Church-State Relationships in the United States.*

28. Frank H. Yost, "When the Churches Met at Amsterdam," *Signs of the Times,* May 15, 1951, pp. 10, 11, 14, 15.

29. Carlyle B. Haynes, "Catholics and Labor Unions," *Review and Herald,* beginning Jan. 12, 1950, and continuing weekly through Feb. 9, 1950.

30. Alvin W. Johnson, "The Appointment of an Ambassador to the Vatican," *Review and Herald,* Dec. 6 and 13, 1951. Robert A. Graham in *Vatican Diplomacy* interprets the Myron C. Taylor "mission" beginning in 1939 and the later mission, presumably of Mark Clark, as a natural result of the new international responsibilities of both the United States and the Vatican. Anson Stokes, *Church and State in the United States,* Vol. 2, pp. 96ff. gives an excellent description of the whole affair. He mentions the Vatican attitude to Taylor, but cites President Roosevelt's letter in reply to Dr. G. A. Buttrick, president of the Federal Council of the Churches of Christ in America, reaffirming the United States President's original position. In the revised one-volume edition of the original Stokes book, Anson Phelps Stokes and Leo Pfeffer, *Church and State in the United States* (New York: Harper & Row, 1964), pages 278ff., it is pointed out that in spite of promises to recall the Vatican representative after Taylor resigned, President Truman announced he would officially send General Mark Clark as a way of combating communism.

31. Arthur S. Maxwell, "Our Cover," *Signs of the Times,* May 27, 1952, p. 2.

32. Glenn L. Archer, "Keep America Free," *Signs of the Times,* May 27, 1952, p. 2.

33. Heber H. Votaw, "This Number of *Liberty,*" *Liberty,* first quarter, 1952, p. 5.

34. Rodney E. Finney, *These Times,* February, 1952, pp. 18, 19, 34; *These Times* is a Seventh-day Adventist journal established in 1891 under the title *The Southern Agent;* the name changed in 1892 to *The Southern Watchman,* and in 1901 it became *The Watchman;* in 1905 it again changed to *The Watchman Magazine,* changing once more, in 1917, to *Our Times.* Finally, in 1946 it became *These Times.*

35. Charles Clayton Morrison, *The Unfinished Reformation* (New York: Harper & Brothers, 1951), pages 26-47.

36. Frederick Lee, "Church Union Now," *Review and Herald,* Aug. 20 and 27, 1953, pp. 11, 12 and 13, 14.

37. Arthur S. Maxwell, "Evanston Memories," *Signs of the Times,* Oct. 12, 1954, pp. 3, 4, 15.

38. A. S. Maxwell, "Struggle for Unity," *Signs of the Times,* Oct. 19, 1954, pp. 3, 4, 14, 15.

39. F. D. Nichol, "Comments on the World Council of Churches," *Review and Herald,* Sept. 23, 1954, pp. 14, 15.

Chapter 7

SUNDAY ENFORCEMENT REVIVED

By the mid-1950's Adventists were emphasizing the superficiality of the then current religious revival. Commenting on the "new piety," *Review* Editor Nichol reflected on the possibility that the recent increased interest in religion might have stemmed from a fear of the future. The threat of communism, and the possibility of atomic destruction were causing greater numbers to look to Christianity as a refuge from the coming storm.[1] The revival of enforced Sunday observance concerned Seventh-day Adventists.

Increasingly, they noted, lax Sunday observance provided too facile a symbol to illustrate the degeneracy and materialism of the times and too convenient a reason for tampering with religious liberty through legal measures. Joining the revived Sunday enforcement cadres came business leaders aggravated by competitors who opened for business on Sunday. They readily supported Sunday-closing enforcement, hoping to end this "unfair" competition.[2]

Rapid suburban development and the multiplication of automobiles enabled Americans to shop where they wished. And Sunday gave them the chance. Large commercial outlets, the "discount houses," opened along the main highways to take advantage of the increasingly mobile shoppers. Utilizing rural locations, these businessmen reduced overhead and secured ample parking facilities. Thus they were able to underprice downtown merchants, who retaliated by supporting Sunday closing legislation.[3]

Powerful new support emanated from Roman Catholic sources. Opposition to communism and "secularism" impelled Roman Catholic leaders to forsake the old "Continental" concept of a holiday-like Sunday in favor of new crusading alliances with "downtown" businessmen and trade union interests aiming to shorten the labor week. If the powerful trade union interests should lend their full support to business and religious groups, they would be capable of exerting enormous political pressure.[4] Adventists could do little to prevent such a confluence of action.

At that time the legal view of Sunday observance legislation held that the laws were designed to preserve the social and economic welfare of the population. They were not, in this view, religious laws. But religious and social interests could work together to effect the passing of Sunday laws.

Adventists, noting that the results of these laws produced a type of religious persecution, insisted that they were not "social" but religious.[5] They argued that Americans had a five-day work week. Why did they need an enforced rest day?

Adventists deeply distrusted this concerted activity by religious and social groups. They felt that the instrumental activity of the anticipated successful Sunday enforcement would come from the labor unions. Coalitions of labor and church groups were already distributing automobile bumper stickers and advertising in local papers. As Adventists watched, they saw a time when stronger measures would be taken.[6]

They found welcome allies in Sabbath-keeping Jewish merchants who worked through the Rabbinical Council of America to pressure state legislators to rectify the "injustice" to Jews prevented from earning their living on Sunday, having already rested on Saturday.[7] The practically universal endorsement of the New York Jewish community supported the Asch-Rosenblatt bill which was recommended to the New York State Legislature by the New York City Council. In spite of its powerful backing, it was rejected on the grounds that it would weaken the force of existing Sunday laws.[8]

Liberty magazine publicized the implications of the defeat of this Jewish legislative effort by publishing an article by Dean M. Kelley, chairman of the board of social and economic relations of the Methodist New York East Conference. Dr. Kelley stressed the "characteristic" nature of differences between the Jews and the Roman Catholics over the issue, and the rather emotional climate in which the "battle" was fought. He suggested that Roman Catholic sources had spread rumors of Macy's and Gimbels staying open seven days a week and of Christians and Jews operating in partnership to open stores every day of the week. Every shopkeeper in New York, these rumors suggested, was forced to register his faith, and declare his choice of Sabbath. Within this confused atmosphere, the Roman Catholic hierarchy tried to represent itself as the new guardian of the legalistic Puritan Sunday. This extraordinary change of direction was explicable, in Kelley's opinion, by Rome's conception of itself as "arbiter and proprietor of all legislation concerned with moral and religious issues." Protestant apathy and the failure to recognize the implications of the bill had allowed the Catholic voting bloc to triumph.[9]

To Adventists the rising tempo of the Sunday crusade resulting from the efforts of Roman Catholics, Protestants, and organized labor suggested a consistent and concerted pattern of cooperation.[10] During the General Conference spring session held in Cleveland in 1958, J. A. Buckwalter, the secretary of the Religious Liberty Department, described the critical state of Sunday law issues. Around the country, he reported, demands for strict Sunday enforcement burgeoned at state and local levels. The religious liberty department, reported its secretary, met with some success in combating these laws; but so far the Supreme Court had refused to review the cases on the grounds that the First Amendment did not apply. The high court regarded Sunday laws as social rather than religious.

The strenuous efforts by the Roman Catholic hierarchy and strong labor unions sparked new proposals for Sunday laws and prompted tightening of existing legislation. Merchant associations supported these efforts in order to prevent "unfair competition" from stores open on Sunday. Buckwalter revealed that these arguments were used to demonstrate that Sunday laws served an economic and social, not religious, purpose.[11]

Adventists felt that the public was so far removed from religious tyranny that it was unwary of the dangers involved in the medieval theory of church-state union. Thus they explained the widespread public apathy. Had they remained sufficiently conscious of their birthright of freedom, Sunday law advocates would have failed in their efforts to classify Sunday measures as health legislation or labor safeguards.[12]

General Conference officers at their 1958 autumn session discussed what could be done to arouse public opinion to the dangerous implications behind new Sunday bills. The officers considered that the trends toward uniformity and conformity "were reviving a pattern of coercion and conditioning the mind of the masses against religious liberty." They decided to train religious liberty representatives to develop a program of public education in religious liberty, and called for efforts to widen the circulation of *Liberty*.[13]

Liberty personnel contended that Sunday legislation was not demanded by the American people, but was, in most cases, pushed through by determined minorities taking advantage of public apathy. *Liberty* used a South Carolina city as a typical example.

There Sunday advocates claimed that a duly constituted referendum had proved that the people of Spartanburg, South Carolina, wished to uphold statutes prohibiting work, sports, and public amusements on Sunday. *Liberty,* citing an interview of a cross section of Spartanburg's citizens, showed that most of them had failed to vote during the referendum. A vociferous minority, organized and directed by a few local clergy, had actually railroaded the referendum through. When the majority of Spartanburg's citizenry saw the way the Sunday law actually operated, they desired its repeal.[14]

This desire was not unique. The inconsistencies of Sunday legislation usually aroused public antipathy. Since commercial interests played such a significant part, confusion over which items could justifiably be sold on that day created a multitude of arbitrary and irrational applications. Exemptions became a continual source of headaches for police charged with enforcement. Smoker's supply shops, for instance could sell tobacco on Sunday while grocery stores were forbidden to sell milk.[15]

Enforcement in New Jersey resort communities proved particularly difficult. Various classes of tradesmen relied on tourists who did most of their buying on Sunday. For this reason the state government tended to leave Sunday regulations to local county option. Stores in resort areas remained open on Sunday, while Sunday-closing laws in neighboring counties shut down stores. Buyers near such a county line, then, naturally crossed over into the resort counties to do their Sunday shopping—much to the

7—C.S.R.

irritation of merchants in their own counties. This practice evoked a rash of complaints of unfairness and discrimination. Owners of many small businesses, caught in this web, went bankrupt and were forced to close.[16] Finally Gundaker Central Motors of Belmar, New Jersey, went to court. Its suit claimed that these laws discriminated between businesses engaged in selling nonessential products for Sunday use. Although winning in the New Jersey Superior Court, on the appeal in the New Jersey Supreme Court, Justice Arthur Vanderbilt reversed the earlier ruling, stating that to provide relief from the constant huckstering of business interests, public interest had the right to demand that commercial enterprises close on one day of the week. The fact that Sunday held religious significance to most people did not, he said, invalidate the state's right to choose it as the community rest day.[17] The Federal Supreme Court refused to review the state supreme court's decision on the grounds that the case did not present "a substantial Federal question."[18]

But the struggle continued to mount. In 1959 Pennsylvania passed a new Sunday law. This law raised the fine for Sunday violation from four dollars to 100 dollars for a first offense, or for a second violation an amount up to 200 dollars.

These stiffer penalties were intended to discourage earlier practices of merchants who paid fines rather than lose remunerative Sunday trade. For example, a highway discount house called "Two Guys From Harrison" paid fines for all employees convicted of violating the Pennsylvania Sunday-closing law. With its multimillion dollar Sunday business the store was far better off financially to pay this multiplicity of fines rather than to lose its flood of Sunday trade. But the amount of the new fines reversed the net gain to a net loss, and "Two Guys From Harrison" went to court.[19]

This store faced a purely secular problem. Simple economics demanded Sunday trade. But Orthodox Jewish merchants in downtown Philadelphia sustained economic injury because of their religious beliefs. Out of religious convictions they closed their store on Saturday and opened it on Sunday. In effect, the Sunday law penalized them because they worshiped on a day different from that of most of the Christian community. They joined "Two Guys

From Harrison" in an appeal. But a Federal District Court in Pennsylvania upheld that state's Sunday-closing requirement. The two groups then appealed to the United States Supreme Court. Had it followed its own precedent, the high court would have refused to review the cases. But while the Federal District Court in Pennsylvania had upheld that state's Sunday law, its counterpart in Massachusetts had reversed a decision of the Massachusetts Supreme Court which had enforced that state's Sunday laws. Confronted by two opposing Federal court decisions, the United States Supreme Court was compelled to change its policy of more than 50 years and to accept several Sunday law cases for Constitutional review.[20]

The Massachusetts case concerned the Crown Kosher Supermarket of Springfield. This company, operated by Orthodox Jews, sold kosher products primarily for members of Orthodox Jewry. This company and most of its customers observed their Sabbath from sundown Friday to sundown Saturday. Their commonly shared beliefs enabled the supermarket to sell a large proportion of its produce on Sunday. If compelled to close on that day, the company claimed, it would sustain such a loss as to encounter vital economic injury.[21]

Dr. Leo Pfeffer, a constitutional lawyer, argued the case before the Massachusetts Supreme Court and later before the First United States Circuit Court of Appeals, contending that Sunday laws could not be divorced from their religious origins. The fact that they were not simply secular laws enacted by the state police power was evident, he reasoned, since courts had consistently recognized the religious nature of these laws. He pointed out the frequent occurrence of the term "Lord's Day" in these ordinances and noted that in many cases they limited Sunday sports events until after church services had ended. Obviously, said Mr. Pfeffer, this particular restriction was intended to prevent people from indulging in activities possibly more attractive to them than their attendance at church. Sunday's selection as a day of rest constituted *prima facie* evidence that the involved states acted to prevent the secularization of Sunday. Any day could serve as a community rest day for health and social reasons.[22]

A fourth case rounded out the picture for the highest court.

This one, *McGowan* v. *Maryland,* concerned another highway discount store in Anne Arundel County, Maryland.

In all of these cases the appellants argued that Sunday laws violated the First Amendment by establishing a religion and by prohibiting the free exercise of religion. Furthermore, they violated the Fourteenth Amendment in denying to the appellants "equal protection" of the laws.[23]

The Seventh-day Adventist Church entered these cases on an *amicus curiae* or "friend of the court" basis, securing permission to file its own brief opposing the Sunday-closing laws. This document set out the denomination's basic views on religious liberty, including its particular emphasis on the fourth commandment of the Decalogue. It summarized Adventist historical interpretation of the substitution of observance of Saturday with observance of Sunday which took place in the early centuries of the Christian church. It outlined the Adventist position on Biblical predictions of this substitution and suggested "probable" consequences to the nation, should current Sunday law trends continue. Having read copies of this brief, many church members waited anxiously for the outcome.[24] The General Conference autumn session called church members together to pray for a wise Supreme Court decision.[25]

Meanwhile, other groups were supporting the movement for Sunday closing. The Retail Dealers International Association Union filed its own *amicus curiae* brief with the United States Supreme Court, asking that the court should uphold the "community day of rest" so invaluable in American life.[26]

Arguments presented to the Supreme Court by the attorneys for Massachusetts, Pennsylvania, and Maryland asserted that Sunday-closing laws in modern times could not be regarded as violating any principle of church-state separation and that they operated as any other health, welfare, or safety law. All such laws, they stressed, were maintained for the protection and benefit of the community. Legislation in this area was therefore a proper exercise of the state's police power. Since all civic functions focus on Sunday, it was logical that the state should protect it as the day of community rest.[27]

Opposing attorneys argued that Sunday-closing laws penalized their clients directly and solely for religious reasons, impairing the "free exercise" of their religion. In two cases, the appellants were Orthodox Jews forced to suffer for their faith.[28]

Attorneys for the supermarket chain "Two Guys From Harrison" were unable to appeal on the same basis, since their case involved no claim of religious infringement. However, they did argue that the Pennsylvania and New Jersey Sunday laws were unconstitutional and illegal and represented an establishment of religion.

In the ruling, the majority of the Supreme Court upheld the Sunday laws, specifying that these ordinances were now secular in character, and therefore did not constitute a religious establishment.[29] Only Justice William O. Douglas dissented, maintaining that the religious "parentage" of these Sunday laws demonstrated the fallacy of the Supreme Court majority.

Admitting the religious origin of Sunday laws, the majority decision nevertheless decided that the purpose of these laws had changed with their contemporary usage. Their central purpose now, said the majority, was to provide a uniform rest day for all citizens. Admitting also that Sunday-closing laws made Sabbath observance more expensive for those who kept any other day, the Court nevertheless ruled that this was simply an unfortunate result, which did not disturb the constitutionality of the laws.[30]

Discussing these rulings, Adventist writers wondered what value could be attached to the wording of state statutes, since the Supreme Court had decided that the phraseology constituted no evidence of any religious nature.[31]

The Court majority also decided that exemptions and "one day in seven laws" were unsatisfactory because of their tendency to undermine the state's provisions of a single day in the week free from commercial noise and activity.

This decision, commented *Liberty,* illustrated the failure of the Court to recognize how many states already had provided such exemptions and how few individuals heeded them.[32]

Religious motivation, suggested Editor Hegstad, was inherent and evident in the phraseology of Sunday laws, employing such terms as "worldly," "secular," "Sabbath breaking," "desecration," "profane," and "holy time." These could hardly be termed vestigial appendages. Furthermore, contemporary journalists also used such religious phrases when writing about current Sunday laws. And Catholic contributors to *Life* magazine had unblushingly used Biblical terms when referring to Sunday business. Religious motivation was further illustrated by the actions of those seeking such laws. Protestants mounted ministerial drives to preserve Sunday as a day of "worship and prayer." While some secular and social organizations, such as labor unions and downtown merchants, appeared less interested in religious issues, they, too, had supported Sunday legislation, argued Hegstad, recognizing the importance of the religious interests behind Sunday laws and working in concert with them. Politicians as well, Hegstad asserted, knowing the political potential of these religious groups, had consequently supported the legislation, even using the same religious terminology. "Just how religious," queried Hegstad, "does a law have to get to be religious?[33]

Chaos accompanied the renewed Sunday law "crackdown." Retailers who depended on Sunday sales ridiculed the laws by displaying derisive placards and cartoons. Tourists preferred to visit states where Sunday pressures were least acute and "vacation" districts with Sunday laws lost heavily in tourist trade. Fines for Sunday-law violators showed wide discrepancies. Some judges handed down minimum fines and suspended sentences while others rigorously enforced the laws. Economic confusion reigned. Exemptions and exceptions were seen to be arbitrary and capricious. Expressions like "hodgepodge," "inconsistency," "discrimination," and "chaos" were sprinkled liberally in newspaper items on Sunday laws.[34]

Buoyed by their Supreme Court victory, Sunday law forces quickly launched drives in Colorado, Maine, and Missouri.[35] The Lord's Day Alliance of the United States, for example, an interdenominational organization seeking enforced observance of Sunday throughout the country, formed committees to campaign for Sunday laws in New York, New Jersey, Pennsylvania, Ohio, Wisconsin, Indiana, and Colorado, and ten other states.[36]

But the inherent intolerance in their drives for Sunday legislation showed through and roused many people. In Minnesota a statewide survey showed that 65 percent of the people believed that Sunday observance was a matter for the individual's own conscience and should not be enforced by law, although they applied this opinion to small stores rather than large multiple complexes.[37] Despite public opinion, the Minneapolis city council voted ten to two to override the Mayor's veto of a Sunday closing ordinance, although it did approve an exemption for stores closing on Saturday.[38]

Differences of opinion on Sunday enforcement created great inequities along some state borders. The Kansas State Supreme Court disallowed its Sunday-closing law, while Missouri's chief legal tribunal upheld that state's blue law. In consequence, Kansas shops along the common state border, remaining open on Sunday, gained major trading advantages over Missouri establishments, which were closed on that day.

Meanwhile, in Kentucky the court of appeals overruled a lower court and insisted that the state Sunday laws were constitutional, although it did allow exemptions for businesses closed on Saturday for religious reasons.[39]

In New York the legislature's codes committee listened to a variety of speakers, including Adventists, who urged an exemption from the New York Sunday law for those who observed the seventh day. Governor Rockefeller supported this exemption clause, but it was generally opposed by Roman Catholics within the state.

In Michigan a new Sunday bill exempted seventh-day Sabbath keepers.

In Massachusetts the state senate allowed a similar exemption clause in its Sunday law. But a Roman Catholic newspaper, *The Pilot,* attacked all senators voting for the exemption. Listing their names so that priests could urge their parishioners to write letters of protest, the paper called for reconsideration of the earlier decision. *The Pilot* had its way. After a second vote, the amendment was defeated 31 to 8. Commenting, M. E. Loewen, Secretary of the Seventh-day Adventist Religious Liberty Department, called this one of the "most glaring evidences of Catholic political pressure for Sunday laws witnessed by the Seventh-day Adventist Religious Liberty Department for many years."[40]

In 1963 Adventists found an outstanding Sunday test case

when an Adventist woman in South Carolina was refused unemployment compensation because she declined a job requiring work on the seventh day of the week. The South Carolina Supreme Court ruled against her. But, supported by the General Conference, she took her case to the Supreme Court. And this highest court struck down the law which penalized her, declaring it unconstitutional since she was being penalized because of her religion. The Supreme Court decided that the South Carolina unemployment compensation law, which provided protection for the Sunday observer, should have provided equal protection for the seventh-day keeper.[41]

This decision helped to clarify the Supreme Court's attitude toward Sunday laws. It classified them as social and welfare enactments, but in some cases, where discrimination against individuals due to their religious views could be shown, the Court ruled against the Sunday laws.

Reacting to the South Carolina decision, *Review* Editor Nichol expressed satisfaction that the highest legal tribunal of the nation was still willing to invest time and advocacy to ensure the just rights of one lone Adventist. The nation still favored the right of an individual to religious liberty. Also, Nichol noted, the ecumenical mood currently recognized religious liberty as still the only road to true Christian unity.

REFERENCES AND NOTES

1. F. D. Nichol, "The New Religious Look in America," *Review and Herald,* Jan. 20, 1955, p. 8. In this editorial Nichol is commenting on an article by A. R. Eckhardt on the current emphasis on religion. See A. R. Eckhardt, "The New Look in American Piety," *The Christian Century,* Nov. 17, 1954, pp. 1395-1397; Eckhardt later embodied his conclusions in *The New Surge of Piety in America: An Appraisal* (New York: National Council of YMCA Associated Press, 1958). Eckhardt treated the "new piety" as an "American culture religion" emphasizing peace of mind, personal adjustment, and the treatment of God as "the Man upstairs," or the "friendly Neighbor."

2. F. D. Nichol, "Sunday Legislation Propaganda," *Review and Herald,* Jan. 20, 1955, p. 8.

3. Hiley H. Ward, *Space-Age Sunday* (New York: The Macmillan Company, 1960), pages 9-14, suggests that within the heart of the Sunday controversy is the age-old church tradition, beset by the problems of the new age.

4. Bob Senser, "Stop This Sunday Shopping," *Catholic Digest,* October,

1954, pp. 9-12; also Cardinal Cushing criticized a three-judge Federal court in 1959 for declaring the Massachusetts Sunday law unconstitutional where it affected a kosher market case. *Boston Pilot,* June 27, 1959.

5. Editorial, "Labor's Role in National Affairs," *Review and Herald,* Feb. 10, 1955, p. 10; Nichol, "New Agitation for Sunday Laws," *Ibid.,* April 4, 1957, pp. 8, 9.

6. Kenneth H. Wood, Jr., "The Sinister Shadow of Today's Religious Horizon," *Review and Herald,* Feb. 20, 1958, pp. 16, 17, 25. Wood was a prominent contributor to the *Review and Herald* who became editor of the magazine in 1966 on the death of F. D. Nichol.

7. News item, "Rabbis Ask Revision of Sunday Trade Laws," *Review and Herald,* March 6, 1958, p. 5. Also editorial, "Democracy and the Sabbath," in the New York *Post* of March 23, 1958.

8. Statement of legislative principles, New York State Council of Churches, 1958; cited in "Intolerance? The Sunday Law Issue in New York," *Liberty,* third quarter, 1958, p. 25. If the powerful New York Jewish community was thus unable to mitigate the Sunday laws, Adventist perturbation can easily be understood.

9. Dean M. Kelley, "Sabbath Observance and Eight Dilemmas of Protestantism," *Liberty,* fourth quarter, 1958, pp. 10-12.

10. *Ibid.,* pp. 13, 14.

11. Alvin W. Johnson, "The Religious Liberty Department," General Conference Report [spring session] No. 3, *Review and Herald,* June 23, 1958, pp. 71, 72.

12. J. A. Buckwalter, "Why Seventh-day Adventists Oppose Sunday Laws," *Liberty,* fourth quarter, 1958, p. 5.

13. F. R. Millard, "1958 Autumn Council Actions," *Review and Herald,* Nov. 27, 1958, p. 7.

14. Roland R. Hegstad, "A Street Called Liberty," *Liberty,* January-February, 1960, pp. 10-14, 29.

15. Charles S. Longacre, "Glaring Inconsistencies in Sunday Laws," *Liberty,* fourth quarter, 1958, pp. 27-29.

16. C. S. Longacre, "Constitutionality of New Jersey Sunday Law Questioned," *Liberty,* first quarter, 1959, pp. 29, 30; "Outpuritanizing the Puritans," *Ibid.,* p. 30.

17. Hiley H. Ward, *Space-age Sunday* (New York: Macmillan Company, 1960), page 15.

18. *Ibid.;* also Melvin W. Adams, "Supreme Court to Review Constitutionality of Sunday Laws," *Liberty News,* May, 1960, p. 1.

19. Richard Cohen, *Sunday in the Sixties* (Public Affairs Pamphlet No. 327, Public Affairs Committee Inc., 1962), pages 12, 13.

20. Melvin W. Adams, "High Court to Hear Another Blue Law Appeal," *Liberty News,* July, 1960, p. 1.

21. Warren L. Johns, *Dateline Sunday, U.S.A.* (Mountain View: Pacific Press Publishing Association, 1967), pages 115, 116.

22. Leo Pfeffer, "Sunday Laws Are Religious," *Liberty,* January-February, 1960, pp. 9, 30, 31.

23. Johns, *op. cit.,* pp. 119-132; Melvin W. Adams, "Supreme Court to Review Constitutionality of Sunday Laws," *Liberty News,* May, 1960, pp. 1, 2.

24. M. W. Adams, "Seventh-day Adventists File Brief With the United States Supreme Court," *Liberty News,* Oct. 14, 1960, pp. 1, 2.

25. W. R. Beach, "Actions Taken at the 1960 Biennial Autumn Council," *Review and Herald,* Nov. 24, 1960, p. 21.

26. Adams, "NADA Backing Sunday Laws"; "Union Filed Brief on Sunday Laws," *Liberty News,* November, 1960, pp. 3, 4.

27. The cases considered by the Supreme Court at this time included: *McGowan v. Maryland,* 366 U.S. 420 (1961); *Gallagher v. Crown Kosher Super Market,* 336 U.S. 617 (1961); *Two Guys from Harrison v. Mc-Genley,* 366 U.S. 582 (1961); *Braunfeld v. Brown,* 366 U.S. 599 (1961).

28. See *Braunfeld v. Brown,* 366 U.S. 616, 610 (1961). Both Justice P. Stewart and Justice William J. Brennan agreed with William O. Douglas that the "free exercise" of religion was impaired by the enforcement of these Sunday laws.

29. *McGowan v. Maryland,* 366 U.S. 561-581 (1961).

30. Adams, "Sunday Laws Before the Supreme Court," *Liberty News,* December, 1960, pp. 1, 2.

31. Adams, "Arrest 45 at '2 Guys' in Sale Ban," *Liberty News,* March, 1961, p. 3. See also Hiley H. Ward, *Space-Age Sunday,* p. 98. Ward emphasizes the effect of these arrests on employees of the organization who thus acquired a criminal record.

32. Editorial "The Supreme Court Sunday Law Decisions: Do They Close the Long Battle to Obtain Recognition of Minority Rights in the Field of Religion?" *Liberty,* November-December, 1961, pp. 14-17, 22.

33. Roland R. Hegstad, "Modern Sunday Laws Not Religion?" *Liberty,* November-December, 1961, pp. 26, 27.

34. M. Carol Hetzell, "Chaos on Sunday," *Liberty,* March-April 1962, pp. 9-13.

35. Adams, "Protestants and Catholics Push City's 'Save Our Sunday' Drive"; "Main Priest Asks Boycott of Stores Opening on Sunday"; "Ruling Spurs Full-scale Enforcement of Missouri Sunday Laws," *Liberty News,* March, 1962, 12:17.

36. "Expansion Program Planned by Lord's Day Alliance," *Ibid.,* April, 1962, p. 20.

37. "Only 30% Minnesotans Cite Need for Sunday Laws," *Ibid.,* May, 1962, p. 24.

38. "Minneapolis City Council Overrides Veto of Sunday-closing Ordinance," *Ibid.,* p. 25; Andrew Naftalin, Mayor of Minneapolis, "Why I Vetoed the Minneapolis Sunday Closing Ordinance," *Liberty,* January-February, 1963, pp. 7, 8.

39. Adams, "Kansas' Sunday Closing Law Is Ruled Unconstitutional"; "Kentucky Sunday Closing Law Is Held Constitutional," *Liberty News,* May, 1962, p. 25.

40. Adams, "Rockefeller Backs Sunday Bill That Would Exempt Sabbatarians"; "New York Legislative Hearing"; "Michigan House Sunday Bill Would Exempt Sabbatarians"; *Ibid.,* June, 1962, pp. 31-34; "Massachusetts Sunday Law Pressure," *Ibid.,* August, 1962, p. 43.

41. Nichol, "A Seventh-day Adventist and the Supreme Court," *Review and Herald,* July 11, 1963, pp. 12, 13.

Chapter 8

RELIGIOUS LIBERTY AND ECUMENISM

During the 1960's Adventists, in their desire to ensure continued religious liberty, eyed ecumenical trends with a concern based partly on eschatological expectations and partly on prospects for more immediate practical results. The Vatican II Council, for example, which began on October 13, 1962, evoked an outburst of Adventist comment.

W. L. Emmerson, editor of the British Adventist magazine *Our Times,* noted that with only a week left before the opening of the council, Pope John XXIII visited the Catholic shrine at Loretto to invoke the Virgin Mary's aid. This action, he predicted, together with the proposal that Pius XI, who had called Vatican I, would be canonized as a saint during Vatican II, suggested how little the forthcoming council was likely to alter basic Roman Catholic positions recognized by the First Vatican Council or even the Council of Trent. John XXIII's opening address, said Emmerson, confirmed this idea. At this time reunion with Protestantism, he concluded, seemed impossible. To achieve even the limited degree of unity sought by Cardinal Bea's secretariat could prove extremely difficult.[1]

Secretary of the Northern European Division of Seventh-day Adventists, B. B. Beach, sounded a similar note. Basing his opinion on published Roman Catholic materials and personal contacts with high Roman Catholic leaders, he ascertained that the Roman view of Christian unity depended on seeing the "separated brethren" recognize Roman Catholicism as the one true church. Pope John XXIII's encyclicals, *Ad Petri Cathedrum* (To the Seat of Peter) and *Aeterna Dei Sapientia* (God's Everlasting Wisdom) both indicated his goodwill and benevolence towards non-Catholics. But the pontiff remained adamant in requiring Protestant acceptance of papal authority. Even ecumenically minded Cardinal Bea, said Dr. Beach, admitted that although the Roman Catholic

Church might compromise on liturgy, organization, and church polity, it would not do so on doctrine.[2]

Dr. Jean Nussbaum, Adventist religious liberty secretary for Southern Europe, interviewed Greek Orthodox Patriarch Athenagoras on developments at the Vatican. Nussbaum judged that both the Orthodox patriarch and the pope based their desire for unity on their common opposition to communism. This approach, Nussbaum feared, might form corrupt alliances and apply force to achieve victory in Europe over the common civil laws in order to secure unity in religion. This tactic had always produced disastrous results. Christ's concept of Christian union was a spiritual ideal realized only through a rejection of human traditions in favor of Bible teachings. Only by a common recognition of the total sovereignty of God's Word could mankind forget its differences and thereby realize true unity.[3]

Associate editor of the *Review,* R. F. Cottrell, assessed developing Roman Catholic ecumenism from the standpoint of Roman Catholic attitudes to the Bible. The "progressive advocates of the unique authority of the Scripture," he suggested, had ranged themselves against "conservative champions of the equal authority of tradition."[4]

Observing the revolutionary strength of these dynamic new forces emerging in the Roman Catholic Church, Cottrell saw that a new interest in the Bible had created bonds of union between Roman Catholics and Protestants. Liberal Protestants and Catholics, he wrote, had been experiencing a rapprochement on the sense and import of Scripture since 1943, the year Cardinal Bea wrote for Pius XI the encyclical *Divino Afflate Spiritu* (The Inspiration of the Holy Spirit). In the ensuing years spiritual affinity between liberal Catholics and Protestants had continued to deepen.

Cottrell emphasized, however, that although liberal Roman Catholic theologians empathized with liberal Protestant theologians in their approach to Scripture, *conservative* Protestants and *conservative* Roman Catholics still found little in common in this area. These conservatives held that liberal theologians, whether Catholic or Protestant, paid only nominal respect to the Bible, treating it as little more than a human production. The most liberal Roman Catholic Bible student, stressed Cottrell, depreciated and minimized the message of Scripture by subjecting it to the magisterium, or teaching authority, of the Church.[5]

In sum, Cottrell dismissed the upcoming Vatican II as an "adroitly staged first act in a play whose plot was intended to reach a climax in the submission of all Christendom to the authority of Rome."[6] Obviously, Seventh-day Adventist eschatological views greatly influenced Cottrell's thought, since, on the surface at least, in the actual developments of the council surprisingly little evidence emerged to substantiate such a conclusion.

On April 28, 1963, Father Hans Kung addressed a predominantly Roman Catholic audience at Georgetown University on "The Church and Freedom." Cottrell, who attended, later wrote that he was impressed by the apparent widespread sentiment among Roman Catholics for greater religious liberty and an end to religious intolerance and bigotry within their church. Kung, he stated, proved himself a convincing spokesman.[7]

Also impressed with the trends toward greater religious tolerance within both Roman Catholicism and Protestantism, *Liberty* Editor Roland R. Hegstad commented on Dr. A. F. Carrillo de Albornoz's call for a commonly acceptable definition of religious freedom as a basis for ecumenical growth.[8] While appreciating Dr. Carrillo's emphasis on the need for all religious denominations and sects to define their point of view on this vital subject, Hegstad argued that even if Roman Catholicism should define its position, the acid test of its sincerity would have to come in such Roman Catholic-oriented countries as Spain and Colombia. Would they allow dissenters the right to propagate their religious beliefs freely? Failing that, such a "definition" would have no practical value.[9]

Developments among Protestants also indicated an increasing concern for religious liberty. At its 175th general assembly, the United Presbyterian Church voiced its opposition to government-forced or "sponsored" Bible reading and prayer in public schools and to state enforcement of Sunday laws. The assembly also voted against "grants from tax funds to parochial schools."[10]

Some Protestant groups showed themselves particularly zealous about enlarging religious freedom in certain parts of the modern world. H. Ward Hill, an Adventist minister attending the Fourth

World Conference on Faith and Order at Montreal in July, 1963, argued that if this conference "failed," it would be because of its great concentration on religious divisions in the church. There was no attempt there, he urged, to gloss over essential doctrinal differences to achieve a superficial harmony of interests. Dr. W. A. Visser 't Hooft, secretary general of the World Council of Churches, stated very clearly that "a theological peace . . . gained at the expense of truth would not be the peace of Christ." The recognition of this principle, said this Adventist pastor, showed the difference between religious productiveness and religious pogroms.[11]

H. W. Lowe, a second Adventist observer there, suggested that the absence of fundamentalist evangelicals should cause delegates to consider smaller sects that had so far kept out of the main ecumenical patterns. While admitting that "the excessive and fanatical literalism of certain sections of fundamentalism" was as reprehensible as the "excessive and repressive authoritarianism of dominant institutional religions," he insisted that ecumenists should pay attention to the genuine misgivings of minority evangelicals. Understanding here, he considered, could prevent indifference to or persecution of these groups.[12]

Despite their emphasis on eschatology, Seventh-day Adventists recognized the significance of these religious liberty trends and endeavored to benefit from them. Delegates to the General Conference autumn council of 1963 voted a generous subsidy to send *Liberty* magazine subscriptions to influential men in all parts of the country.[13] They noted that the "once nearly solid front of church support for Sunday-closing laws" had been breached. The Presbyterians had been foremost. But other Protestant and Roman Catholic spokesmen were also voicing opposition to enforced Sunday closing. The New York legislature had passed a fair Sabbath law exempting keepers of the seventh-day Sabbath. Ecumenical leaders had spoken favorably of religious liberty. Public polls had indicated a high public resentment of Sunday laws.[14] In the light of these developments, Adventists, in common with other Protestants, observed with keen interest Roman Catholic deliberations on religious liberty.

Religious liberty was an agenda topic at the second session of the Second Vatican Council. John Courtney Murray, a leading Roman Catholic religious liberty apologist, whose views had prevented his attendance at Vatican II's first session, had prepared the substantial questions for council debate. Many Adventist writers believed that the Roman Catholic Church would now accept at least part of the new religious liberty concept. They hoped it would repudiate its older "thesis-hypothesis" concept—the traditional Roman Catholic view that man is never free to act in opposition to divinely revealed truth. According to this old position, "error" had no rights, and the ideal situation, or "thesis," exists when and where Roman Catholic principles can be fully applied to the annihilation of all opposing "error." At certain times and places, however, this was recognized as often impossible, and in such cases the principle of "hypothesis" should obtain, and the church would deviate from the ideal situation and condone error to the extent considered expedient.[15]

When no religious liberty declaration was announced, Adventists wondered if Roman Catholic conservatives had outmaneuvered the liberals through delaying tactics. Then, when some limited liberty statements were finally issued, Adventists considered them far from adequate. Adventist London Editor W. L. Emmerson summarized the announcements for *Liberty*. He pointed out that they failed to define proper rights for all people in religious education and evangelistic witnessing, or to recognize freedom for an individual to change religious affiliations. While Roman Catholic religious liberty apologists were emphasizing the need for an ordering of the common good in society, said Emmerson, they were also laying the groundwork for Rome's claim to be the sole authoritative source of eternal law, designed by God to guide the state in enacting laws for the citizen's good.

This "new" Roman Catholic theory, said Emmerson, that Rome's attitude to society had varied through the centuries according to society's needs, amounted to toleration rather than endorsement of true freedom. The Roman Church may therefore tolerate some things today which it had not tolerated in the past and would not tolerate in the future.

While liberal democracies remained a bulwark against anti-Catholic communism, for example, the Roman Catholic Church would probably endorse the settled order. But suppose this situation should change? Suppose the communist threat should be eliminated. The Roman Church might then relate itself to society very differently.

Pursuing this thought, Emmerson argued that the papal decree on mass media, proclaimed at the Council's final session on December 4, 1963, stressed the civil authority's duty to protect society from misuse of mass media. Although he admitted that this provision might conceivably have value, Emmerson warned that it would allow "Roman Catholic press censorship for the common good."[16]

Liberty Editor Hegstad agreed with Emmerson's thesis that Roman Catholic pronouncements on religious liberty were dependent for their value on their phraseology. Such commitments as the Archbishop of Tarragona's declaration at a recent Madrid press conference, he suggested, had aroused rather than alleviated Protestant suspicions. The Cardinal's assertion that he favored freedom of worship for non-Catholics in Spain, provided this right was not abused by attempting to proselytize Roman Catholics, raised questions as to what this definition of freedom really meant. With Emmerson, Hegstad concluded that Vatican II could assuage Protestant fears of Roman Catholic intolerance only if it granted to Protestants the rights of evangelistic witness in every Roman Catholic country.[17]

Emmerson further emphasized the fact that Roman Catholic progressives desired an unequivocal stand on religious liberty. Since non-Catholics demanded evidence that the Roman Catholic Church had actually forsaken its intolerance as witnessed by history, it must provide this assurance if the ecumenical movement was to succeed. Further deliberations must be fortified by a clear Roman Catholic religious liberty declaration. The very continuance of Protestant-Catholic dialogue depended on such a declaration.[18] Yet the Roman Catholic conservatives, rallying around the Spanish hierarchy, had succeeded in delaying this action and in making the declaration ambiguous.[19]

Emmerson described the conservative "time bomb": Cardinal Tisserant had announced that there would be no preliminary vote on the religious liberty decision before the council adjourned.

Even though more than one thousand bishops, led by the United States hierarchy, appealed directly to Pope Paul VI, the pope refused to intervene, and the disappointed liberals saw the session close with no religious liberty declaration.[20]

Adventists realized that the acid test of any Roman Catholic declaration on liberty would have to come in a country intolerant of religious liberty, such as Spain. They reacted favorably when Spanish lay opinion, polled concerning freedom of worship for non-Catholics, registered nearly 49 percent for equal rights of worship for non-Catholics. This poll indicated to Adventists that in a country with strong Roman Catholic traditions, lay opinion was veering toward more liberal attitudes.[21] This changing climate of thought, if combined with a papal religious liberty declaration, offered real promise.[22]

Adventist writers appreciated the apparent reasonableness of Vatican II's religious liberty schema, but bridled at the amendment which stated that all men are obligated to accept the Catholic faith to the degree they understand it.[23] They equally opposed another assertion that religious liberty principles, because of historical circumstances involving some peoples with a long Catholic tradition, do not militate against special recognition being given to the Roman Catholic Church in the legal constitution of the state. This, adduced Emmerson, could only lead not to liberty but, at best, to a very precarious toleration.[24]

This view found support from other statements which, as *Liberty's* Hegstad suggested, provided loopholes wide enough "to accommodate the whole Spanish Inquisition." If the individual's religious freedom was subject to "public order as determined by law," Hegstad argued, in how many dangerous ways could this be interpreted?[25]

The long struggle for a religious liberty declaration climaxed finally on November 19, 1965, with an affirmative vote of 1,954, and 249 opposing. Both the Catholic and non-Catholic press hailed the declaration as a cornerstone in the development of religious freedom.

Commenting on this enthusiastic reception, W. L. Emmerson, *Liberty's* London correspondent, discovered three distinct attitudes among Catholics on this issue at Vatican II:

8—C.S.R.

1. The progressives busily engaged themselves in pushing through the schemata, determined to provide full religious liberty to all people and to advance Catholic truth solely by spiritual methods.

2. The conservatives concerned with the "rights" of "truth" formed a staunch opposing wing. Undoubtedly, suggested Emmerson, these conservatives accounted for inconsistencies in the religious liberty declaration.

3. The moderates, standing midway, formed the great deciding bulk of delegates. While accepting the conservatives' arguments that the state had the right to recognize one religion above all others, these moderates did side with the progressives in saying that while doing so the state should safeguard the religious liberty of other groups.[26]

While vigilantly spotting the apparent departures from recognizing full religious liberty, Adventists did detect that a shift of position was taking place in lands where religious freedom might be at least anticipated. In Spain during one year, 1965, for example, 13 more Seventh-day Adventist churches received permission to open. And reports from a Baptist official returning from that country indicated the relative ease with which Protestants were now able to import religious literature.[27]

In April, 1966, a religious liberty bill pending in Spain inspired Adventist representatives to interview the Spanish foreign minister, Fernando María Castiella, to discover, if possible, the nature of the proposed legislation and to make a film documentary on the resulting new Spanish religious liberties. They asked how such an issue came within the jurisdiction of the foreign minister.

Señor Castiella explained that he had adequate diplomatic ties to discover the mind of the Vatican and to appreciate international reactions to governmental treatment of the Protestant minority.[28]

His thorough understanding of the concepts of religious freedom—extending far beyond the Vatican II declaration—astonished his Adventist interviewers. Vatican II had stressed the church's need to adjust its religious liberty position to contemporary conditions. Liberty must be shaped to the best interests of "public peace, morality, and justice." The application of liberty could vary in different places and times. But the Spanish minister had formed his convictions about religious liberty after observing the weaknesses of religious life in his own country.

A former ambassador to the Holy See, Castiella had become convinced that the only real basis for Christian vitality is personal commitment, a quality he found sadly lacking in his country, a country that denied the sovereignty of personal religious conviction.[29]

Indeed, Spain seemed to be shaping up as a critical testing ground for the genuineness of Vatican Council II's religious liberty declaration. With a leading authority of deep convictions implementing the new spirit of liberty, registered Protestants were worshiping openly and were freely distributing their religious literature. Protestants still felt dissatisfaction over the requirement that they must register as Protestants, but in general the religious liberty situation constantly improved.[30]

However much their eschatological beliefs might brake rising Seventh-day Adventist hopes in the future development of the ecumenical movement, they were for the time, at least, enjoying some of the fruits it was producing. The Roman Catholic religious liberty declaration had eased the difficulties of Protestants in Spain and Italy.

The World Council of Churches had also demonstrated a praiseworthy regard for rights of religious minorities. This World Council attitude was clearly demonstrated when, to achieve friendlier relations with conservative evangelicals, its representative met with Seventh-day Adventists at the Adventist Lake Geneva Sanitarium to discuss their doctrinal views and ecclesiastical policies. Dr. M. B. Handspicker, assistant to Dr. Lukas Vischer, director of the secretariat on faith and order, embodied the results of these discussions in an article for *The Ecumenical Review.* Apart from a few minor disagreements, R. F. Cottrell, writing in the *Review,* regarded Dr. Handspicker's analysis as scrupulously honest, opening opportunities for dialogue, and deserving proper response from Adventists. Cottrell even suggested that God might consider the Seventh-day Adventist Church recreant if it failed to take advantage of new opportunities to develop friendlier relations with Christians of other denominations.[31]

Briefly describing Seventh-day Adventist backgrounds, Dr.

Handspicker indicated in his article that for most of the denomination's history, it had remained separate from other Christian bodies, going so far as to refer to these bodies as "daughters of Babylon" because they received "modernist" teachings. But, he suggested, a more conciliatory atmosphere now prevailed, and since the council's constitution was neutral on doctrinal and ecclesiological questions, there was no reason that Seventh-day Adventists should not witness within the framework of the World Council of Churches.[32]

Responding to this implied invitation, Cottrell explained that Seventh-day Adventists could not join the World Council of Churches because such an arrangement might limit their world witness. The World Council did not encourage "conversions" from other churches, whereas Adventists did. The council did not recognize a geographically unlimited missionary program by any one denomination, whereas Adventists did and were actively engaged in such a program. The council held that the churches should speak jointly on matters of public policy, whereas Adventists could not share this popular ecumenical belief. Although they believed that morality is involved in public policy, Adventists, said Cottrell, still could not agree to turn from a worldwide evangelistic mission to secular issues, a concern of the state. While the church should state its ethical position, there should be no church involvement in secular political affairs.

From July 30 to August 8, 1967, the World Council of Churches commission on faith and order convened at Bristol, England. There Commission Director Lukas Vischer spoke of widening contacts with both the Roman Catholic Church and conservative Protestant groups. Referring specifically to closer relations with Pentecostals and Seventh-day Adventists, he emphasized that the commission had revised its constitution to raise its ceiling on possible membership from 120 to 150. Since the additional 30 members on the commission represented denominations which were not members of the World Council, it was evident that the World Council of Churches was making strenuous efforts to reach both Roman Catholics and conservative Protestant groups.[33]

These Bristol discussions prepared the way for the World Council's fourth assembly at Uppsala, Sweden, from July 4 to

19, 1968. On July 6 Cardinal Bea, president of the Vatican secretariat for Christian unity, addressed the assembly, expressing the desire of many Roman Catholics to be a part of the great ecumenical movement. Reports from the six sections of the assembly included, among others, those titled "The Holy Spirit and the Catholicity of the Church," "Renewal in Mission," "World Economic and Social Developments," "Toward Justice and Peace in International Affairs," "The Worship of God in a Secular Age," and "Toward a New Style of Living in a Secular Age."

Review Editor Kenneth H. Wood expressed his disappointment that these sections stressed the "horizontal" rather than the "vertical" aspects of life. The assembly's theme that the struggle of millions of people to achieve social justice was a means of hastening the kingdom of God on earth sounded strangely in his Adventist ears. Adventists, he explained, conceive the kingdom of God on earth as an end result of the personal, literal return of Jesus Christ. To Adventists this is the only hope for the world.

From these World Council sections, however, the sole report that in any way could be termed by Adventists as "encouragingly eschatological" was the one which presented "Catholicity" as the gift of God. This report stressed that Christ's kingdom could only be fulfilled and fully realized at His coming. Editor Wood deeply regretted that the interest in the second coming of Christ, so noticeable at the Evanston meeting, was almost undetectable at Uppsala. In a later summary of his reactions to the Uppsala gathering, he expressed the deep desire of Adventists to maintain an attitude of friendly cooperation with other Christians, recognizing the spiritual commitment of these members of the World Council of Churches. But Seventh-day Adventists, wrote the editor of the official organ of the denomination, could not agree with the "strange mixture" of politics, economics, and religion that prevailed during the two weeks of the assembly. They could not participate in such a program, for the World Council of Churches defined world evangelism in a sense Adventists could not accept. While Adventists had the friendliest feeling toward the council and sent representatives to the commission to share information on topics of mutual interest, they could not conscientiously take part in the total program.[34]

REFERENCES AND NOTES

1. W. L. Emmerson, "That They All May Be One . . . , Father," *Liberty*, March-April, 1963, pp. 12-15.

2. B. B. Beach, "Obstacles to Unity," *Ibid.*, pp. 16, 17, 28, 29.

3. Jean Nussbaum, "Can Christian Unity Be Achieved?" *Ibid.*, May-June, 1963, pp. 20-22.

4. R. F. Cottrell, "On the Eve of the Council," *Review and Herald*, Jan. 10, 1963, p. 13; "To Let Fresh Air In," *Ibid.*, Jan. 24, 1963, p. 13; "Peter's Bark Changes Course," *Ibid.*, Jan. 31, 1963, p. 13; "The Import of Vatican Council II for Adventists," *Ibid.*, Feb. 7, 1963, p. 13.

5. Cottrell, "From Battlefields to Bonds of Unity," *Signs of the Times*, October, 1963, pp. 7-10.

6. Cottrell, "The Import of Vatican Council II for Adventists," *Review and Herald*, Feb. 7, 1963, p. 13.

7. Cottrell, "The Church and Freedom," *Review and Herald*, May 30, 1963, p. 15.

8. This is the appeal by A. F. Carrillo de Albornoz in *The Basis of Religious Liberty* (New York: Associated Press, 1963). Dr. Carrillo, of course, fully recognized the Spanish problem and explained the difficulties involved in the granting of religious liberty in Spain: the covert hostility of the priests, popular sentiment, extreme integrists, and problems attending practical implementation of religious liberty principles at the local level. See Carrillo, "Roman Catholicism and Religious Liberty," *A Journal of Church and State*, spring, 1964, p. 190.

9. Roland R. Hegstad, "Ecumenism and Religious Liberty," *Liberty*, September-October, 1963, p. 30.

10. F. D. Nichol, "Further Comments on Religious Liberty," *Review and Herald*, Aug. 1, 1963, pp. 14, 15. See also *Relations Between Church and State in the United States of America* (Adopted by the 175th General Assembly, May, 1963. Office of the General Assembly, Witherspoon Building, Philadelphia, Pennsylvania), pages 1-38.

11. H. Ward Hill, "Montreal: The Fourth World Conference on Faith and Order—Failure?" *Liberty*, November-December, 1963, pp. 20-23.

12. H. W. Lowe, "Toward a World Church," *Review and Herald*, Aug. 29, 1963, pp. 2, 3; *Ibid.*, Sept. 5, 1963, pp. 6-8.

13. Duane S. Johnson, "The 1963 Autumn Council," *Review and Herald*, Nov. 21, 1963, pp. 1, 8.

14. Gordon F. Dalrymple, "Churches Against Sunday Laws," *Liberty*, January-February, 1964, pp. 14-17.

15. Cottrell, "Vatican II and Religious Liberty," *Review and Herald*, Dec. 19, 1963, p. 17.

16. Emmerson, "Rome and Religious Liberty," *Liberty*, March-April, 1964, pp. 20-24.

17. Hegstad, "Catholic Statement Can Assuage Protestant Fears," *Liberty*, May-June, 1964, p. 29.

18. Bishop Emile Josef DeSmedt, of Bruges, Belgium, a leading Roman Catholic progressive, fully admitted that the church needed to change its image. He opened the religious liberty subject for general debate in November, 1963, with a detailed *Relatio* (introduction).

19. Emmerson, "What Will Vatican II Say About Freedom?" *Liberty,* September-October, 1964, pp. 20-23.

20. Emmerson, "Council Battleground," *Liberty,* March-April, 1965, pp. 20-22, 32.

21. Editorial, *Liberty,* July-August, 1965, p. 32.

22. B. B. Beach, "Catholicism and Liberty," *Liberty,* September-October, 1965, pp. 23-25, 32, 33.

23. Cottrell, "The Religious Liberty Schema," *Review and Herald,* Dec. 9, 1965, p. 12.

24. Emmerson, "Rome Speaks on Religious Liberty," *Liberty,* November-December, 1965, pp. 7-10.

25. Hegstad, "Religious Liberty and Public Order," *Ibid.,* pp. 28, 29.

26. Emmerson, "The Religious Liberty Schema," *Liberty,* January-February, 1966, pp. 10-12, 33, 34. Note that no Seventh-day Adventist writers on the subject of the Roman Catholic Religious Liberty Declaration in Vatican II appear to have recognized the importance of this declaration in placing a tool in the hands of minority groups in Roman Catholic-oriented countries with which they could defend and publicize their religious freedom. Nor did they sufficiently emphasize that the declaration was itself an expression of the widespread human desire for religious freedom which could be effective in implementing the decisions of the Council. On these two points note Philip Wogaman, *Protestant Faith and Religious Liberty* (Nashville: Abingdon Press, 1967), pages 21, 22, 27-31, 40. Thomas T. Love, "De Liberate Religiosa: An Interpretive Analysis," *A Journal of Church and State,* winter, 1966, takes an opposing view. He stresses that from the Roman Catholic emphasis on the "special civil recognition" of a religious tradition in the constitutional "order of society" there should be drawn the implication that within a state shaped too exclusively by a single religious tradition, genuine freedom and equality of the citizens would be virtually impossible.

27. Loewen, "Spain: A Progress Report," *Liberty,* May-June, 1966, p. 29; Hegstad, "A Report on Spain," *Ibid.,* July-August, 1966, p. 30.

28. Hegstad, "The Spanish Religious Liberty Document," *Ibid.,* September-October, 1966, pp. 7-9.

29. Benjamin Riffel, "Adventists in Spain May Now Worship Openly," *Review and Herald,* Oct. 19, 1967, p. 22.

30. Hegstad, "Spain's Improving Religious Climate," *Review and Herald,* May 16, 1968, pp. 16, 17.

31. Cottrell, "The World Council Looks at Seventh-day Adventists," *Review and Herald,* March 23, 1967, pp. 12, 13.

32. *Ibid.,* April 6, 1967, pp. 13, 14.

33. Earle Hilgert, "The Faith and Order Commission," *Review and Herald,* Oct. 12, 1967, pp. 4, 5; *Ibid.,* Oct. 19, 1967, pp. 5, 6.

34. Kenneth H. Wood, "Trends and Crosscurrents at the WCC Fourth Assembly," *Review and Herald,* a series beginning with July 25, and continuing through Sept. 5, 1968; "Eight Convictions and Observations," *Ibid.,* Nov. 7 and 14, 1968.

Chapter 9

CHURCH, STATE, AND EDUCATION

Seventh-day Adventists have invested a large proportion of their funds in their educational system. This investment has enabled them to create an educational establishment which rivals that of some of the largest churches in the United States.

In 1870, shortly after the denomination was founded, the Seventh-day Adventist Church had neither elementary nor secondary schools. By 1910, they were financing more than 1,000 elementary schools besides a few secondary schools and colleges.[1] But by the close of 1971 the denomination's total count of elementary schools had passed 4,000, and it operated more than 400 secondary schools and 50 colleges.[2] It is understandable that the size and scope of this educational program imposes a huge financial burden upon the Seventh-day Adventist Church.

Although the financial problem will inevitably increase as the rate of the church's growth continues, Seventh-day Adventist Church leaders still plan to expand the denomination's educational work as the demand for education continues to grow. Adventists consider the training of their youth basic to the life of their church.[3] The Adventist philosophy of education places Scripture at the center of the school training system. And Adventists believe that the church, not the state, should supervise and develop this training.[4]

In the past Adventists have held that no churches should use state funds to maintain their parochial school system, but that they should educate their own youth in their own doctrines, from their own resources. Simple consistency requires the Seventh-day Adventist Church to abide by the same principle they have espoused for all churches. Specifically, they should refrain from accepting state funds to educate their youth in the tenets of Seventh-day Adventism.

State money used to maintain parochial as well as public

schools could eventuate in a particular church establishment obtaining a privileged status in the educational and cultural life of the nation. Such a religious group could gain a controlling position in shaping the thought and fixing the loyalty of the next generation. Their worldwide mission program has brought Adventists into a painful cognizance of the effects of church control in countries like Spain and Colombia, where a dominant church dictates the religious and educational life of the country.[5]

In the late 1940's Roman Catholic spokesmen aroused Seventh-day Adventists by their demands that state legislatures provide supplementary funds for Catholic parochial school systems, complaining that the separated system subjects Roman Catholics to "double taxation."

Adventists countered that the application of such church pressures placed state governments with large Roman Catholic populations in a difficult position. In Wisconsin, for example, Catholic pressures obliged the legislature to conduct a referendum to discover whether the electorate desired a constitutional amendment legalizing state assistance to parochial schools. Although at least 35 secular newspapers favored the amendment, Wisconsin citizens rejected the proposition. Similar Catholic political pressure in New Jersey forced the state legislature to rule that children attending either public or parochial school should be transported at state expense. One New Jersey township's board of education actually reimbursed some Roman Catholic parents for their children's public bus transport to their parochial schools. When a district taxpayer challenged the board's right to disburse tax funds in this manner, the resulting legal case passed up through the lower courts and finally reached the United States Supreme Court.[6]

Ruling on this Everson case, the Supreme Court validated the use of tax funds to transport children to parochial schools. Actually, none of the justices disputed the importance of the separationist principle, but the five-to-four decision revealed a rift among the justices on how that principle should be applied.

Adventists considered the constitutional issues in the case best stated in the Rutledge dissent. Alvin W. Johnson and Frank H. Yost, in their 1948 revision of Johnson's original book *The Legal Status of Church-State Relationships in the United States*, indicate how closely the view of Justice Edward Rutledge represented the views of the religious liberty department of the Seventh-day Adventist Church.[7]

Paralleling arguments used in Rutledge's dissent, Johnson and Yost trace James Madison's role in achieving religious freedom in America. Viewing religious liberty as a right rather than a privilege, Madison struggled with conservative religious forces in Virginia to disestablish the Episcopal Church. This religiopolitical conflict climaxed in the struggle over the assessment bill. Sponsored by Patrick Henry, then governor of Virginia, this measure would have taxed all citizens for the support of religion. In its final, amended form, however, the bill provided that the taxpayer, should he care to do so, could allot his share of the tax revenue to education rather than to religion. This was considered a quite liberal and enlightened measure. Even so, Madison continued to oppose it. His *Memorial and Remonstrance* finally aroused such popular protest against the assessment bill that the Virginia assembly killed it.

This struggle for religious liberty in Virginia laid the foundation for the First Amendment. Johnson and Yost agreed with Rutledge that Madison epitomized the whole struggle for the First Amendment. He opposed interference by the civil power in matters of religion and viewed both "free exercise" of religion and absence of any church establishment as two facets of the same principle.

Johnson and Yost stress that the First Amendment has expressed a continuing American tendency toward the separation of church and state. Although some theocrats argued that the nascent United States should set up a "Christian" form of government, the nation's Founding Fathers decided that the Government should be free from the controls of churchmen. The Northwest Ordinance of 1787 further protected the religious beliefs of individuals living in the new territories. Even diplomatic treaties of the time contained guarantees of religious freedom. Thus the church-state separationist principle continued to play an important part in American history, reaching its climax when the infidel James G. Blaine introduced a constitutional amendment ensuring that no state should make any law respecting an establishment of religion or prohibiting its free exercise. This proposal could have prohibited any public tax funds from ever being utilized by any religious sect.[8]

Overwhelmingly successful in the House, Blaine's proposal failed to gain a necessary Senate majority. According to Johnson and Yost, this was a tragic failure, since from that time the movement toward Sunday laws and for the diversion of Government money to parochial schools picked up considerable impetus.

Since provisions of the First Amendment apply directly to Congress and not to state legislatures, the United States Supreme Court could use only indirect means to achieve the ends set out in the First Amendment. For example, in *Gitlow* v. *United States* (1925), Justice Sanford applied the "due process" clause of the Fourteenth Amendment to a New York statute against "criminal anarchy." The Court invoked the Fourteenth Amendment in this instance to protect the freedom of speech and press. But this case did not really touch the religious question.[9] This came to the fore in *Cantwell* v. *Connecticut* (1940), when the Supreme Court again cited the Fourteenth Amendment to prevent a state from denying to a Jehovah's Witness his right to spread his religious views by unsolicited home visitation.[10]

The Seventh-day Adventist denomination summarized its conviction that religious liberty interests were best served by the aplication of the First Amendment at all levels of government when a resolution passed the General Conference at the 1947 spring session in Los Angeles: "*Resolved:* That we reaffirm our belief that for pupils to ride free of charge to and from Adventist schools in public school buses is in principle contrary to the historic position of the Seventh-day Adventist Church, that church and state be kept separate, . . . and further, *We Recommend,* That because of the principle concerned, Seventh-day Adventists do not use buses which are operated at public expense for the free transportation of their children to and from our church schools."[11]

Further propounding the church's view of separationism, *Liberty* published an article by the able constitutional lawyer, Leo Pfeffer, arguing that in both the previous Everson and the current McCollum cases,[12] the Supreme Court had applied the Fourteenth Amendment. Roman Catholics, Pfeffer suggested, liked the Everson ruling because it favored their immediate interests and supported the New Jersey board of education in providing transportation costs to parochial schools. But, said Pfeffer, despite the fact that the McCollum decision, in applying First Amendment principles to the states, followed the same pattern as the Everson case, Roman Catholics disliked this ruling simply because this case sustained Vashti McCollum's contention that the Illinois law permitting religious instruction on a "released time" basis was unconstitutional. Roman Catholics here viewed the case solely in terms of their own material self-interests rather than from principle, consistency, or in terms of the constitutional issues at stake.[13] Roman Catholics seemed more interested in getting something out of the Supreme Court decisions than in the constitutional principles on which the decisions were based. Catholic writers tended to inveigh against the Supreme Court for supporting a dangerous secularism within the public school system.[14]

Adventist views were directly opposite to those of the Catholics. They disliked the Everson decision and liked the McCollum ruling. In the McCollum case they had submitted an *amicus curiae* brief objecting to the "unconstitutionality" of the Illinois law which permitted the teaching of religion in state schools.[15] The almost unanimous ruling (8-1) of the Court harmonized with the views of church-state separationism embraced by most Adventists.[16]

Controversy over state aid to parochial schools reached a high point after Representative G. A. Barden of North Carolina introduced his bill, H.R. 4043, in 1949. Proposing an appropriation of 300 million dollars to support American public schools, this bill specifically excluded parochial institutions from sharing in the appropriation. Asserting that the bill was designed to assist communist Russia in its war against religion, many priests advised their parishioners to write their Congressmen denouncing the measure. Francis Cardinal Spellman vigorously attacked Representative Barden and crossed verbal swords with Methodist Bishop Oxnam, vice-president of the strictly separationist POAU. On the same issue he later clashed with Mrs. Franklin D. Roosevelt.

The New York cleric asserted that, by refusing to support "religious" factors in American education, these individuals demonstrated a very "un-American" spirit. They returned Spellman's fire with equal fervor, the national press supplying full coverage to the conflict.[17] Adventist religious liberty leaders, Heber H. Votaw, C. S. Longacre, and Frank H. Yost, wrote to the embattled Representative Barden, pledging their support.[18] Adventists took particular exception to the "double taxation" argument, the staple Roman Catholic rationale in their quest for Federal funds to finance their schools. Adventists insisted that Roman Catholics ought to shoulder this responsibility voluntarily, out of their desire to foster Roman Catholicism. They could not expect the Government to pay for their efforts to spread Catholic doctrines. Should the nation's citizenry be forced to pay for religious schooling, the system could well eventuate into a form of church education supported by the Government in which a powerful and ascendant religion is able to dominate other and smaller religious groups. This was in fact the situation in a number of countries.[19]

By 1952 another relevant Supreme Court decision injected a new element into the mix. In the McCollum case the Supreme Court had definitely ruled the "released time" programs unconstitutional. "Dismissed time" programs, however, did not involve the use of state equipment and were therefore less subject to charges of religious interference with state education.

Gary, Indiana, operated the first "dismissed time" plan, authorizing school authorities to dismiss pupils who desired religious education. These pupils were to go to church or synagogue for a period of religious teaching during the final part of the school day. The Zorach case, which came before the Supreme Court on July 28, 1948, tested the constitutionality of this practice. Opponents of "dismissed time" contended that in essence it was no different from "released time," since both plans exerted the influence of the school to make them effective. But the Supreme Court did not support this contention and decided by 6-3 that "dismissed time" was constitutional.[20]

Assessing the case, *Liberty* argued that the system as operated in New York did indeed use the coercive power of the state to secure attendance at religious services. Paragraph 4 of section 154 of the statute in question required that public school authorities be provided with attendance reports for the religious courses.

Admitting that "dismissed time" caused less interference with state educational machinery than "released time," *Liberty* maintained that it still introduced a measure of state coercion in matters religious.[21]

During this period Adventists held as consistently and as closely as possible to "church-state separation" in all matters involving religious instruction in public schools and state aid to parochial schools.

To denominational leaders this view accorded best with Madison's and Jefferson's intentions as demonstrated in Virginia's historic struggle for freedom from its church-state establishment. And, at least in the United States, it harmonized with the historical positions and eschatological interpretation of the denomination. But would Adventists cling as tenaciously to this commitment when their own economic interests were at stake? This question was soon put to the test.

During October, 1948, the Central California Conference of Seventh-day Adventists acquired Camp McQuade on the Monterey Peninsula as a "free" Government gift. This 300-acre tract containing 273 buildings, Adventists converted into Monterey Bay Academy. But the seemingly happy arrangement quickly turned into a knotty intramural debate.

Several Adventist laymen, disillusioned by the "inconsistency" of the denomination's position, wrote to the General Conference headquarters demanding that the church either admit its inconsistency and purchase the property or repudiate the entire transaction.[22] H. H. Votaw, Religious Liberty secretary, emphasized to the General Conference Committee that he had personally opposed the acquisition of Camp McQuade, fearing just such a reaction. Now his worst fears were realized. As he saw it, the only honorable solution was for the church to return the property.[23]

At the 1949 Autumn Council session delegates discussed the problem and drew up a policy. Denominational institutions should not accept Government gifts of money, lands, equipment, or buildings, except for war surplus and other grants to medical institutions. Hospitals, sanitariums, and other medical training institutions were, they determined, in a different category from other types of denominational institutions. Because of the remunerative value to their communities, they could accept such grants.[24]

From this time forward, denominational policy on state aid to religious institutions grew ever more complex. Committees established to study the problem seemed to lack a consistently cohesive thrust. After the passage of the National Defense Education Act in 1958, denominational leaders faced growing difficulty in restraining educational administrators from eagerly accepting proffered Government aid. Loma Linda University in southern California and Pacific Union College in northern California, both Adventist-owned and operated institutions, contracted with the Federal Government to receive research grants from the National Institutes of Health.

Since these grants paid for research done by colleges and medical institutions, Adventists considered them as payment received for services rendered to the Government, namely the results of their research. From 1958 Loma Linda accepted funds from the National Institutes of Health in increasing amounts. Loma Linda University accepted $1,943,278, the smaller Pacific Union College accepted $115,975 and Union College in Nebraska gained $8,050.[25] The acceptance of these funds was justified by the assertion that they were payments received for services rendered under contract.

When the Hill-Burton program was originated in 1946, it had provided Seventh-day Adventist medical institutions with over a million dollars to be expended on new medical facilities. W. A. Loveless, a prominent Seventh-day Adventist minister, has argued that Hill-Burton grants to Adventist groups violate the First Amendment since Adventist hospitals, no less than denominational schools and colleges, are religious institutions. They pray with patients, broadcast religious programs, have Adventist chaplains visit patients, and distribute Adventist literature. On the other hand, other Adventists have countered that these facets of SDA hospital work are only incidental to the main purpose of restoring health, a nonreligious activity.

In 1962 the Seventh-day Adventist Hinsdale Sanitarium, affiliated with the Andrews University complex in southwestern Michigan, accepted $1,003,037 in tax-generated funds, the grant coming not from the Hill-Burton program but from public health funds. This money was used to enlarge Hinsdale's housing facilities for nurses in training. Meanwhile other Adventist institutions also accepted public health service grants for nurse-training programs.[26] Loma Linda further accepted $83,498 in Government grants through the Federal Vocational Rehabilitation Plan to rehabilitate disabled persons. Loma Linda used these funds to educate more students in rehabilitation skills.[27]

These grants were received for medically-related programs, and denominational leaders explained that in providing a public medical service their institutions were serving the Government. This argument carefully distinguished between medical and religious phases of the total Adventist thrust. This was a reasonably convincing argument, but Adventist educational institutions could not so easily make this claim. Both Seventh-day Adventist colleges and universities greatly stressed the centrality of the Bible to their entire system of teaching, including history, the sciences, physical training, and everything else.

Yet Seventh-day Adventist colleges and universities had also benefited from state funds. Pacific Union College, alone among Adventist colleges, had first joined the National Defense Education Act loan plan on the ground that the student rather than the college received the money.[28] But other Seventh-day Adventist institutions had also accepted large amounts of material from the Surplus Property Act of 1944. They had maintained that they were free to buy at greatly reduced prices any surplus Government property, as long as they could demonstrate, as the law required, that it would be used for public benefit.[29] The important point was that the whole Seventh-day Adventist denomination had begun to profit from this kind of Government largess from 1950 onward.[30]

This easy symbiosis was somewhat disturbed by POAU's strong and public advocacy of "complete" separation of church and state, stressing that religious institutions which accepted Federal assistance were breaching the wall of separation. Quoting the Baptist general convention of Texas as stating that such participation violated "moral, spiritual, and constitutional aspects of the principle of church-state separation," POAU insisted that true separationism demanded refusal of Hill-Burton grants and rejection of student loan programs on the ground that scholarhip aid practices had degenerated into a conduit for the state subsidy of churches.[31]

Some Adventists questioned whether separationism should be interpreted in this strict way and suggested a broader approach. Several Adventist counselors and educational administrators, already involved in various grants and subsidies from the state, advanced arguments favoring even further involvement. A questionnaire circulated by W. A. Loveless among Adventist educational administrators revealed considerable dissatisfaction with existing denominational church-state policy among those polled. Many school administrators saw no reason why Adventist policy should allow *medical* institutions to accept Government grants but refuse similar benefits to strictly *educational* institutions.

A nebulous sort of consensus seemed to emerge among administrators to the effect that colleges could use Government money for *building-expansion,* but not for *operating expenses.* Educators who voiced this view held that in the past the denomination had derived its church-state policy from a particular tradition of separationist theory, rather than from a necessarily fresh and practical approach to actual church-state issues confronting Adventists in the mid-twentieth century. These educators commonly believed the church should restudy its entire position in this matter, paying greater heed to the views of its involved educators.[32]

The dissenting views of some educators within the denomination, however, did not greatly alter Adventist expression to the world on this topic. *Liberty* published an article by C. Stanley Lowell, a leading figure in POAU, exposing current Roman Catholic efforts to gain additional Government aid for its vast school system. Catholic Action, Lowell charged, had organized scores of front groups to undermine the wall of separation. The Roman Catholic Church, he wrote, had mapped out a long-term plan designed, first, to secure small concessions, and, eventually, to gain total Government financing.[33]

One result of such massive Government aid, Lowell declared, would be such a mushrooming of Catholic schools in the United States that the same undesirable sociological and cultural results already observable in France, in Spain, and in other European

9—C.S.R.

and South American countries would likewise occur in North America.

Roman Catholic leaders, on the other hand, tried to persuade taxpayers to accept the additional burdens of helping to finance Catholic schools by appealing to the church's role in ameliorating community social problems. Since public schools were unable to cope with increasing numbers of pupils, the Roman Catholic Church was assisting the nation by teaching many of these children, thus lightening the educational load which must otherwise be carried by the state. The church should therefore be reimbursed from public funds.

In an appeal to religious sentiment, Roman Catholic leaders charged that secularism was rampant in the public schools. The fact that no religion was taught in public schools, they argued, far from representing official governmental neutrality, actually signified a governmental drift toward agnosticism and even atheism. How did such schools differ significantly, they asked, from those conducted by communists?[34]

This kind of argument gained wide public support after the important *Engle* v. *Vitale* case of July 25, 1962. On this occasion, by a 6 to 1 majority the Supreme Court declared that the state of New York could not force teachers to recite a twenty-two word "nondenominational" prayer in that state's public schools. Such a requirement, ruled the Court, constituted a violation of the First Amendment to the Constitution.[35] As press reports circulated across the country, criticism of the Court mounted to unprecedented heights; and the Roman Catholic argument of secularism in the public schools gained enormous support, especially among conservative Protestants, a class traditionally opposed to Roman Catholics.[36]

Adventists reacted quickly against this "misinformed public opinion" as did POAU. *Liberty* Editor Roland Hegstad pointed out that the Supreme Court decision had been misunderstood. The Court did not forbid any student or teacher from saying any prayer in the classroom. Rather, it forbade the governmentally *forced* recitation of a prayer. As Justice Hugo Black stated, it was not the business of the state to compose official prayers for classroom use.

This, maintained Hegstad, was no anti-God decision. Nor did it spring from any secular outlook. It was directed against state-enforced religion, and in free America this was the only constitutional position. The decision really highlighted two factors, said Hegstad. It emphasized constitutional barriers against state-directed religious practices. And it ruled that religious instruction of children was the personal responsibility of their parents. Properly understood, the prayer decision should be viewed as a far-seeing effort to place spiritual issues where they properly belong —outside the realm of state dictation.[37]

Two additional Court cases, involving Bible reading in the schools, raised further questions.

In one, initiated in Abingdon Township, Pennsylvania, two Unitarians, Edward and Sidney Schempp, objected to a Pennsylvania law requiring at least ten Bible verses to be read to pupils without comment each day on the ground that the law was unconstitutional. A Federal district court had upheld their contention.

A second legal case initiated in Baltimore where two professing atheists—Mrs. Madalyn Murray and her son William J. Murray III—challenged the constitutionality of forced reading of Bible verses. When the Maryland court of appeals denied the appellants and upheld this law, the Murrays then appealed to the Supreme Court.

Liberty Editor Hegstad particularly noted an interchange between Justice Hugo Black and Pennsylvania's deputy attorney-general. The state representative asked the justices to consider the consequences if they ruled out the possibility of enforced Bible reading in public schools. Justice Black retorted by asking Pennsylvania's deputy attorney-general to consider the results if they did not.[38]

These cases stirred Adventists deeply. From earliest times, the denomination had recoiled from the prospects of a police-enforced "Christian America." Officially enforced classroom prayers and religious readings had always conjured up images of the persecution of religious dissenters. David McAllister, pioneer supporter of the National Reform Association, had early authored a pamphlet on the constitutionality of Bible reading in the nation's public schools.[39] And Seventh-day Adventists had consistently opposed the National Reform Association and its president in their endeavors to enforce religious observances.

Now, as the specter again arose, Adventists felt compelled to expose its dangers. *Liberty* published an article by Dean Kelley asking whether "a state religion was emerging in the United States." Stressing that recent tendencies in the United States were fostering an embryonic state religion, Kelley adduced such evidence for his affirmation as the superficiality of "resurgent religion," the hunger for tax money to finance religious schools, the current emphasis on religious language and symbolism, and the desire to incorporate religious practices in public schools. God, said Kelley, was being transmuted into the "Great American," leading the nation as His "chosen people" in a "holy crusade" against the infidel.[40]

Once again the old fear of state-enforced religion destroying religious liberty in America loomed before Adventist eyes. They believed the Supreme Court stood on sound ground in declaring unconstitutional any form of police-enforced religious practices in the tax-supported public schools. They agreed with the Schempp-Murray verdict. They agreed with Justice Clark when he maintained that this ruling continued the Court's consistent interpretation of the "nonestablishment clause." They agreed that nothing in the "free exercise" clause should be interpreted as allowing a majority to use state police power to ensure the dominance of its particular beliefs.[41]

Public controversy over church-state issues continued throughout 1965, public passion flaring fiercely over the Supreme Court decision in the Schempp-Murray cases. And out of this controversy came the Becker Amendment introduced into the eighty-ninth Congress in order to void the Supreme Court's earlier decision.

Religious groups organized to demonstrate through polls and petitions that the majority of Americans favor "regular prayer and Bible reading" in the nation's public schools. *The Christian Herald* circulated ballots asserting that the Supreme Court had outlawed prayer and/or Bible study in public schools.[42]

To counter the false impression in the public mind, *Liberty* circulated a poll asking whether its readers favored a religious amendment giving power to the Government to compose prayers and to require children to recite them. Furthermore, asked the tenacious little magazine, did readers wish to give this power to Government even if dissenting children were allowed to absent themselves?[43]

By early 1966, the late Senator Everett Dirksen was reduced to championing a watered-down amendment designed to placate any potential opposition. The bill now stressed: "Nothing contained in this Constitution shall prohibit the authority administering any school, school system, educational administration . . . from providing for or permitting the voluntary participation by students or others in prayer. Nothing contained in this article shall authorize any such authority to prescribe the form or content of any prayer."[44]

Adventists reacted with typical élan. Religious liberty leaders observed that the proposed amendment was so ambiguous as to be capable of many and various interpretations, some of which might well lead to further encroachments of the state upon the church and the church upon the state. Since the First Amendment was itself subject to Court interpretation, they deemed it inadvisable to add further words which might be construed in ways destructive to religious freedom.[45]

During the hearings before the subcommittee on constitutional amendments, various groups—Jewish, Protestant, Roman Catholic, and Seventh-day Adventist—spoke against the proposed amendment. Jewish spokesmen said it would place the Government's "stamp of approval" on a devotional act. Nonparticipating children, labeled nonconformist, might possibly be subjected to social and psychological pressures.[46] Others emphasized the possibly deleterious effects the proposal might exercise upon teachers. If they should personally object to the devotional form, they might be forced into hypocritical concealment of their feelings in order to obey a state-ordered religious exercise contrary to their own beliefs. Their only alternative might be to withdraw from the school system. Any minority groups could thus easily be reduced into the stature of "second class citizens."[47]

By a narrow margin of nine votes, opponents of the measure prevailed in committee and although the bill's proponents succeeded in forcing it out, it finally expired on the Senate floor.[48]

Adventists wiped their brows in relief and returned to their own persistent nemesis—whether or not to accept tax-generated funds from a willing Government. Many Seventh-day Adventist educational administrators felt that the most difficult problem in this area was the least mentioned, due to the fact that an increasingly vital need to finance church-sponsored undergraduate colleges existed throughout North America.

From their standpoint this predicament threatened the very existence of Seventh-day Adventist religious education. Most of the institutions felt a critical lack of adequate classroom space, laboratory facilities, and dormitory accommodations. In addition, almost without exception they operated in the red. To try to meet this problem by raising already high tuition fees could result in a disastrous exodus of Adventist youth to tax-supported colleges and universities. Faced with declining enrollments, some administrators of financially faltering colleges saw little profit in worrying about the future state interference, which strict Adventist separationists feared, if the decline of Adventism should result anyway from the deterioration of its school system.[49]

Eyeing proffered financial relief from the national treasury, several Adventist educational administrators continued to express the opinion that the "traditional" position of the Seventh-day Adventist Church on church-state relations did indeed stem more from church tradition than from Biblical doctrine or ethical principle. "Is total separationism sacrosanct?" asked Charles Fleming, Jr., a college financial administrator. Asserting that no direct support for absolute separation of church and state could be found in the Bible, Fleming cited Ellen G. White, who in her arguments utilizing Old Testament passages, he said, specifically instructed the denomination to accept help. Referring to the Solusi land transaction in South Africa, he emphasized that Cecil Rhodes was premier of Cape Colony as well as president of the British South Africa Company, when the denomination accepted land from that corporation.[50]

Other Adventist educational leaders also spoke up. Veteran college and university administrator and historian F. O. Rittenhouse viewed the historical problem. For a century after the founding of the United States, he said, the nation knew little of complete separationism. Citizens of the young country heard little dissent over tax-supported Protestant institutions. Contending that complete separationist doctrine, really descended from weak "historical credentials," he set out three areas for consideration: First, the responsibilities residing peculiarly and uniquely in the state; second, the "inalienable rights of free men"; third, mutual understandings and shared responsibility.[51]

From the time of Chief Justice Marshall, he reasoned, the Supreme Court had defended practically every ingredient of personal freedom as envisioned by the Founding Fathers. Notwithstanding this, in an increasingly complex society, it is impossible to hold a completely doctrinaire attitude regarding church-state separation. In common with most other churches, Adventists were already accepting school lunch aid, Government surplus property, school bus transportation, Government scholarships, tax exemption for their institutions, welfare and health services, and Hill-Burton funds for their hospitals. Since the denomination had accepted tax exemption from the very beginning, why could it not just as well receive Government grants? No supportable qualitative distinction existed. They were opposite sides of the same coin.[52]

These variations of opinion came into the foreground in 1968 after a panel discussion which was moderated by Neal C. Wilson, chairman of the Seventh-day Adventist church-state committee for North America. [53]

During this discussion a college president, one of the panel members, urged a "three wall" theory of church-state relations which emphasized the "in-between" zone as that place where church and state activities overlap. Asked by moderator Wilson to define this "in-between" activity, the panelist mentioned examples: military chaplains, church tax exemption, donation of state lands for religious purposes, financial grants to church-supported hospitals, and free textbooks to church schools.

A second panelist, also an educational administrator, added that the issue of Government aid was one of public policy rather than morality.

These two educators then asserted that a careful, "discriminating acceptance of Government aid" was a "logical development of the highest form of religious liberty." Since religious liberty must eventually become a key topic among Americans, they asked, should not Seventh-day Adventists discriminate now, so that thinking men could appreciate the denomination's evangelical answer to world problems?

The publication of this discussion in the denomination's official organ, the *Review and Herald,* elicited a flood of reader comment. A great number of letters, beginning with the *Review* issue of November 7, 1968, in the main disagreed with the panel's evident consensus and supported the traditional position on church-state separation.[54] Most of the published letters based their comments on the assumption that the traditional view was the correct one and that only faith could solve the financial problems. Several educational administrators also wrote letters to the *Review* proposing that under certain conditions state funds could be accepted.[55]

Thoughtful persons who opposed such acceptance wrote as well, discussing the important issues at stake and evaluating the possible consequences of accepting tax dollars. Some of these stated that since the denomination did not wish to employ teachers differing in religious or scientific philosophy from the Seventh-day Adventist beliefs, the church could not compromise its basic position by accepting Government funds. Roland R. Hegstad, of the Religious Liberty Department, set forth two reasons for refusing Government money. First, legislative guarantees of noninterference are of little value unless endorsed by the United States Supreme Court; second, society insisted on controlling the policy of institutions accepting subsidies from the Government. Thus acceptance of public funds could drastically alter Adventist educational policy.[56]

Warren L. Johns, legal advisor to the Seventh-day Adventist church-state council, outlined basic differences of opinion among Adventists on the question of acceptance of state aid for education. According to him, those who believed in accepting Government help as a means of meeting financial needs of Adventist education urged the following points:

1. There is nothing in the Scriptures or in the writings of Ellen G. White prohibiting Government aid to a church institution.

2. The acceptance of Government aid is not a moral issue.
3. Seventh-day Adventist parochial education is subsidized by the Government in many overseas countries.
4. Church members pay their taxes for public education, and acceptance of Government funds provides a means of getting back a portion of these taxes.
5. Programs of Government subsidies currently contain no unreasonable demand or controls.
6. To accept Government help rather than let parochial education go out of business is to accept the lesser of two evils.
7. The church should not be bound by nineteenth-century church-state concepts in coping with twentieth-century problems.[57]

Those who opposed accepting Government aid set forth these points:

1. Direct Government financing of parochial education conflicts with existing guidelines separating church and state, as established by decisions of the United States Supreme Court.
2. Government support of church institutions represents a false church and constitutes evidence of spiritual weakness. There is a moral issue which is implicit in the prophetic symbolism which stands as a foundation doctrine of the Seventh-day Adventist Church.
3. In many overseas countries where Government aid is available to parochial education, the Seventh-day Adventist Church has not accepted it. Furthermore, in some cases where Government aid has been accepted, problems have resulted.
4. The absence or the existence of "controls" now in a Government subsidy program is immaterial. The "power to control" inherent in any Governmental program can be invoked at the whim of the Government.
5. If the church accepts Government support of its educational institutions, Adventist arguments against Government support of other religious institutions, such as coerced Sunday observance, will be inconsistent.
6. Acceptance of Government funds will weaken traditional

sacrificial support by the church laity, and dollars gained from the Government would likely be offset by dollars lost from diminished membership support.[58]

Up to the close of 1968, the issue of state aid for Seventh-day Adventist colleges remained hotly contested.[59] But in February, 1969, the membership of the North American Division Committee on Administration (consisting of officers of the General Conference, Union Conference presidents, and college administrators from the North American division) was summoned to Washington, D.C., to consider the action of the medical department of Loma Linda University. During the previous year this department had accepted more than $1,750,000 in Federal aid. After considerable discussion the committee took the view that by virtue of its role as a public service institution rather than as simply a church educational institution, Loma Linda University was eligible to accept Federal aid. But the committee repudiated all suggestion that other Seventh-day Adventist educational institutions could follow suit. Respecting these this committee voted to implement the decision formerly taken at the autumn council of 1965. In this way the church sought to reaffirm its historic separationist position.

From 1969 most Seventh-day Adventists could agree that the maintenance of separation between church and state was increasingly difficult. Adventists realized that Roman Catholics *did* serve non-Catholic disadvantaged people within its educational institutions, often free of charge. Certainly this Roman Catholic endeavor to reach the inner city ghettoes was a commendable public service. However, Adventists also recognized that the practice also involved extensive religious indoctrination. Similarly, certain Eastern states had been paying part of the salaries of mathematics, science, and physical education teachers in Roman Catholic parochial schools. Proponents of this practice explained that these teachers were contributing to secular education, but Seventh-day Adventists could recognize that these were examples which blurred all distinction between "secular" and "religious." Adventists noted also that several cases involving Federal grants to sectarian colleges had now reached the courts.

Up to 1968, the taxpayer, whose hard-earned dollars various

denominational institutions were coveting, had no voice in determining whether or not he wanted his money used to support such institutions. In that year, however, a Supreme Court decision, *Flast* v. *Cohen,* at last gave him his opportunity.[60] The Court decided that the "Frothingham doctrine," which held that individual taxpayers could not challenge the expenditure of Federal funds, did not apply to Federal grants and loans to religious institutions. Thus, after this decision, no religious educational institution could rest securely in the possession of Federal funds. Its rights to these moneys could now be challenged by any taxpayer.

Nor did taxpayers waste time deciding whether or not to challenge. They challenged. And the Supreme Court agreed to consider three legal cases involving Pennsylvania, Rhode Island, and Connecticut Roman Catholic educational institutions.

In harmony with their rights under the recent Flast-Cohen Supreme Court ruling, taxpayers challenged the constitutional basis of Pennsylvania and Rhode Island to pay parochial school teachers for teaching secular subjects in Catholic schools. They also challenged the right of Catholic colleges in Connecticut to accept Federal grants for the erection of buildings to house secular educational activities.

In the Pennsylvania case (*Lemon* v. *Kurtzman*) and the (*Di-Cenzo*) Rhode Island case, the Supreme Court ruled that state aid is unconstitutional when received for educational supplies in the teaching of secular subjects in a church-related high school.

But in the Connecticut case (*Tilton* v. *Richardson*) the Court emphasized that church-related colleges were not debarred from participation in the construction grants program of the Federal Higher Education Facilities Act of 1963. In this Connecticut case the Supreme Court ruled that since the purposes and instruction offered by these Catholic colleges involved no serious or extensive religious mission and no compulsory religious indoctrination, their religious affiliations constituted no deterrent to their receiving the taxpayer's funds. But the Court carefully stressed that should religious instruction become compulsory on these campuses, the case would be radically altered.

Thus the Court made clear that what the Government could subsidize it could also regulate.

In the other cases the Court noted the complex problem of deciding the constitutionality of various demands which parochial schools might make if Federal moneys should be opened to them. Admitting this problem, Chief Justice Warren Burger observed that the "wall of separation" had already become a "blurred, indistinct, and variable barrier."

The constitutionally recognized power of the Government to control the use to which taxpayer's moneys were put became even more clearly evident in a case involving the Catholic University of America in Washington, D.C. Student representatives from the university invited the rather controversial Miss Ti-Grace Atkinson to address a student group on the university campus. She being a spokesman for women's liberation, birth control, and abortion, who had already made a series of provocative statements, President Clarence J. Walter cancelled her appointment.

Considering the Catholic position on the above topics, the action of the administration could hardly be considered unusual or unduly strict. But because this Catholic institution had already accepted Government funds, the student representatives were able to secure a court injunction from a Federal court forcing the administration to lift its ban and to allow Miss Atkinson to speak.

Obviously the university's acceptance of Government funds had opened the way for the Government to act swiftly to prevent "discrimination" against un-Catholic opinions and teachings in the Catholic institution. And Miss Ti-Grace Atkinson did indeed proceed with her lecture.[61]

These developments provided a background against which Adventists viewed their own dilemma. Certainly the Supreme Court had sharply demonstrated that if the denomination should rashly take Government funds without a full understanding of the issues involved, it might lose control over some aspects of its own educational institutions.

Since Seventh-day Adventists commonly agree that the church must retain complete religious autonomy within its own system of education, agreement is also common that only certain funds may be accepted. However, some Adventist educators have expressed the opinion that the church could cooperate with the Government if a "voucher" plan [62] should be introduced by which tax-generated money might be given to the *student* rather than to the *institution*.

At this writing most Adventists oppose this plan. Undoubtedly this question will be further discussed, especially if the financial problems of Adventist schools continue to mount, and as the Government's policies become more detailed and explicit.

In any case, as threats to religious liberty continue to appear, Adventists will continue their historical vigilance. When Representative Chalmers P. Wylie (R-Ohio) introduced to the House of Representatives a constitutional prayer amendment obviously intended to void the Supreme Court decision outlawing forced school prayers, Adventists and some other religious groups did much to publicize fully the dangerous implications in the bill which would permit forced "nondenominational prayers in public buildings." On September 21, 1971, this bill was commonly considered unbeatable. But by the day of the vote, November 8, 1971, by a margin of 28 votes this proposed amendment was killed— a defeat which gave tribute to the work done by Adventists and other opponents.[63]

By the close of 1972 it was clear to the Seventh-day Adventist leadership that a precise policy must be formed to guide the church in its working relationships with the United States Government. General Conference officers, Union Conference presidents, educational leaders, and religious liberty spokesmen used the occasion of their meeting at the Autumn Council in Mexico City to explore fully and discuss at length the North American Division Working Policy in respect to a number of problems, but particularly with regard to church-state relationships. The church needed to restudy this subject because of the confusion in the minds of so many educators, church administrators, and laymen. Many individuals had come to believe that the apparent variance between practice and policy in denominational church-state relations might finally lead to a loss of confidence in the credibility and integrity of church leadership, hence had arisen the necessity to clarify the denomination's position on this subject of church-state relations.[64]

First the traditional separationist views of the Seventh-day Adventist Church were reaffirmed.[65] Then it was emphasized that Government aid could be accepted provided it did not jeopardize denominational independence and freedom of action. Under all circumstances the spiritual goals of the church must be kept to the fore, and any denominational educational institution accepting Government aid should officially record that the new arrangement was not necessary for its continued viability. This must be demonstrated in terms of the percentage of its budget which came from Government aid. It must affirm that it would terminate such an arrangement at any time it should endanger the college or the school's basic religious objectives or its relation to the Seventh-day Adventist Church as a whole.

To ensure denominational control of its own educational institutions the council further stated that by June 1, 1973, the boards of trustees of all denominational church colleges and universities in the United States should report on all types of Governmental (local, state, or Federal) aid they had received. Following this report, the Church-state Committee associated with the North American Division Committee on Administration would counsel the various institutions on their specific aid programs. If the committee should determine that any institution was becoming dependent upon state aid, the institution must end that situation.

To further clarify the denomination's church-state position with the lay members of its own church body, with the general public, and with the United States Government, Seventh-day Adventist Church leadership also required that any application to the United States Government for loans or grants must be accompanied by an approved statement of the Adventist philosophy of higher education.[66] There must be no misunderstanding as to the church's position. Finally, the projected General Conference session of 1975 was specified as a settled date by which all Seventh-day Adventist educational institutions must be in complete harmony with the newly stated church policy. However, the Mexico City church-state report strongly affirmed that the denomination continue to consider the buying of Government surplus, the carrying out of research programs paid for by Government funds and established by Government contract, and issues affecting public health as distinctly different from other forms of Government aid. Consequently, the work of the Loma Linda Schools of Medicine, Dentistry, and Health were viewed as somewhat unique from other Seventh-day Adventist educational institutions in the way all of the provisions should be applied.

Thus the year 1972 closed with an important and definitive clarification of the Seventh-day Adventist position respecting church-state relationships. As we have seen in this book, consistently throughout the denomination's history its leadership has recognized the importance of good relations with the Government and the general public. This rapport is essential to the maintenance of religious liberty so necessary for the continuation of Seventh-day Adventist evangelistic programs and missionary endeavor. The recent restatement of policy on church-state relations follows this same tradition. In addition to this, the denomination continues to inform both its own members and the general public on its stand on religious liberty issues by sending free the *Liberty* magazine to judges, congressmen, and other leaders; by conducting weekend discussions on religious liberty; and by placing church-state materials in college and university libraries.

REFERENCES AND NOTES

1. Bill Oliphant, ed., *Seventh-day Adventists Today* (Nashville: Southern Publishing Association, 1966), pages 44, 45, 54, 62, 63.

2. *109th Annual Statistical Report of Seventh-day Adventists,* 1971, compiled by Jesse O. Gibson, Statistical Secretary, General Conference of Seventh-day Adventists, Takoma Park, Washington, D.C. 20012. School Statistics, pages 7, 8.

3. Hiram William Sauer, "The Seventh-day Adventist School as a Determining Factor in Church Membership," (unpublished master's thesis, Pacific Union College, Angwin, California, 1950), pages 3-6.

4. John David Hardt, "Historical Development of Seventh-day Adventist College Curricula" (published master's thesis, Pacific Union College, Angwin, 1942), pages 12, 13.

5. For example, consider the work of Jean Nussbaum, Seventh-day Adventist Religious Liberty secretary in Europe. His work during the thirties was vital in securing new freedoms for Adventist minority groups in some of the European countries; cf. "Tributes to Jean Nussbaum, M.D.," *Liberty,* March-April, 1968, pp. 17-20; also concerning this position see Justice William O. Douglas, *The Bible and the Schools* (Boston: Little, Brown and Company, 1966), pages 33ff., where Douglas argues the case for the secular government and its advantages to the citizen.

6. *Everson* v. *Board of Education,* 330 U.S. 1-74. Both the majority decision and the very close minority dissent in this Supreme Court ruling represent important illustrations of separationist interpretation.

7. This seems very apparent in reading Johnson and Yost's account and comparing it with Justice Edward Rutledge's dissenting opinion. Johnson and Yost were both leaders in the Religious Liberty Department. The 1948 revision of the book is entitled *Separation of Church and State in the United States* (Minneapolis: University of Minnesota Press, 1948).

8. Johnson and Yost, *op. cit.,* pp. 30ff., suggest that the movement for the secularization of public schools reached its greatest height with this amendment proposal; William A. Blakely, *American State Papers,* pages 204ff., argues that if Blaine's proposal had been adopted, it would have done away with all forms of state patronage and support for religion. Since that time, he suggests, the current moved the other way, as evidenced in the revival of Sunday laws. Mark DeWolfe Howe, *Cases on Church and State in the United States* (Cambridge: Harvard University Press, 1952), pages 86-88, explains the background of the Blaine Amendment as the endeavor of the Republican Party to meet what many Protestants considered as the Roman Catholic threat. The "embers of the Know Nothing movement were still burning."

9. *Gitlow* v. *United States,* 268 U.S. 652 (1925). Richard C. Kim, "The Constitution, the Supreme Court, and Religious Liberty," *A Journal of Church and State,* autumn, 1964, discusses the case among others from the standpoint that it represented the gradual application of the Fourteenth Amendment on the state scene. William H. Marnell, *The First Amendment* (Garden City: Doubleday and Company, 1964), pages 174ff., also considers this case from a similar view.

10. *Cantwell* v. *Connecticut,* 310 U.S. 296 (1940). *Ibid.* Note also Joseph Tussman, *The Supreme Court on Church and State,* pages 72-80.

11. J. I. Robinson, "Spring Council Proceedings, Los Angeles, April 16-23, 1947," *Review and Herald,* May 29, 1947, p. 14.

12. *McCollum* v. *Board of Education,* 333 U.S. 203 (1948). Mrs. Vashti McCollum, the appellant, protested an Illinois law permitting "released time" basis for religious instruction in the Champaign, Illinois, public schools. This case is discussed in Stokes, *Church and State in the United States,* Vol. 2, pp. 515ff.; Donald E. Boles, *The Bible, Religion, and the Public Schools* (Ames: Iowa State University Press, 1963), pages 162ff.

13. Leo Pfeffer, "The Meaning of the First Amendment," *Liberty,* second quarter, 1949, pp. 5-10.

14. Donald E. Boles, *op. cit.,* p. 167.

15. General Conference Religious Liberty Department, "On the Religious Liberty Front," *Review and Herald,* Jan. 1, 1948, p. 10.

16. Mark DeWolfe Howe, ed., *Cases on Church and State in the United States,* pages 364ff., provides a transcript of *McCollum* v. *Board of Education,* 333 U.S. 203 (1948).

17. Frank H. Yost, "On the Religious Liberty Front," *Review and Herald,* Nov. 3, 1949, p. 19; Yost, "The Press Comments on the Roosevelt-Spellman Dispute," *Liberty,* fourth quarter, 1949. Anson P. Stokes and Leo Pfeffer, *Church and State in the United States* (New York: Harper & Row, 1964), pages 436-442, gives an excellent description of the Roosevelt-Spellman controversy.

18. William A. Loveless, "Federal Aid and the Church-operated College: A Case Study" (unpublished doctoral dissertation, University of Maryland, 1964), page 77.

19. C. S. Longacre, "Imposition of Double Taxation," *Liberty,* second quarter, 1950, pp. 28, 29.

20. *Zorach* v. *Clauson,* 343 U.S. 306 (1952). For a record of the case and its findings see Joseph Tussman, *The Supreme Court on Church and State,* pages 264-274; also Donald E. Boles, *The Bible, Religion, and the Public Schools,* pages 169-176.

21. Yost, "The New York System of Weekday Religious Instructions," *Liberty,* third quarter, 1952, pp. 5-8.

22. Letter From the Laymen's Committee, For General Circulation, undated (mimeographed); cited by W. A. Loveless, *op. cit.* pp. 77, 78.

23. Letter from H. H. Votaw, Religious Liberty Department secretary to members of the General Conference Committee, July 5, 1959; cited by Loveless, *op. cit.,* pp. 78, 79.

24. "Actions of the Autumn Council of the General Conference Committee, Nov. 7-16, 1949, at St. Louis, Missouri," pp. 26, 27; cited by Loveless, *op.* cit., p. 80.

25. Loveless, *op. cit.,* p. 125.

26. *Ibid.,* pp. 128-130.

27. *Ibid.,* pp. 144, 145.

28. *Ibid.,* pp. 124, 125.

29. "Public benefit" allowance could be as high as a reduction of 95 percent leaving only 5 percent to be paid by the buyer.

30. Loveless, *op. cit.,* pp. 134, 135.

31. C. Stanley Lowell and Herbert C. Southgate, "POAU Position on Church-state Relations," *A Journal of Church and State,* May, 1963, p. 41.

32. Loveless, *op. cit.,* pp. 90, 190.

33. C. Stanley Lowell, "Shall the State Subsidize Church Schools?" *Liberty,* September-October, 1960, pp. 11-15.

34. Dean M. Kelley, "Parochial Schools and Public Funds," *Liberty,* November-December, 1963, pp. 14-16, 30.

35. *Engle* v. *Vitale,* 370 U.S. 421 (1962). Stokes and Pfeffer, *op. cit.,* pp. 142-144, give a brief description of this case. (Two justices took no part in the decision rendered.)

36. Many of these arguments were based on Luke 18:16, Christ's words being "Suffer little children to come to Me and forbid them not." This caption was used by the *Evening Star* of Washington, D.C., Tuesday, June 26, 1962; cited by editorial, *Liberty,* September-October, 1962; note also William A. Hachter, "Journalism and the Prayer Decision," *Liberty,* July-August, 1963, pp. 18-21, 31.

37. Roland R. Hegstad, "Supreme Court Prayer Decision Misunderstood," *Liberty,* September-October, 1962, p. 32.

38. Hegstad, "The Bible—Holy Book or Tranquilizing Pill," *Liberty,* July-August, 1963, pp. 12-17; the two cases of *Abingdon School District* v. *Schempp,* 374 U.S. 203 (1963), and *Murray* v. *Curlett,* 374 U.S. 203 (1963), are collectively described as the Schempp-Murray Case and briefly dealt with in Stokes and Pfeffer, *op. cit.,* pp. 144-147.

39. David McAllister, *Constitutionality of Reading of the Bible in the Public Schools* (Pittsburgh: National Reform Association, 1902).

40. Dean Kelley, "Beyond Separation of Church and State," *Liberty,* July-August, 1963, pp. 24, 25; note the expanded version of this article in *A Journal of Church and State,* November, 1963, pp. 181ff. A similar emphasis is given in Sidney E. Mead, "The Nation With the Soul of a Church," *Church History,* September, 1967, p. 262. Winthrop S. Hudson, *The Great Tradition of the American Churches* (New York: Harper & Brothers, 1953); and Franklin H. Littell, *From State Church to Pluralism* (Chicago: Adline Press, 1962), also discussed the decline of internal church discipline and doctrine with its resultant creation of an accompanying dependence on the doctrine of a "national Christianity."

41. Don A. Roth, "The Becker Amendment," *Liberty,* November-December, 1964, pp. 15-17.

42. Morris K. Udall (Congressman from Arizona), "Do We Want Another Bible War?" *Liberty,* March-April, 1965, pp. 12-15.

43. Hegstad, "Prayer Poll Ballot?" *Liberty,* March-April, 1965, pp. 16, 17.

44. S. J. Res. 148, 89th Congress, 2nd session. *Hearings Before the Subcommittee on Constitutional Amendments of the Committee on the Judiciary of United States Senate Eighty-Ninth Congress Second Session on Senate Joint Resolution 148 Relating to Prayer in Public Schools* (Washington, D.C.: U.S. Government Printing Office, 1966), page 1.

45. W. Melvin Adams, "Hearing on Dirksen Amendment," *Liberty,* September-October, 1966, p. 30.

46. *Hearings Before the Subcommittee,* pages 489ff.

47. *Ibid.,* pp. 532ff.

48. Adams, "Senate Rejects Prayer Bill," *Liberty News,* November, 1966, p. 1.

49. Charles Fleming, Jr., "The Case for Accepting Federal Funds," (paper read to Nashville Chapter Association of Adventist Forums, Nashville, Tennessee, Dec. 7, 1968) (mimeographed), p. 2.

50. *Ibid.,* pp. 3-5.

51. F. O. Rittenhouse, "The Seventh-day Adventist Church and Religious Liberty," (statement presented at the Annual Freedoms Award Dinner of the Church-State Council, San Francisco, California, Nov. 5, 1967); Harold D. Hammett, "Separation of Church and State: By One Wall or Two?" *A Journal of Church and State,* spring, 1965, pp. 196ff., also uses the idea of a "third wall" involving mutual overlapping of relationships between church and state.

52. *Ibid.,* p. 3. See also Philip Wogaman, "The Changing Role of Government, and the Myth of Separation," *A Journal of Church and State,* May, 1963, pp. 61ff. Dr. Wogaman stressed that there is a great deal of difference between "separationism" in a sparsely populated agrarian society and the same concept in the complex world of today.

53. "Church-State Relations: A Panel Discussion Setting Forth Some of the Issues Involved in Accepting Federal Aid for Denominational Schools." *Review and Herald,* September 26, 1968, pp. 1-7.

54. "Response to Church-State Panel" (Letters From Readers), *Review and Herald,* Nov. 7, 1968, p. 15.

55. Richard Hammill, "More on Federal Aid" (Letters From Readers), *Review and Herald,* Nov. 14, 1968, p. 15. Hammill is president of Andrews University, Berrien Springs, Michigan. Raymond Moore, "Apprehension Over Federal Aid," (Letters From Readers), *Review and Herald,* Dec. 12, 1968, p. 16.

56. Hegstad, "Government Aid to Seventh-day Adventist Education in the Light of the Future" (paper read at the North American Division Quadrennial Council for Higher Education, Andrews University, Michigan, Aug. 22, 1968).

57. Warren L. Johns, "Should Adventist Churches Take Federal Aid for Their Colleges?" *Pacific Union Recorder,* June 10, 1968, p. 1.

58. Gleaned from letters published in *Review and Herald* from Nov. 7, 1968 to March 6, 1969.

59. See *Review and Herald,* March 6, 1969, pp. 1, 2, and March 13, 1969, pp. 9-12, for a thorough discussion of the problem at that time.

60. *Liberty News,* October, 1968, p. 73; November, 1968, p. 79; March, 1969, pp. 16-18. *Flast v. Cohen,* 392 U.S. 83 (1968).

61. *Liberty News,* May, 1971, p. 23.

62. *Liberty News,* December, 1970, p. 65. *Note:* The general idea of this voucher plan is developed by Donald Rumsfield of the Office of Economic Opportunity. He describes the plan as an experiment to allow the parents, by receiving vouchers which they can apply to any institution, to exercise their influence on the quality of education. The plan also escapes the odium that it provides money for church-related schools. The money is given to the student to spend as he or his parents wish.

63. *Liberty News,* March, 1972, pp. 15, 16.

64. For a summary of the reasons for adopting a new policy see Neal C. Wilson, "A New Policy on Government Aid," *Review and Herald,* Dec. 7, 1972, pp. 18, 30.

65. For a complete statement of the new policy see *Review and Herald,* Dec. 14, 1972, pp. 26, 27.

66. The statement points out that it "endeavors to set forth how and why Seventh-day Adventist colleges and universities differ from—not how they resemble others." It quotes from Ellen G. White's statement of purpose for education as recorded in *Testimonies,* Vol. 4, p. 425, and goes on to point out that each of these schools "is more than a church-related institution; it is a church institution." And it affirms that in such a school "religion is not merely one among many academic disciplines; a religious world view pervades the fundamental philosophy of the school."—Wilson, *Review and Herald,* Dec. 7, 1972, p. 18.

HIGHLIGHTS

GENERAL INDEX

11—C.S.R.

F
M

Milofsky, David.

Playing from memory

c.1
783

DATE			

PLAYING
FROM
MEMORY

A NOVEL BY

David Milofsky

SIMON AND SCHUSTER

NEW YORK

Designed by Wayne Kirn

Manufactured in the United States of America

1 2 3 4 5 6 7 8 9 10
Library of Congress Cataloging in Publication Data
Milofsky, David.
Playing from memory.
I. Title.
PZ4.M6598Pl   [PS3563.I444]   813'.54
80–18600
ISBN 0-671-25252-6

I would like to acknowledge the contribution of my father, Bernard Milofsky. Some of the
musical scenes in this book are based on his unpublished novel *The Fiddlers Four*. I am
grateful to him for his advice and support.

To Jaqueline,
and to my mother and father

Part One

1

THE APPLAUSE was thunderous. It rolled out of the tiered seats, enveloping the musicians, resonating through the huge, vaulted hall, until finally it crested and began to subside. Heinz Ober consented to an encore. Schumann, Ben would remember later. Again the auditorium was flooded with noise. A man in the front row stood and shouted, "Bravo, bravo, maestro, more!" But Ober would never play a second encore. He stood and bowed stiffly from the waist. Then he indicated his colleagues with a broad sweeping motion. When the audience tired of clapping, Ober pointed at Antoine Beaulieu, who led the quartet offstage. As the junior member, Ben always exited last. He counted a beat, two beats, then followed Ober. He was ten feet from the wings, his mind blank, his eyes on Ober's polished heel, when abruptly he felt his feet go out from under and saw the stage coming up at him.

He was flying, now soaring, arms outstretched, reaching for the receding tails of Ober's tuxedo. It seemed to take ages to hit the floor; he floated, weightless, outside himself, not believing what was happening to him. Then he was on the stage, shoulder tucked instinctively to blunt the impact of his fall. Ben smelled sawdust as he rolled into the accompanist's stand. But even the sharp pain in his side seemed imaginary. The whole thing was too absurd to be true.

Perhaps his fall would go unnoticed. People were in a hurry to get home, they were reaching for their coats and purses. He would crawl like an

7

Indian scout into the wings on his hands and knees. Who would see; who cared anyway? But to his dismay, nothing worked. Arms, legs, nothing. He lay as if paralyzed, his vision blurred, his limbs useless. He saw his right leg jerk convulsively, and then, feeling the flood of sensation return to his body, he swept his left hand in a wide arc, looking for his glasses.

He replaced the wire-rimmed spectacles and the world snapped into focus. There was a short, gray woman facing him in front, eyes wide in horror. Ben smiled weakly. It's okay, he wanted to say; a minor miscalculation, nothing more, nothing broken, go home now. Everything's fine. But having made eye contact, the woman became hysterical, pointed at him. "Help! He fell down! Look, help!"

Nervous whispers rose in the hall. Those who had been hurrying to leave turned now to look. Ben felt his cheeks flush with embarrassment.

"Get up," someone hissed from offstage.

He felt a hand under his arm, and he pushed unsteadily to his feet. The woman who had cried out was still standing in front of him, staring. A group of elegant matrons with frosted hair approached. Ben raised his right hand to hold them off, and was surprised to see his fiddle secure in it. Through it all, he had managed to protect his instrument. There was comfort in that.

He considered making a little speech; perhaps he could imply it was all part of the concert; something light to leaven Ober's rather predictable program. But then, sadly, he realized there was nothing he wanted to say. He made a deep bow and walked offstage.

2

OBER WAS WAITING. The others seemed to have gone to the artists' room. He would apologize to them later. "Ben, Ben," Ober said.

"You're repeating yourself."

"No jokes, this is serious. What happened to you?"

"You saw it," Ben said. "I fell on my ass."

Ober was usually the picture of composure, but now he was beside himself. "Of course I saw. I have eyes. But *how* did you fall? That's what I want to know."

Ben's self-assurance wavered. "I fell. How does anyone fall? I tripped, I guess."

"You tripped? On what? There is nothing to trip on! The stage is clean! Here, don't believe me, go look for yourself."

"I don't have to, I trust you, Heinz. I tripped over my own feet. I lost my balance. It happens, I'm a klutz, I fall down a lot. Why don't you ask about Cleveland, or that shower stall in Boston, or my broken wrist in Madison last year, it's the same."

"Very good, you take the words out of my mouth. I would very much like answers to all these questions."

"And I already told you. The throw rug in the hotel came out from under me, the fireplug was hidden, shower stalls are slippery. I sued the city of Madison and won; the court believed me, why don't you?"

Ober lowered his head, chastened. "I'm sorry, Benjy, I . . ."

"Ah, to hell with it. You're right, it's not normal. I don't know what's wrong." Suddenly he felt light-headed again and walked over to the wall and sat on a desk.

Heinz followed, and when he spoke, he was sympathetic. "Benjy, we are friends, you are like a son to me."

"Sure, Heinz, I know. I appreciate it."

"But I am worried; as you say, it's not normal. I am concerned for your welfare, that is all."

"And the welfare of the quartet."

"Of course. That is my responsibility as leader."

"Sure," Ben said. He couldn't blame Heinz. They couldn't have him falling down at concerts.

"I understand how you feel," Ober continued. "It is like being under attack, as if your body is in revolt. It is upsetting, I know. But it is not only you that is affected. I too am concerned when my second violinist falls and breaks his arm. Now you fall again. This is very serious. Careers, you know, can hang on just such an incident. As musicians, our bodies are terribly important. Beyond interpretation, beyond theory, we must have marvelous co-ordination, we must be alert, we must eat properly, we must exercise, we must—"

"I know all that," Ben said abruptly. Next Ober would get into orgone theory and blame it all on Ben's refusal to sit in the goddamned box he had brought back from New York.

Heinz was insulted. "All I meant was that we can never afford to take our health for granted."

"I know," Ben said. But he also knew it went beyond that. Ober would not be a left-handed fiddler today had he not broken his arm in two places when he was thirteen years old. The arm took more than a year to mend and never did heal properly. Ober had been forced to switch his bow arm; and he said his tone had never been the same.

"Look, Heinz, I know what you mean. I agree with you; it's very serious. But I don't know what to tell you."

"All I ask is that you see my doctor."

"Not that orgone guy?"

"Very funny. Very amusing. I mean the head of the medical school at the university. He also has a private practice; there is no reason anyone else need hear about it. But I must know if there is anything seriously wrong with you. If there is, we will fix it; if not, then we can forget about the whole thing. Agreed?"

And what if they couldn't fix it, as Ober said. What then? But there

10

was no point in arguing. "All right," Ben said. "What the hell. I went to a doctor in New York and another in Cleveland. Neither of them found anything, but if it will make you feel better, I'll go see the guy at the medical school. What harm can it do?"

"Exactly," Heinz said, pleased to have convinced Ben. "Now come, there will be people waiting for us, a reception."

"I think I'll just stay here for a while," Ben said. "I'm a little shaky; I'd just as soon not see anybody right away."

"As you wish, my boy," Heinz said. "I'll make excuses for you." He tapped Ben's shoulder and moved off toward the greenroom.

3

BEN SAT on the desk, still holding his fiddle under one arm. His broad shoulders and long trunk made him appear taller than his five feet eight inches, but he was not a big man. Now he peeled off the toupee, revealing a nearly bald head with a neat fringe of brown hair and a pate that gleamed in the stage lights. Heinz claimed his pink scalp distracted audiences, which insulted Ben, but he let it pass. There were more important things to worry about. Now he lit a cigarette and sucked on it, his cheeks hollow with the effort. Everything seemed hard tonight.

Color distracted him. Turquoise just out of his field of vision. Then he remembered: Dory was meeting him. They were going for a short vacation, had been planning it for weeks. He turned to see his wife watching him.

"Have you been here long?"

Dory ignored the question. She put her arms around him and held him tight. The turquoise shawl blocked his view, so Ben closed his eyes. He smelled her perfume; violets, he thought. She kissed his neck, then pulled away. "Are you all right?"

"I feel fine," Ben said. There was no point in worrying her. "I don't know what happened. Suddenly I was flat on my face. How did it look?"

"I couldn't see anything. Everyone was standing up and pointing. It was awful, like the circus. By the time I could see, you were on your knees. I was scared."

"I just tripped." Then, elaborately casual, Ben said, "Heinz wants me to see his doctor."

12

"But you've already done that. They always say you're fine."

"Maybe I am. Except for a few moments, I'm the way I always was. I feel a little weak, but we've been on tour, late nights, lousy food, all that. It's not so unusual."

Dory looked exhausted. Her dark hair curled onto her neck and accentuated her pale skin. Her eyes were round and sad; she had been crying. "Oh, Ben, what are we going to do now?"

It was not so much a question as a plea, and Ben felt helpless to answer. He took Dory in his arms and held her. He stroked her hair and neck; to him, she seemed fragile as a bird, bones exposed, as if she might break. "I don't know for sure," he began. "But we'll get by. We always have, haven't we?"

Dory nodded and blew her nose. "I guess so. Don't you have to go to the reception?"

"In a minute. I want to sit here for a while longer. You're tired. Why don't you go back to the hotel?"

"I think I will. Somehow I'm not up to seeing Heinz tonight. You'll be along soon?"

Ben nodded. "I won't be long."

Alone again, Ben shivered slightly. When he put his fingers to his forehead, they felt like ice. The fall had upset him more than he let on. He didn't want to upset Dory and he didn't entirely trust Heinz. He couldn't afford to.

What was it he had said? Careers could hang on such a fall? Hang. It was an odd word to use, and Ober was meticulous in his speech, as he was in everything else. Did he think this was the beginning of the end for Ben? Was Heinz trying to ease him out? It was ironic, since Ben had always thought of Ober as his savior, mentor, the man who had rescued him from a life of radio orchestras and free-lance jobs. They had met on a Tuesday. Ben remembered because normally he came to the union hall only on Fridays. He would pick up his check, then go to Wurlitzer's to cash it and buy strings. Often he went to Lindy's for lunch. But a friend called to say Ober wanted to meet him. Sitting backstage, it all seemed very vivid to him. He knew it was 1957, that he was in Chicago, that ten years had somehow gone by, and that he was crowding middle age, but it seemed as if he had never been away.

The musicians' union was at Fiftieth Street and Sixth Avenue. As Ben climbed to the second floor, the sound of a thousand voices engulfed him. At the top of the stairs, he paused before entering the room.

The musicians swarmed over an area a city block long. They were packed in groups, like fish, in different parts of the hall, with buffer zones separating them. Jazz musicians met at the rear, near Fifty-first Street, and spread toward the middle. The classical musicians were on the Fiftieth Street side. Recording musicians, radio men, those who played in orchestras for Broadway shows or worked at Radio City or the Roxy, filled the middle. On the fringes were men who belonged to no particular group. Displaced persons who made twenty dollars on Saturday night playing for a college dance, a wedding or bar mitzvah.

Anyone who revered musicians as virtuosos with poetic souls should see them here, Ben thought. They were as poetic as dockworkers shaping up for the morning call. Most of the men he knew were Jews like himself, who saw music as a means of escape from their families, a way out of the ghetto and the sweatshop.

The boys he had played with in the All-American Youth Orchestra were just off the boat or at best first-generation. Still, if ever the idea of American equality worked, it was here, in the union hall. For the most part the rules were brutally fair: either you played exceptionally well or you were out. Go teach piano in Brooklyn or high school in New Jersey.

Ben had always been among the best. From the start, when his father got the idea of Ben's learning the fiddle so that one day he could work his way through medical school, his talent had been large and unmistakable. Moshe took Ben to a Hebrew teacher who played the violin. The melamed insisted on having the boy play for his friend, who was concertmaster of the National Symphony. Moshe never dreamed music would become an end in itself. To him, music was essentially frivolous, something to take up the slack on a Sunday afternoon or relieve the monotony of prayer in the synagogue. But not a job. He went along with the melamed and lived to regret it.

The concertmaster was impressed. He took Ben on as a private student. At twelve Ben made his concert debut. He won scholarships to Peabody and then to Curtis. At fifteen, in the dead of the Depression, he was earning three times as much money as his father. Still, Moshe did not trust music. It wasn't steady; here today, gone tomorrow. He wanted Ben to go to medical school. But the family needed the money.

For Ben, music was liberation. It meant he could leave home and meet people his own age. It meant he had money to spend as he pleased. It meant that at fifteen he was an adult. He had gone to Curtis as an explorer in search of a new land. After Curtis, Ben toured and eventually came to New York. When the union's six-month waiting period had passed, he found a job at WOR and joined a struggling string quartet organized by a friend from Curtis. It was 1943. The world was at war. But Ben had no reason to

14

be unhappy. He failed his army physical because of his eyesight, and he had a girlfriend. He was only twenty-five years old and already making $8,000 a year. Yet in time he grew dissatisfied. He had always thought of himself as a pragmatist when it came to music: he had even shifted from violin to viola at Curtis for a better position. Music was a way to make a living, and a good living at that. But now he felt unfulfilled. In part it was a function of time. Five years before, he was euphoric just to be out on his own; now he took it for granted. Originally he had reveled in making enough money to support himself, but he no longer enjoyed buying things. Then there was the music itself. He was trained to perform on the concert stage, but he spent most of his time in radio orchestras.

He liked free-lancing better. The jobs were sometimes worse than the commercials he did for radio, but often much better. At least he had some control over his life. He could keep an eye out for opportunities and didn't have to punch a clock. After three years of free-lancing, however, he began to question his worth as an artist.

He was twenty-eight now, a veteran. If there was to be a break, shouldn't it have occurred? The musicians he went to school with all seemed to be famous. Leonard Rose, Eudice Shapiro, even Isaac Stern, who was younger. All of them had agents, were on their way. And what was he doing? Playing background music for newsreels. Ben felt the meeting with Heinz Ober might be his last chance.

The noise of the musicians talking formed an almost palpable barrier, like the humid curtain at the entrance to a steam bath. Heinz had said they would recognize each other, but Ben didn't know how.

The pay windows were to the left as he entered the room. Ben stood behind a man who was arguing with the paymaster. A check had been lost, both men were angry. The musician threatened to take the paymaster to the union if he didn't produce the check. "This is the union," the paymaster said with perfect logic. "Sure," the man said, "but you know what I mean."

He reminded Ben of the Cisco Kid. He was tall and dark and had a cocky smile. Each week at WOR, the script seemed the same. Cisco would read his line: "You are the most beautiful señorita the Cisco Kid has ever seen." Then Ben would play a tremolo. Over the months, he came to feel a personal bond with Cisco. He was a good-looking kid, and when he spoke his lines, he leaned over the microphone like a crooner, taking the stand in his hands and stroking it. But Ben had never spoken to Cisco.

The line moved, and Ben stood facing the paymaster. His name was Red, or at least that was what the musicians called him. Though Ben had been coming down to the union hall for years, Red had spoken to him only

15

once, the day Roosevelt died. Then Red looked up and said, "Wasn't that something about Roosevelt, dying like that, I mean?" And Ben had nodded dumbly because there was nothing to say.

"Next," Red called, and Ben moved up.

"Name?"

"Seidler. Ben Seidler."

Red flipped through a pile of checks. He went through the pile again, more carefully. Finally he picked out Ben's check.

"Miss it the first time?" Ben said.

"Next," said Red.

Ben turned away from the window. Now the throng of musicians seemed less formidable. He could see windows of space between the groups. For a moment he enjoyed the feeling of community in the hall. The men stood smiling, laughing at old jokes but more at the memory of time spent together. This was their clubhouse; for many, what social life they had was here. Little old men wandered back and forth selling neckties and violin strings, though no one ever seemed to buy. In a corner two men leaned against the wall playing chess on a pocket board.

"Ben, Ben, over here!" Ben looked and saw Jimmy Shapiro coming to meet him. He had shared a stand with Jimmy at WOR and was fond of him. Jimmy was wearing a chartreuse shirt and black tie. He had gained weight; now gravity seemed to pull at his chest, tugging it down to meet his belt.

"Benjy," Jimmy said, "how long has it been? Where you keeping yourself?" Jimmy chewed the words like a cud, digesting them, then letting the syllables flow out over his teeth, his tongue flitting from side to side to pick up errant bits of saliva displaced in the process.

"Around, I'm around. I play some nights. I come here. Sometimes I travel a little. How's Cisco?"

"You know, it's funny, but I think he misses you. He's never gotten used to the guy who took your place. He talks in the middle of the tremolo, or the fiddler's late. You guys have something going?" Jimmy shimmied his hand in front of his belt. Then he was struck by memory. "Hey, I got to tell you. Heinz Ober's here. Did you know he's looking for you?"

"I'm supposed to meet him. He said we'd recognize each other." He feigned indifference; it was important that Jimmy not think he was desperate.

"He's right," Jimmy said. "He don't look like anyone else. Small, European. Looks like he's got a stick up his ass, know what I mean? Gray hair, mustache, the works, looks like he walked off an album cover, like a fucking count. You can't miss him. Why you meeting Ober anyway?"

16

Ben shrugged. "It's all a mystery," he said. "Stan Goodman called and said Ober wanted to see me. He's looking for someone, I guess. We don't exactly travel in the same social circles."

"I guess not," Jimmy said. "Those guys give me a pain in the ass. They all come over here and put on this terrific show, like America was discovered yesterday. But they aren't too proud to take away our jobs. Fuck them."

"Where did you see Ober?"

"Over against the wall. Ten minutes ago. What's he want you for, anyway? That quartet out west?"

"Ask him."

"What's it called, Casa Bella?"

"Yeah, beautiful house. You'd love those guys, Jim. They're all Europeans. Came over in '44, I think."

"I remember. Ober went out to take over when the old guy died, right? Where are they, anyway?"

"Wisconsin, I think."

"What the hell are they doing there? I thought all they had in Wisconsin was cows."

Ben had a sudden vision of cornfields, an endless plain without Jews or tall buildings. He squeezed Jimmy's arm. "Got to go," he said.

Ben walked the length of the hall, but it was like working his way through a maze. Then he saw Ober. He was standing to the side, adjacent to but distinctly apart from a group of men. Jimmy was right: Ben recognized him instantly. Ober wore a blue serge suit and stood erect, chin jutting forward, revealing neck muscles stretched tight. His hands were cupped under his coattails in the European manner, and his head was imperceptibly tilted to the side, as if he were listening to some private music. Ober was short and thin and looked older than his picture.

"Mr. Ober," Ben said. "Excuse me, I'm Ben Seidler."

Ober turned and looked at him with great interest. His eyebrows were arched, his forehead wrinkled. He bowed slightly, sardonically, as if he were mocking Ben. "We meet at last, Mr. Seidler, it is a pleasure." The older man offered his hand, but Ben felt cheated. Ober shook with his fingers.

"Nice to meet you," Ben said. The line of Ober's mouth was cruel, though it curved into a smile. Ben felt self-conscious towering over him, although he himself was hardly tall. He was suddenly aware that his tie was askew, his shoes unshined, his jacket and slacks a poor match. He was angry with himself. Ober had known Schönberg and was a close friend of Bartók. He had been educated in Vienna, and it annoyed Ben that he must be fulfilling precisely the preconceived notions Ober had of Americans. He sucked in his stomach and pushed his glasses higher on his nose. Then he ran his hand over his head, smoothing the few hairs he had left, and tried to think of something intelligent to say.

"You like this place?" Ober said. Then, "Ah, of course not. It is an awful place, but I love it. When I came to America I used to come here to find jobs. I would take anything. Broadway, the movies, in radio orchestras, really, anything was all right for me. Now, though I have no need of a job, I come here whenever I'm in New York. It is a tradition, you see?"

Ben nodded. It was a tradition for him too. He needed the money. But he wasn't fond of the union hall, of the noise. He couldn't imagine making nostalgic trips back.

"So," Ober said. "Tell me about yourself."

"There isn't much to tell," Ben began. "I'm a fiddler—"

"Yes, yes, of course," Ober interrupted. "But how did you become one? I am interested in your origins, musical and otherwise. You are from a musical family?"

"No. My father is a tailor, I grew up in Washington. When I was eight he arranged for me to have lessons."

"Ah, you started late."

"It was early enough. All I did until I left home was play the fiddle and go to *heder*. My father thought I could earn my way through medical school playing at fraternity parties and bar mitzvahs."

"And did you?"

"Play for fraternities? No. I started college, but I had to leave after my sophomore year. I didn't have time."

"Yes, you were in Baltimore then, weren't you?" Ober nodded, then thought for a moment. "And do you ever wish you had gone on, become a doctor as your father hoped?"

The interrogation was annoying. Ober seemed to be patronizing him. Would he ask these questions of an older man? What was past was past. He *did* wish he had been able to go on, to finish college, whether or not he had become a doctor. To Ben, music was magical; he was gifted, but he had not worked hard at it. Other children had cared more than he did, but he had won the scholarships and, later, the jobs. He had not become a musician out of love for art. That had come later. At first it was simply practicality; even his father knew it would be criminal to waste such a natural resource.

"What about it?" Ober said. He was smiling.

"There was no choice," Ben said. "It was the middle of the Depression. My family needed the money and I was very lucky to get a job. Giving it up for college would have been crazy."

"Perhaps you could have played for the fraternities."

Ober's eyes twinkled with amusement at Ben's discomfort. "I do not mean to insult you," he explained. "I only want to know your feelings about music. Why do you play?"

"I play because I'm very good. From the start it was easy for me. It's hard not to enjoy things one does easily."

"I have the feeling you're putting me on, Mr. Seidler." Ober smiled again, pleased with his colloquial English.

"Not at all. If I hadn't been very good, the melamed wouldn't have passed me on to his friend in the National Symphony; if Steiner hadn't been impressed, I wouldn't have gotten into Peabody; if I hadn't won the prize at Peabody, I wouldn't have been asked to audition for Curtis; and if I hadn't gone to Curtis, I wouldn't have come to New York and you wouldn't be interested in talking to me."

"I see," Ober said, smiling broadly. "And if you were a gifted physicist or a chess genius or a marvelous baseball player, then you would do that?"

"Actually, I've always liked baseball," Ben said. He had. Baseball in the summer, boxing in the winter. Ben remembered himself at age ten, squinting in the dark hot space between the back counter and the wall in the candy store to read box scores in the newspapers. Daily he would calculate the changes in the Washington Senators' batting average. This infuriated Moshe, who thought Americans spent all their time playing games. Jews had no time for such frivolity, he said.

But now Ober asked him something else. "I was wondering about your difficulty getting along with others. Am I right, you've had trouble in the past?"

Now they were getting to the meat. No more chitchat.

"Sometimes," Ben said.

"Do you think we would get along, Mr. Seidler?"

"That depends," Ben said. "Are you hard to get along with?"

"Touché," Ober said. "The answer is yes and no. According to some people, I am very difficult, impossible; others find me charming. But I understand you left the Cincinnati orchestra in the middle of Iowa. Surely that is a great hardship, Mr. Seidler. After all, how many competent violinists are there in Iowa?"

"Benning threw my fiddle on the floor, so I left. He's an anti-Semite, and I told him so. He took me to the union and they upheld me. You can go check if you want."

"I will check nothing. Do you think I am a clerk? And I have no intention of throwing your instrument on the ground, if only because I respect fine craftsmanship. But I don't want to be left looking for a replacement in the middle of my winter tour."

"Look, Mr. Ober, I don't know if we'll be compatible. How could I?

We'll have to wait and see. Don't you want to hear me play? Isn't that more important?"

Ober looked astonished. "My boy," he said. "Do you honestly think I would have come here if I had the slightest question about your ability? I have already heard you play, several times in fact. I heard your concert at the Brooklyn Academy of Music last spring, and I was also at the YMHA in the fall. I missed your debut, but from what I'm told you were not at your best."

"That's right," Ben said. He was impressed and pleased that Ober had taken such an interest in him. "Do you make a habit of scouting like that, or was it just me?"

"I do," said Ober. "I must. You never know when you will need a man, and then there isn't time to spend three months combing the country."

Ben wondered how many other young hopefuls Ober had surveyed and perhaps offered the job. Still, he couldn't help asking Ober's opinion of his playing.

Ober looked at him, his eyes slits at first, then opening slowly, amused. "Not bad," he said. "Not bad at all. Technically, there is no problem. You play very well, brilliantly in fact. I have the feeling, however, that you've never been pressed hard, and I will press you like a grape, Mr. Seidler. I will make demands on you that have never been made before. Whether the resulting brew will be quality or cheap table wine, we cannot know. What is inside you is what I am curious about, and that I can't tell from a few recitals. You have a great deal to learn as an artist, but you are young and I am an excellent teacher. I am hopeful, even optimistic, but you needn't concern yourself about any of this. All you have to do is play exceptionally well."

"All?"

"Yes. Didn't you say that had always been easy?"

Ben smiled now. "There is one thing I have wanted to ask you for a long time—I know the quartet plays entirely from memory, but I don't know why. What possible reason can there be for so much unnecessary work?"

"Unnecessary?" Ober's eyes were wide open now. "Unnecessary," he repeated, drawing the word out, savoring it. "On the contrary, we memorize only because it is an absolute necessity. A necessity, that is, if one wishes to play well—and not only well, but superbly. We must have our attention free to concentrate on the music and on one another. To play as an ensemble, it is important that we know each other intimately. In any case, if you don't really know a composition, you have no business playing it in public."

Ben nodded in agreement, but he wasn't sure. Ober was an enigma. Avuncular one moment, imperious the next, he was asking Ben to move across the country and memorize the entire violin repertoire in six months. Yet the offer was tempting. Ben could continue to play free-lance jobs forever and make a good living, but there was a part of him that was growing rusty from disuse. Ober challenged him to extend himself. Of course, he might find out more than he wanted to know about his limitations, but that was a chance he was willing to take. And Wisconsin was not entirely unattractive. It would be quiet there, peaceful. He imagined long evenings in a community of scholars, grassy meadows dotted with Holsteins, and the sounds of four fiddles tuning. He thought he smelled freshly cut hay, though he hadn't the slightest idea what hay smelled like. He would buy a farm and live alone, at peace with his surroundings, at one with music.

"Good," Ober said. "We have an agreement?"

"I want to come," Ben said. "But I have to close my apartment, and there are some other things—"

"Of course, but they are not important," Ober interrupted. "We will give you a contract for five thousand dollars a season. That is enough? If not, you will tell me and we will argue about it. It is now June. Can we expect you in August?"

It seemed like a long time. "I can be there before that," Ben said.

"Excellent. The sooner, the better. Now, come, I'll take you to Lindy's. I never discuss business when I'm eating."

He took Ben's arm and steered him toward the exit. Then he stopped and looked back at the huge room. "What I don't understand," Ober said, "is how musicians can make such noise. You would think there would be soundproof ceilings, carpets, to absorb the din. That they would have union stewards, like librarians, moving among the men, shushing them continually. It is as if these men are seeking revenge on their art, destroying the beauty of measured sound, melody, dynamics, even discord. Yet they enjoy it. They are like children at play." He shook his head. "This chaos I don't understand. It is madness."

"That's what they call this place. The madhouse."

"Yes," Ober said. "Excellent. One of the reasons I like so much to come here is that it feels so wonderful to leave."

Ben studied the scarred floorboards of the stage, the elaborate fretwork of time, like the chiaroscuro of an aging face. How many of the marks had been made since he left New York? What part of the hall's history was his own?

21

Ober had been right. He was an excellent teacher, and Ben had learned more than he had imagined possible. He had matured into an artist capable of commanding the stage. Some critics even compared him favorably with the leader. Each year Heinz gave him more important solos. It seemed incredible now that he had been so arrogant in the initial interview. He had known nothing, and in the confidence of ignoramuses imagined that therefore there was nothing to know.

Memorizing was the least of it. That was only the necessary basis on which the rest depended. Ober made him study facsimiles of the original scores of Mozart sonatas, Beethoven string quartets, trios, duos. He had listened to lectures on the modern tendency to play everything too fast and the inadequate education of American musicians. Ober insisted on authenticity, so Ben spent hours with scissors and glue pasting together corrected scores. Then there were the rehearsals. Day after day, week after week, for months, years, Ober was never satisfied. Repeatedly he stopped to criticize one player or another. At turns biting and sarcastic, he could also be sweet, wheedling, or imploring, his goal always to goad them into playing better than they knew they could.

Surprisingly, Ben had. They all had. The Casa Bella became famous for its precision in performance, for the artists' sensitivity to the ensemble, and for Ober's interpretations of the masters. They recorded as a quartet and individually made an annual tour of the East. Tenured chairs were rumored to be in the offing, and even Ben, the youngest, had been approached by an agent who wished to arrange a solo tour for him in the off-season. The future seemed bright, or at least it had. Now Ben didn't know what to expect.

The stage lights went out and the lights backstage dimmed. A man in overalls appeared to Ben's left, carrying a broom.

Ben got quickly off the desk, steady now. "I didn't mean to hold you up," he said.

"Makes no difference to me," the man said.

"I'm with the quartet," Ben said. "We played a concert here; the others are already at the reception." The man said nothing more, though he did not seem unfriendly. Ben nodded to him. "Well, I'm on my way out." And he walked offstage, toward the greenroom.

4

As BEN DROVE, Dory drifted in and out of sleep. Even now, awake, she didn't open her eyes. She lay there trying to remember the dream. It was in Kentucky somewhere, and she was with her grandfather, who had been a Baptist deacon. They were driving through the cemetery. Every few hundred feet they would stop to decorate a grave with flowers. Her grandfather would then step back and tell her something about the person buried there. One had been a doctor, one a carpenter, another a U.S. senator. Yet there was nothing morbid or unpleasant as she recalled it now. What Dory remembered was her grandfather's large, dry hands, and the smell of after-shave talcum.

All her life men had doted on her. She was her grandfather's favorite, and her father's. They had loved and respected her, and this made her trust men in general. She had been disappointed with the boys she met in art school, but more than that, she was surprised. She did not expect men to feel threatened by her intelligence.

As different as Ben was from her father, they were alike in their indulgence of her. After the boys were born, Ben had insisted they buy a house so Dory could have a studio. Then he had hired a sitter to take care of the house and cook, for Ben said art was more important than dusting furniture.

It seemed impossible that housework had ever been a serious problem. In retrospect, life was idyllic. But the future scared her. What if Ben couldn't work? What would happen to them, how would they live? Ben had always taken care of these things. She had depended on his being there; it had simply never occurred to her that he might not be able to support them. She told herself she was overreacting. Ben had fallen down onstage; it was embarrassing, but little more. Why should she fear the worst? But it wasn't an isolated occurrence, rather part of a developing pattern: an accident, sudden weakness, followed by a return to normality, which would convince them nothing had ever happened. But last night Heinz Ober and a thousand other people had seen Ben fall. There was no denying that. Dory knew she should try to comfort Ben, reassure him, but she could think of nothing that would help. She wanted only to lie back and sleep. If she kept her eyes closed, she could preserve the illusion that Ben had never fallen in the concert hall, that nothing unusual had happened.

They drove north, north through wealthy lakeside suburbs thick with golf clubs and Ford station wagons, past factories with long lines of cars arranged in battalions at their flanks; north past shopping plazas with signs on stilts as high as trees saying "Cheese!"—like photographers trying to wring smiles from sullen children. The sun was low in the sky, red-orange against the sere winter landscape, its rays bleeding on the sparse patches of snow lining the highway.

Ben felt meditative. They had decided not to postpone the vacation. What was the point of rushing back for the latest medical opinion? It would wait. They had slept late and ordered breakfast in the hotel room. While Ben visited a fiddle maker to have his bows restrung, Dory went to the art museum. In midafternoon they met back at the hotel.

He looked over at his wife. Dory was asleep, the sun bringing a blush to her cheeks. In the warmth of the car, Ben felt confident. Things would work out, they always had. At an age when many men were just hitting their stride, he was a veteran of twenty years on the concert stage. Many would be satisfied with what he had already done. What had really changed, after all? He had fallen down a few times, but none of the doctors could find anything wrong with him. It was ridiculous to feel hopeless.

They drove north, within themselves, quarantined by thought, memory. And while each feared the future, they were certain of each other.

They had met in 1947, the year after Ben joined the quartet. At the end of the spring season, the others dispersed: Richler went to New York, where he had a small instrument business; Beaulieu returned to France; Ober was also leaving for Europe, but he was going to Vienna. Ben decided to stay in Madison. The year before, he had visited Washington, but found it impossible. If his mother, Sarah, wasn't complaining about his clothes, she was trying to marry him off. He went out a few times, but the heavy so-lemnity of the girls frightened him. Even to kiss one of them would amount to an engagement. This summer, he would stay in Wisconsin.

At first, he enjoyed himself. He took long walks along Lake Mendota, sometimes going as far as Picnic Point, from which he could see the south-ern curve of the lake, and its long, slow slide from the elegance of the Edgewater Hotel, to Maple Bluff, and finally to the insane asylum safely iso-lated across the water from the town. He started swimming again. After two weeks he was able to swim a half-mile, then a mile. By the end of June he could swim across the lake and back.

Still, he felt dissatisfied, bored. After a full day he was pleasantly aroused, but not tired enough to sleep. He lived in a state of readiness, but he wasn't preparing for anything.

He called friends and went to some dinner parties. There were a few blind dates, but nothing worked out. Ben was lonely, but either too tongue-tied or too brash for the women he met. He needed someone who under-stood him, at least someone he could talk to, and such a woman did not seem to exist in Wisconsin.

Toward the end of June, Ben started feeling anxious. If he wanted to meet a girl, the summer was the best time. It was important that he move, take action. He decided to go east.

As he boarded the train, it occurred to him that he was really looking for a wife. The realization was sudden and powerful, but not unpleasant. It was as if, having floundered aimlessly for years, he had found his true mis-sion in life. Home and family, the little woman, pipe and slippers, kids, a dog, all inside a small bungalow on a half-acre of prime Madison real estate. Was that so bad? It seemed incredible that he hadn't thought of it before. As the train moved slowly out of town, he realized that he was sweating. It felt good to be excited again.

In the past, it had made sense to remain single. He had been traveling or living the unsettled life of a studio musician. He had stayed in furnished rooms and eaten in luncheonettes. But now he was artist-in-residence at a major university and made more money than he could spend. He could af-ford to get married, and he wanted a family. It was as simple as that, and as complex.

But how should he go about finding a wife? There was no way to au-dition for marriage, no booking agents, no contractors, no union hall in which arrangements could be made. It was a strategic problem; he knew what he wanted, but not how to get it. He thought of little else on the long train ride.

25

Ben called Phil Early from the station in Philadelphia. They had been friends at Curtis; now Phil played with Ormandy.

"Phil, I want to get married," Ben said.

"What do you think I am, a *shadchen?*"

"Okay, forget it."

"Hold on, don't get insulted. Where's your sense of humor? Let me ask Janie."

Ben waited, feeling humiliated. Then Phil was back. "Listen, Ben, this is funny, but Janie does have a friend. Her name is Dorothy Bryan, she went to Central High School in Washington."

"It's possible," Ben said. "I didn't know anyone at Central."

"Well, she grew up in Kentucky and now she's in New York, studying pottery at Alfred University. If you can catch up with her, you might give it a try."

"It's not really important," Ben said. "But is she Jewish?"

"Not unless they're letting Jews in the DAR these days. But what do you expect on short notice?"

"I just thought I'd ask. I said it wasn't important."

"Your mother's going to love this girl," Phil said. "Her family goes back to the Jamestown settlement. She's even related to Daniel Boone. She was going with this poet who was digging graves in the Jewish cemetery when Janie met her."

"You've got to admit we're an unusual people. Imagine, we've got poets digging our graves. Give me her address and I'll get in touch," Ben said.

He wrote Dory at Alfred, explaining how he had gotten her name. He had looked her up in his Central yearbook and thought he recognized her. Perhaps they could have dinner? But Dory's reply was not encouraging. The poet/gravedigger was gone. She was busy putting together her graduate show and was seeing no men except for her pottery instructor, who was Viennese. The potter had forsaken his native tongue in protest of the Nazis, and since he had an imperfect command of English, they seldom spoke. Dory had learned to enjoy the perfection of solitude.

Ben was not easily discouraged. He liked the tone of Dory's letter. She must be damned independent; a loner sufficient unto herself. He wanted more than ever to meet her. In the weeks that followed, he sent flowers, candy, books, records, and a stream of letters outlining plans for dates. They could meet in the city and go to a concert. If she couldn't make it into the city, he would come to Alfred. Or they could meet in between for a picnic. How could she know if they had anything in common without meeting him? He was interested in things other than music, and she must be, too. If he didn't hear from her, he'd write again in a week.

Dory was unprepared for Ben's assault. She was slim and attractive in an austere way, but the boys that called her lacked imagination. A bottle of Scotch and into bed was their idea of a successful evening. Her most interesting lover had been the gravedigger, who had a Harley-Davidson and used to drive at top speed between the rows of graves at night screaming curses at the dead.

Ben was something else. Dory was dismayed by his gifts and tried at first to return them. Inevitably she was overwhelmed and gave in. But she wondered what sort of man would send presents to a woman he'd never even met. And such gifts. They were more like graduation presents. Shakespeare's complete works; the late Beethoven string quartets; gift assortments of fruit and candy; and flowers, more flowers than she'd ever seen outside a garden. Single-handed, Ben had pulled the local florist out of a seasonal slump. The delivery boy told Dory it was like homecoming weekend.

Though Ben's attentions were embarrassing, Dory was flattered. She found herself stopping in front of mirrors, trying to discern the peculiar quality that had attracted her unknown suitor. She felt desired and yet unattainable, like a character in a Victorian novel.

But when Dory finally wrote Ben, it was because she was going to be in New York anyway, on business, in mid-July. They could meet for lunch then, she wrote, if he was still interested.

Dory's teacher had a friend who owned a pottery factory on Staten Island. Dory took the ferry, then a bus, and arrived at the small brick building shortly after eleven. The man said little, but reached immediately for her portfolio. He flipped through her sketches, giving them little more than a cursory examination. Then he closed the folder and handed it back to her. "I'll take all you can make," he said.

Dory left the building feeling euphoric and astonished by her success. In her excitement, she almost forgot Ben, and when she got to Manhattan, she took the wrong subway and ended up in Brooklyn. By the time she reached the restaurant, it was after two, and Ben was furious.

At first, Dory didn't notice. She had enjoyed being lost. She hadn't been out of Alfred for six months and had forgotten what it was like to be crowded together below ground, to feel in a concrete way that one did really share the world with others. The first thing she noticed about Ben was that he wore a fedora tilted back on his forehead. None of the boys she knew wore hats, and it made him seem older.

She started to apologize, but Ben cut her off. "I am a musician," he said. "My life is dominated by time. If I begin my solo a tenth of a second late—a tenth of a second, mind you—the leader bites my head off and the

27

others are furious with me for days. My sense of timing is so precise that I can take my pulse by a piece of music, correcting for mistakes in the music simultaneously. It infuriates me to have to wait. And I've been standing here for forty-five minutes."

Dory just stared. Was this the man who sent flowers and candy? The same man who had been begging for a date for weeks? "I'm sorry," she said finally. "I didn't know it would matter so much to you. I just got lost, I couldn't help it."

Ben smiled slightly. He was no matinee idol, but he had an attractive smile that changed the rather somber set of his features. He had good, large teeth and delicate lines around his small, dark eyes. Now when he looked at her, his eyes were warm. "Well, as long as we're here, we might as well get something to eat," he said.

As soon as they entered the restaurant, however, Ben's expression changed again. Now his lips were pursed, his forehead wrinkled. He seemed to be in pain. There was a piano playing in the background, and whenever the pianist hit a note, Ben seemed to wince. He followed the conversation fitfully and finally signaled the maître d'.

"Yes, Mr. Seidler," the man said. "Something I can do?"

"George, you know I'm a professional musician," Ben said. The maître d' nodded. "That's why I originally came here," Ben continued. "Because it was so close to Carnegie Hall. I've brought many friends over the years because the food is superb. You know this?"

George smiled, waiting for Ben to get to the point. Of course, there might be no point. Seidler often liked to talk and was extravagant in his praise. "Yes, thank you very much," George said.

"The only reason I bring music up is that it has made me unusually sensitive to sound. Anyone would object to a cement mixer under his bedroom window, but I am bothered by almost imperceptible noises, such as a baby crying in another apartment or a bartender mixing drinks."

"Is the bartender bothering you?" George asked.

"Oh, no, it was just an example. The trouble is the pianist. You see, your piano is out of tune, and while the man plays quite well, the instrument sounds awful." He looked at George. "I understand that this can't matter to anyone else, and I don't mean to be unreasonable. But it is very important to me. It makes it difficult to enjoy my lunch."

"I understand entirely," George said. "Allow me to apologize for the restaurant. I didn't realize the piano was out of tune; how could I? But I'm very grateful to you for calling it to my attention." He bowed to Ben and Dory and walked across the room. He spoke briefly to the pianist, who gathered together his music and left. No one else seemed to notice, but Ben heaved a sigh of relief.

"Do you usually complain about the music in restaurants?" Dory said.

"Always, but it seldom does any good. Most people think I'm a pain in the ass. They laugh, until they realize I am serious, then they get insulted. *They* get insulted. That's why I like George. It doesn't matter whether he really understands. What's important to him is the happiness of his customers. That's what makes George exceptional; and the food he serves reflects this."

"But aren't you embarrassed, complaining like that? Everyone is bothered by little things."

"It's not a little thing. Not to me. We're all bothered by big things all the time, and we never do anything about it because we're afraid of being embarrassed. Our greatest fear is of bringing attention to ourselves by asking for something, even things we have a right to demand."

"Don't you think that's childish, though? You can't have everything you want."

"Okay, some things you have to accept. But you don't have to like it. Suppose you were eating in a place where the decor was in exceptionally bad taste. Wouldn't it offend you?"

"Almost every restaurant is done in terrible taste. I just try to ignore it."

"Exactly, and why should you? After all, your visual sense is probably the most highly developed; if you close it off, how much of the rest of you suffers?"

"But that's absurd. What should the maître d' do, tear down the pictures, rip the paper off the walls?"

"All right, the analogy isn't exact, but you get my point. It's important, right? And this wasn't an insoluble problem. George could do something about it. You see?"

Ben looked at her, eyebrows raised, waiting for a reply. When she said nothing, he looked down at his menu. "I can recommend the scampi," he said.

In Dory's family, mealtime had been reserved for superficial conversations about vacations and other people's pets and children. Her father thought argument was bad for the digestion. Ben talked nonstop through the meal, asking naive questions about art one minute, talking about his life in music the next. "I don't know anything about art," he said. "I had a deprived childhood."

Dory couldn't tell if he was joking. It seemed to be true, but why tell her? Usually people who knew nothing about art tried to impress her with their knowledge. What did she think of Picasso or Cézanne? he asked. What would anyone think? They were excellent artists. But that did not satisfy Ben. What was so excellent about them? He knew their names, that was all. Where could he see their work? Which collections were the best? Would she come with him to the galleries?—he needed private instruction.

Dory was amused by the questions, but thought them poignant too. Ben was so eager to please, without seeming to know how. He would make the grand gesture, then look to see what effect it had. Dory found herself challenged by him. He seemed to really listen to what she said. If she mentioned a book, he would write down the title on a napkin in small block letters. She was impressed by his determination to learn, and daunted by his intensity. There was also the fact that while most of her friends were still in graduate school, Ben had been playing with the best musicians in America for ten years.

Dory wondered what would become of him. What would he look like if he wore clothes that fit? He wasn't an unattractive man. What if he actually went home and read Joyce and Huxley and Camus? What if he went to the Fifty-seventh Street galleries and the Guggenheim? She was interested not only by Ben as she saw him, but by the idea of what he might become. He was willing to make a fool of himself and clearly didn't give a damn what others thought about it. To Dory, who had always been cautious, this was his most appealing quality.

She looked at him appraisingly. He had a long, intelligent forehead, and though he was going bald, it did not bother her. His upper body was slack and undefined, but his arms were strong and lean. His hands were muscular with thin elongated fingers that seemed elegant to Dory. They were the hands, she thought, of a concert artist or a strangler. As they talked, Ben's fingers stroked his wineglass, and Dory imagined they were stroking her instead.

When Ben asked about her family, Dory talked easily and at some length. She told him about the women of Bryan's Station, Kentucky, who had gone out for water in defiance of hostile Indians; how her ancestors came to America on *The Arc and the Dove*; how her grandfather owned the largest bank in Kentucky before the Civil War; and how her father had gone off to mine gold in Colorado before coming home to marry her mother. She told him about the uproar because her father was Episcopalian while her mother was Baptist. Her father had been an engineer before he died suddenly of a heart attack. One year later, her mother died as well, of a broken heart.

Ben listened quietly, marveling at the difference in their lives, and the fact that they had met at all. While Dory talked of the courage and honor of her illustrious relatives, he thought of Moshe cheating the *schvartzes* on Seventh Street. And why not? Was his father worried about losing banks to the Yankees or preserving his integrity? He couldn't afford to be. To him, the issue was, had always been, simple survival. Even Ben, who understood the concepts of honor and decency, couldn't embrace them. They were the province of the *goyim*, he thought, but the words sounded nice when Dory said them.

The waiter came to refill their cups. Dory was suddenly aware that the restaurant was nearly empty, that it was midafternoon. She had talked too much. What could Ben care about her family? She felt like a fool. The coffee was lukewarm, but she drank it to cover her discomfort. When she looked up, Ben was looking at her seriously. "You know," he said, "it's still possible that we won't get married."

Dory graduated from Alfred at the end of the summer session, but she had rented a cold-water flat in Chelsea for the month of August. She went to life classes at the Art Students League and made ceramic tiles for the man on Staten Island. Each week she read and ignored a letter from a maiden aunt who wanted her to come back to Kentucky.

Dory told Ben she wanted time to be alone, that they could see each other, but within limits. Ben called every day. He respected her as an artist, he said. Of course she must work, but she also needed to eat. They could have meals together. He knew some excellent restaurants. But just when Dory was most irritated by his presence, he would disappear for a few days, and she would wonder where he had gone, until he turned up again with a new place to eat. He had uncanny timing and seemed to know exactly how far he could push her without becoming overbearing. Dory began to wonder after a while if Ben was as naive as he seemed.

When she wasn't with Ben, Dory immersed herself in her work and enjoyed her new neighborhood. Next door, a sailor in the merchant marine and his common-law wife carried on nightly battles. Dory could hear them screaming at each other through the walls, with their cries often punctuated by loud crashes. Afterward, the man would sometimes appear at her door to ask her over for a drink, but whenever she accepted his offer the apartment looked immaculate and she would wonder if she had imagined everything.

There was a tavern on the first floor which was patronized by Irish politicians and their myrmidons. On humid summer nights they would spill onto the sidewalk below Dory's small balcony and call out to her, but she

31

never acknowledged them. Late at night, the men would fight, lobbing slow rights and lefts, elongated by drink, and Dory would take up her sketchbook and make line drawings.

Ben had taken a room on Sixty-eighth Street. After dinner he would often take Dory to concerts given by friends. He taught her to follow the score and soon she was as intolerant as he of those who sat in the audience and slept or gossiped. She was no longer able to wander in and out of the music; either she was totally involved or completely confused. It was easy to miss a page, and she struggled to keep up. In time she came to a new appreciation of music. Though she wasn't a musician, she began to listen like one.

When she finished working in the afternoon, Ben would sometimes stop by. He would study her latest pot until she was sure he hated it. Then he would say, "I like it better than the others; this is your best so far." Though she knew he wanted to please her, Dory did not doubt his sincerity. It was certainly true that he exaggerated her talent, but his appreciation was real. The odd thing was, the more Ben praised her, the more Dory wanted to be the person he thought she was, the person he admired so much. Long before she had any idea of falling in love with Ben, she was infatuated with his image of her.

Yet his intensity, his devotion, alarmed her. Her first commitment was to art. She had no intention of marrying at all, she had no desire to be a mother, a housewife, and told Ben, so as not to mislead him.

"I understand," Ben said. "I'm going back to Wisconsin soon anyway. But what's wrong with our having a few meals together now and then?"

Dory had to admit there was nothing wrong with that.

Over the Labor Day weekend, a friend offered Ben his cottage on Long Island. They rented a car and drove out on Saturday morning. Dory was surprised to see Ben had a swimmer's body, with well-developed shoulders and a deep chest. His clothes hung on him like draperies, but he was built like an athlete. He swam strongly, without grace, plunging into the water again and again. Back on the beach, without his glasses, he squinted in her direction until she gestured to him. Then he approached awkwardly, his body hair clinging tightly to his chest, as though it was painted on.

As they ate lunch, Dory noticed Ben's face was flushed. "You're starting to burn," she said. "You'd better put on a hat."

Ben only shrugged. "I used to be jealous of the kids at the Jewish Community Center who went to Florida in the winter. I thought only rich people could get tan. Funny thing is, it's true. In Madison, I go swimming a lot, but I never tan."

"I never tan either," Dory said.

"That's just liberal guilt," Ben said. "Noblesse oblige, like landlords going to church with their serfs. You're probably the only one in your family that doesn't."

Dory felt herself choking. She thought of her father in the hospital, his skin red and cracked, brittle as glass. She coughed and put down her sandwich. "My father almost died of sunstroke. My mother always said he wouldn't have had a heart attack if it weren't for that."

"Oh, Dory," Ben said. "I'm sorry, I didn't mean anything. I was just kidding." Instinctively, he moved closer to her. Dory leaned on him, her eyes closed. How odd to be here with Ben talking of her father, she thought. He had been so different.

Ben stroked her hair. "Oh, Dory, Dory, I hate to see you cry. Poor girl, poor girl." He lifted her chin, looking into her eyes, large and now swollen with tears. Then he kissed her, mixing his saliva with the tears, tasting her sorrow. Dory responded, confused at first, still thinking of her father, and then passionately, eagerly.

She felt Ben's strong arms under her, lifting her, fitting their bodies together. As if magically, they were nude, the sand grainy beneath them, and then Ben was inside her, his hips moving rhythmically, his breath coming fast. Dory felt panic; she hadn't meant for this to happen. But then she was aroused, alive to Ben, and it didn't matter what she meant or thought she meant. The water was blue in the distance and then the water was gone. There was only Ben, in her, around her, over her, protecting, nurturing, bringing her to herself.

Ben was due in Madison the third week of September. The question of marriage had not bothered Dory before, but as the days went by, it began to seem more important. She knew that soon they would be a thousand miles apart. Her resolve to stay in New York was wavering. She could be an artist anywhere; cold-water flats no longer seemed romantic to her.

Marriage was on Ben's mind too. He had started the summer bored with himself, unsure of his future. Marriage was a diversion. He would go out and find a wife in two months. But had he really expected to succeed? He couldn't remember, but now he was faced with the most important decision of his life, and things seemed very confused. He knew he loved Dory, but he also wanted his parents to love and accept her. And he knew without asking that his mother would hate Dory because she wasn't Jewish. So Ben hesitated, not, he told himself, because he had doubts about Dory or his love for her, but because he was reluctant to expose her to the fury of Sarah Seidler. Sensing this, Dory said nothing and they parted on an indecisive note that left them both slightly disappointed.

Before returning to the Midwest, Ben went to Washington. He wanted to talk to his parents, to introduce the subject of marriage indirectly before telling them about Dory, but he didn't know how. While he considered the question, he allowed his mother to feed him. When he lived at home, Ben had always been fat, but with exercise he had gotten his weight down. Sarah knew she could not remedy a decade's damage in three days, but she was determined to try. Ben resented her, but did not want to fight. They had more important things to discuss than his physique. Finally he decided his father was more approachable and went to him one morning, as Moshe was working over his sewing machine.

"Pop," Ben said. "What do you think of marriage? In general, I mean."

"Think, who thinks about it? You get married, you're young and healthy, and then it's thirty years later and you've got a son asking you questions."

Ben smiled. "The reason I asked is that I'm thinking about it, getting married, I mean."

Moshe looked at him, his eyes wide. "You got some trouble, Benjy, some girl?"

"No, Jesus, it isn't that, Pop. I just felt better about talking to you than Ma. You're a man . . . "

"That's what I said. You got a problem, I understand, it happens. Maybe I can help."

"I don't think so," Ben said. "My problem is that I'm in love with a girl who happens to be a gentile."

"Oy, that I can't help," Moshe said. He shook his head mournfully and wiped his hands on his apron, though they weren't dirty. "Benjy, you asked, so I'll tell. Your mother and me, we don't get on so well, okay, I know, you know, everybody knows that. We fight, we yell; it ain't perfect, but what you're talking about is worse."

"Why, Pop? We don't fight, we don't yell at each other, we're in love. So what's wrong with that?"

"Sure you're in love. You're in love now. But how about ten, twenty years from now?"

"What's the worst that could happen? Maybe we'd be like you and Ma."

"Wise guy. Listen, Benjy, you think I don't know what it is to love? You think you invented it? I know how you feel, believe me. But this is different, Jews and *goyim* getting married. You think it's enough that you love each other, that you don't fight. Okay, it makes sense, but life doesn't work that way, Benjy. This is something rabbis, smarter people than you and me, don't understand. What they know is, it's no good, that's good enough for me." Moshe shook his head again. Then: "You told your mother?"

"I thought I'd start with you."

"Start and end with me, take my advice. When you tell your mother, I'll take a walk."

"I don't want to hear it, not a word, not a word," Sarah screamed. To make sure, she wrapped a towel around her head and pressed her hands tightly against her ears.

For a few minutes Ben tried to outshout his mother, but it was hopeless. "Not a word, not a word," she cried whenever he said anything associated with Dory. Finally he rose to leave the room, whereupon Sarah said, "Where do you think you're going, mister?"

"It doesn't make much sense to try to talk to you," Ben said. "I might as well go back to Wisconsin."

"You'll take your *shiksa* with you?"

"What do you care? You won't meet her, you won't come to the wedding, you won't even hear her name. What difference does it make to you what I do with her?"

"Listen to him. He leaves his mother's house and goes away forever without saying good-bye to his father."

"Who says I'm going forever? I've got a job. I'm going to work."

"You marry this girl, and to me, to your father, it's the same as you're dead."

"It's that important to you? You'd break up the family just because I marry a gentile?"

"See if your father doesn't sit *shiva* for you."

"Why is it so goddamned important?"

"Very nice. Now he's swearing. You lived here for sixteen years. We gave you a religious education. You were *bar-mitzvah*. I have to tell you why it's important?"

"I know what the rabbi would say. I'm asking you."

Sarah sighed. "Benjy, your father and I came to this country when we were children. All our lives we worked hard, why, so we could send you and your brothers to school, so you could live different lives. Now you come home talking about prostitutes, I should be happy?"

"Prostitutes?"

Pity was in her eyes. "Be sensible, Ben. What respectable Christian girl would marry a Jew?"

Ober was only slightly more understanding. "This is what happens when I let you go off by yourself," he said. "You find a woman. Well, I

35

suppose worse things could happen, but if I had my choice, all my musicians would have to swear an oath of celibacy before joining the quartet." They were sitting in Ober's small office looking out at Science Hall and the lake beyond. Ober never looked directly at Ben when he talked; his gaze focused on some distant object. He sighed. "At least she's an artist," he said. "She'll understand."

Ben nodded. "I told her about you, about the rehearsals."

"I can imagine what you told her," Ober said. "Ah, well. We will see how it goes; what else can we do?" Ben didn't see that Ober had to do anything. Heinz had been married and divorced twice. Now he was about to take his third wife, a woman twenty-five years younger than he. Ben did not intend to take Ober's advice on marriage. "Your parents," Ober said. "They were married in the old country?"

"No, they were kids when they left. My mother thinks it was her downfall. If the czar had held off the pogroms another ten years, she would have been safely married to a rich Jew in Kiev. My grandfather was a judge in Russia, but here he owned a junkyard; my father was the best she could find."

Ober smiled slowly. "To you it is all so simple. Your mother is a whining shrew complaining endlessly of what might have been and making your father's hard life harder."

Ober was nearly as old as his mother. There was no point in arguing with him. "So you have no objections?"

"Of course I have objections," Ober said. "But if you choose to defy your parents and the laws of Israel, what can I do?" Then his voice lost its sarcasm. "My boy, there is no point in trying to stand in the way of love. Go, get married, be happy."

Ben left Ober's office and walked along the lakefront, beyond the farthest university buildings. He sat on the grass and looked out over the water, thinking of his parents. He could see their point of view, but his feelings about Dory were unchanged. Just as they had left Russia behind, so he would have to desert them. He hoped that in the future they would forgive him and accept his wife, but if not, he could live without them. He got up, brushed off his pants, and went to call Dory.

"Let's get married during the winter tour," Ben said when he reached her. "I'll be in New York anyway. You can just come back to Wisconsin with the quartet."

Dory had been throwing a pot and was unprepared for a proposal. "Are you sure?" she said.

"Sure I'm sure. I just talked to Ober about it."

"Did you need permission?"

"That isn't what I meant. I've been doing some thinking and I've decided that if it's all right with you, I want to get married as soon as possible."

"It's just so sudden. I thought we'd get together at Christmas and talk."

Ben felt dejected. He had a sudden fear that he had waited too long, thought too much. "You've changed your mind, haven't you?"

"Oh, Ben, of course not. I love you and I want to marry you. I just want you to be sure, and I was a little surprised, that's all."

"I don't see why. After all, I proposed on our first date."

"I remember. I thought you were crazy. I may not get another chance, so I'll just say yes and hang up." Dory put the phone in the cradle and realized she was grinning so hard her jaws hurt.

In November, Dory went to Washington. Her parents were dead, but she wanted to tell her friends from college about the wedding. She had always been an awkward girl who read too much, and her sorority sisters had despaired of her. Now they looked at her with new respect. Compared to the gravedigger, this musician sounded all right, promising in fact.

Being in Washington made Dory wonder about Ben's parents. She wanted to observe them without introducing herself, in order to help her understand more about Ben. Besides, life in the ghetto seemed exotic, richly textured and profound. She imagined Ben's father as a wild-haired Moses in flowing robes and his mother as a gay peasant in babushka and long skirts. She wanted to enter into their lives, to understand the sufferings of the Jews and their genius for survival.

One day she walked over to Seventh Street. The street had never been grand. It was made up of small commercial buildings with apartments above the stores. Dory looked in vain for numbers, then suddenly the sign loomed above her: "Seidler—Custom Tailor."

Considering her expectations, the shop was an anticlimax. Moshe shared the building with a chiropractor and the entrance was nearly hidden by a show window which displayed ancient black fabric. A poster leaned against the back wall which depicted a man in top hat and tuxedo. Below the picture was the legend "Clothes Make the Man!" He looked like a gentile.

A bell rang as she opened the door. At first she could see nothing in the darkness; then she saw Moshe, his face illuminated by a small light on the sewing machine. He was smaller tnan Ben, and broader. When he smiled he revealed only blackened gums and two yellow teeth. His bald head bobbed forward as he pushed back his chair and rose from the sewing machine. She had planned to ask directions for the library and leave, but now she felt a mordant curiosity about the little man who walked toward her.

All her life, Dory had been sheltered from such people. Since leaving home, the only Jews she had met were artists and writers, the children of immigrants, but Americans themselves. She knew very little about Jews like Moshe. Her grandfather had grudgingly admitted that they were smart, if slightly crooked, and that they took care of their own and caused no trouble in town.

What else? There were the Jews of the Old Testament. The followers of Moses and King David, the scattered tribes of the Diaspora. But what had this shop to do with Bible stories? Moshe came forward. He seemed to have adjusted his posture to fit the dark tunnel of the room. His body inclined slightly to the left in a modified C-curve. His head tilted forward, though the ceiling was at least three feet overhead. Could this homely man with no teeth really be Ben's father?

"Yes, miss," Moshe said. "Something I can show you?"

Dory was flustered. "I was only looking for the library," she said quickly. "But perhaps you can help me. I'd like to buy a suit for my father. I don't know his size, but he's a big man, over two hundred pounds."

Moshe nodded. "Sit, please," he said. "Maybe you'd like a cup of tea, it's getting cold." Dory was not a typical customer; he didn't know what to make of her.

"Tea would be nice, thank you," Dory said. Moshe disappeared into the back of the store.

Dory was ashamed of her initial reaction. He was Ben's father, bad teeth or not. She imagined the life of privation that had led him to the shabby store. People didn't live this way by choice. Dental checkups would not be the highest priority in his life. And whatever personal failings Moshe might have, he had raised a son to be a concert artist. Ben would never work in a place like this; their children would not even know it existed. Ben's long elegant fingers came to mind, and now she imagined them operating the sewing machine. Perhaps it was all part of the evolutionary process.

Moshe broke the curtain that separated the store from the family living quarters. A stream of Yiddish followed him, but Sarah did not deign to appear. Had she recognized Dory instinctively?

"Here, miss, you'll feel better." Moshe handed Dory a hot towel and a glass of tea with lemon.

Then he started taking down bolts of fabric from the shelves, displaying them first over his arm, then on a small table that he pulled over from the wide wall. Dory had no intention of ordering a suit, but she liked the irony of her patrician father wearing one of Moshe's. Moreover, the fabrics were lovely and it would give her an excuse to return.

"I'm sorry to be so much trouble," she said. "It's hard to decide. My father has gained a lot of weight lately and I don't know his size anymore."

"No trouble at all, miss. You go home, look in his closet, then come back. I'll be here." He winked, as if they were partners in crime, and Dory smiled at her future father-in-law. She was tempted to introduce herself. If they could sit and drink tea together like this, how could Moshe, himself the victim of countless instances of discrimination, reject her for being a gentile? Yet she knew Moshe's polite acceptance of her was only a facade. This was business: the tea, the deferential manner, everything. It would be different if she told him who she was. The knowledge made her weary, and she rose to leave.

"You'll check your father's size, miss, and come back?"

Dory nodded. But she hadn't returned. She spent the rest of the day at the Corcoran Gallery. The next morning she took the train to New York.

They were married in December at the Ethical Culture Society. No rabbi in New York would marry them. For Ben, Judaism was dead, and he wouldn't sit *shiva* for it.

The leader who performed the ceremony was a dignified white-haired man named Joseph Simons. Simons was an intimate of Eleanor Roosevelt and well-known for his activities in behalf of minorities. Ben arrived early with Jimmy Shapiro, who was best man.

As they waited, Ben and Jimmy chatted with Simons. "I'm sorry," the older man said. "I'm sure you told me, but I've forgotten. What is it you do for a living, Mr. Seidler?"

Ben, expansive on his wedding day, smiled and said, "I'm the greatest fiddle player in the world, perhaps in the universe, which, as you know, is constantly expanding."

Simons, nonplused, looked at Jimmy. "Well, Mr. Shapiro, you play in the Philharmonic. Can this be true?"

"Somebody has to be," Jimmy said. "Why not Ben?" The friends laughed together, and Simons, encouraged now to take it as a joke, smiled discreetly.

Then they discussed the service. Ben wanted no mention of God and no references to organized religion. Simons, who was a deist, asked if he would accept transcendentalism. "I had thought of quoting Thoreau," he said.

"I can't stand nature," Ben said.

"I hardly think Thoreau is limited to flower sniffing," Simons replied.

"Say what you like, then, it doesn't really matter." Ben hadn't meant to insult the man. Today, the important thing wasn't the ceremony, but the fact that he and Dory were going to be together. He didn't want anything to spoil that.

Dory arrived with a girlfriend and the four of them arranged themselves before Simons, whose jaw was set in an unyielding line. Jimmy and Dory's friend took their places behind Ben and Dory. Jimmy held the ring and Simons talked about love as the symbolic representation of the perfection of creation.

Ben was surprised to find he was touched by Simons' eloquence. Words were the leader's medium, as music was his. He looked at Dory. She was wearing a simple off-white dress and turquoise scarf. In profile she looked like a Modigliani, long-faced and serene. She was delicate, pure, fragile, and perfect in her attention to Simons. Ben felt inadequate for her, for them. It seemed incredible that he had succeeded in meeting her, let alone persuaded her to marry him.

Now Simons nodded to him. For a moment, Ben's mind was blank. Then he said, "I love you with all my heart. You are the dearest thing in the world to me, more than life itself. I want us to be together always."

Dory was crying. They had agreed not to make pledges, but she was glad Ben had. Of course they couldn't know how they would feel in twenty years, but this was an act of faith, of hope, whatever might happen. "All I need to know about my future," she said, "is that you are part of it."

They exchanged rings and Simons said, "I pronounce you man and wife. Kiss your bride, Mr. Seidler, and congratulations." Then Simons shook hands with both of them. Ben complimented him on his remarks, and Simons looked suspicious, as if he thought Ben was mocking him. "I'm glad you enjoyed it, Mr. Seidler," he said. "Perhaps you'll come to one of our regular meetings sometime?" He nodded to Dory and left the room.

Jimmy had made reservations at a basement restaurant in Chinatown. It was filled with families, and the tables were crowded together in the small room. There was no music, but a photographer took pictures of an embarrassed young Chinese couple surrounded by their families. For a moment Dory felt wistful, thinking of her scattered family and her parents, who were dead. But then Ben squeezed her hand and she felt better. He was her family, and he was enough, at least for now.

The noise of the engine as Ben shifted gears brought Dory back to the present. Though Wisconsin Dells was a few hours from Chicago, it seemed as if they had been driving all day. It was after dark when they reached the resort and were shown to a small cottage in the shadow of huge trees bare of leaves. Inside, the walls were decorated with wax bas-reliefs of fruit. On one side of the bed were apples; on the other, a bunch of grapes. It reminded Dory of a wax museum and depressed her.

They had planned to skate or snowshoe, but a January thaw set in; the river wasn't frozen and the paths had not been cleared. Dory sat huddled in blankets, trying to ignore the sculpture, and Ben made desultory attempts to practice. Finally he stopped and threw his fiddle on the bed.

"What's the matter?"

"Can't you tell? It sounds like I'm at the bottom of a well."

"I thought it was all right."

Ben turned, angry now. "Don't lie to me, Dory. Don't start that. I sounded like shit and I know it and so do you."

"Well, then why are you stopping? If you sound so awful, shouldn't you practice some more?" Immediately, she was sorry she had said it. "I'm sorry, Ben," she said. "I'm not happy either."

"The problem is the dampness," Ben said. "I think the damned thing is warped, that's all. That's why I sound like this."

Dory nodded. "Maybe you should forget about music for a while and just relax."

Ben smiled. "In this place? I was thinking of music as an escape."

"We could go somewhere else. We could go into Milwaukee for a few days and stay at the Schroeder. That might be nice."

Ben sighed. "The resort's only part of the problem," he said. "I think I'd better go home and see Ober's doctor. If he says everything is all right, maybe I'll feel more like a vacation."

Dory tried to catch his eye, but Ben was looking away from her. She had looked forward to the vacation as a chance for Ben to rest after the tour and as a time for them to be alone. She knew, too, that it was a way for her to put off reality. But she couldn't hide forever; Ben was right. "You go and check out," she said. "I'll start packing."

41

5

WHEN THE NURSE stuck her head in the door of the examining room, Ben was only half-dressed. His belly thrust forward, the fly of his trousers giving way beneath the tumescence of his stomach. "Doctor's waiting," the nurse said, and left, as if that was explanation enough. Ben nodded, shaking his head ponderously, like a horse irritated by gnats. Then he sucked in his belly, fastened his belt, and slipped into his jacket. He was wearing his shoes. He looked around the room, feeling he might have left something behind. But there was nothing of his, of anyone's, in the room. It was in every sense sterile, its bland whiteness attesting to the absence of all things personal.

The doctor sat behind his desk. Three paperweights, a pen-and-pencil set, books, papers, and a thin manila folder separated him from his patient. On the wall were the standard diplomas, in Latin, as usual. Dr. Bowen was about fifty. He would have graduated from medical school in the thirties, before the Salk vaccine, before antibiotics. What had he been doing since? Playing golf, buying Cadillacs? Still, Ober recommended him so highly. Ben took the indicated chair.

Dr. Bowen did not look at Ben as he spoke. "We have your test results, Mr. Seidler."

Ben was silent.

"I'm afraid I can't be very encouraging." Now he looked up, his eyes searching the far wall. "At the same time, I don't want to alarm you prematurely." Dr. Bowen shifted now in his chair, unnerved by Ben's continued

42

silence. He put on a pair of glasses and reached for the folder and opened it. "Now, I've double-checked these results and talked to a neurologist at the university hospital, and he agrees that what we're talking about is multiple sclerosis." He looked up. Ben said nothing. "That would explain the blindness."

"Blindness" wasn't quite accurate, Ben thought. He hadn't been completely blind. It was as if he was looking at life through cheesecloth; everything he saw was misty, vague. It hadn't been entirely unpleasant. Then for a while he had double vision; everyone came at him twice. Twice as many people, cars, buildings, streetlights, a world of doppelgängers. That bothered him; one world was enough.

"I suspected as much when you complained of sensory disturbances," the doctor continued. "And the difficulty in walking fit in too. But I didn't want to say anything before we knew for sure." Bowen looked expectant, as if he thought Ben would congratulate him. But Ben could think of nothing appropriate to say. Science had always frustrated him because it was mainly descriptive; scientists told you about things, but not what they were. All Bowen had done was give his symptoms a name; Ben knew little more about the disease than he had before.

"What did you say this was called again?" he asked.

"Multiple sclerosis," Bowen replied. "It's a disease of the central nervous system, the brain, and spinal cord."

"Am I going to die?"

Bowen's mouth twitched in a nervous smile. Just the thing he had feared: the man was going to become upset. "Now, Mr. Seidler, there's no point in worrying about that."

"I'm not worried, I just want to know. It's a natural question, isn't it?"

"Multiple sclerotics usually live to a normal age."

Multiple sclerotics. It sounded like a club. Maybe they had their own logo, stationery, and sweatshirts. Maybe they had functions like potluck suppers and bingo parties and group vacations to health spas. They could all get together periodically and discuss their central nervous systems.

"We don't really know very much about m.s.," said Bowen, interrupting Ben's thoughts. "It seems to hit mostly young people, in their twenties and thirties, like you. And we know it's degenerative."

Degenerative. The word swam in the doctor's mouth like taffy.

"Look, Dr. Bowen," Ben said. "We're both busy, so why don't you stop beating around the bush. I'm not going to break down and cry, but I would like to know how this is going to change my life. I'm a public figure of sorts and I can't keep on walking around like a drunk at two o'clock in the

43

afternoon in downtown Madison. Do I need a cane, a wheelchair, or is there something you can give me to cure it?"

Bowen felt the tension between them and vacillated. "I can't really give you all the answers," he said. "I'm sorry that we don't know more about the disease. There is no known cure and the difficulty in walking will probably recur, though you seem to be in remission now."

"Remission?"

"Yes, the name of the disease refers to the fact that the patient usually experiences multiple attacks, followed by periods of remission. That's why it's so difficult to diagnose. As you say, you feel fine. You will continue to feel that way as long as the remission lasts."

"How long will that be?"

Bowen shrugged. "It's hard to say. Remissions can last for years, or months, or days. Sometimes people with m.s. go into permanent remission."

"You mean they cure themselves?"

"In a manner of speaking, yes."

"So I might be cured right now?"

"I wouldn't count on it."

"I'm not counting on anything, doctor, but it's possible?"

"Just possible. For the rest, there is no sign the disease is inherited, although we don't know much about how people contract it. There's an odd statistic to the effect that you're less likely to catch it if you live in the South, but that won't help."

"So if the remission doesn't last, what can I expect?"

"It depends. I've made an appointment for you with Dr. Richman, the neurologist I consulted at the university. He's the one to talk to about the future. I would guess you'll have another attack sometime in the next year that will leave you weaker than you are now. Then another one, and another, each leaving you progressively worse. At some point you'll start to have real trouble getting around. At first you can use a cane, then a wheelchair. If you're like most people, you'll eventually spend most of your time in bed. Sometimes the blindness comes back, but not always. You'll probably have trouble with your bladder, and your arms and legs will stiffen up unless you exercise regularly. You might have some problems with speech and hearing, but I'm talking about years from now." The doctor leaned forward, concerned. "I don't enjoy telling you all this, Mr. Seidler, but you asked, and, frankly, you might as well know."

"No, doctor, it's perfectly all right," Ben said. "I appreciate it." He spoke carefully, disguising his feelings. "Now I have to go and tell my wife."

He rose and grasped the doctor's hand, squeezing to show his strength. Then Ben walked out of the office. He took the elevator to the main floor and walked around back to the parking lot. It took a moment to find the Plymouth, and when he opened the door he felt a twinge in his wrist. He remembered the night he fell and broke it. In his mind's eye he saw the dark sidewalk again, but not the low pipe snaking over it. It was the first time he sensed something was wrong, the first time he felt he lacked the absolute sense of control over his body he had always taken for granted. It was as if the disease attacked first the cylindrical, sensory space protecting the body, before moving in for the kill. And now? He felt better than he had in months. The sun was shining, the air was crisp and clear. Rivers of water flowed downhill to the storm sewers, and beyond that out into the lakes. He was young and vigorous; it was hard to believe he could be on his back in a few years.

Ben put the car in gear and careened out of the parking lot. He stretched his arm out the window to wave at the attendant and felt cool air under his cuffs. He flexed his hand in the breeze, extending the fingers against the stiffness, and to his surprise, the attendant waved back. Ben drove out Langdon Street and then took Observatory Drive over Bascom Hill for the view of the lake. He felt euphoric, but beneath the euphoria, like a minor chord in a brilliant phrase, was the knowledge that he was seriously ill. He no longer questioned the doctor's competence. It couldn't be easy to be blamed by patients all day for the imperfection of their bodies. Ben felt sorry for the man. Then he felt cold. He pulled in his arm and rolled up the window.

Dory sat in her basement studio surrounded by oils. There were studies of bowls of fruit and drawings of the backyard with its twisted dwarf apple trees below a dark blue sky. A group of paintings of Ben leaned against the wall. He was depicted in every aspect: in profile and full face; wearing a coat and tie and in T-shirt with red horizontal stripes; smiling and solemn; with fiddle and without. She had her husband down. She had done the paintings while pregnant with Charles and remembered complaining to her analyst that her life was limited to Ben and the family. "All we ever do is drink coffee, talk, and look after our son." "How many women know their husbands so well?" the analyst replied.

Now Dory felt she knew nothing, about art or her husband. Ben had been silent about the disease since their return. He had been to the doctor once for tests, but the tests had not yet revealed the problem. Ben practiced and went to the university, but they didn't talk and Dory felt a new tension between them. In self-defense she had gone down to the drugstore one morning and bought a large notebook. If she couldn't talk to Ben about the disease, she would write about it, but so far she hadn't opened the notebook. It was, she thought, a book she was reluctant to write.

She paced in front of her assembled canvases. The paintings seemed dreary, unimaginative. She had to put together a portfolio for Sam Matthews, but she couldn't find anything she liked, and she knew her feelings for Sam were influencing her judgment. This annoyed her. Sam's professional opinion of her hadn't mattered before; now, suddenly, it did.

Dory and Sam had met at a reception for the quartet shortly after she arrived in Madison. Since they were the only people not clustered around the musicians, they found each other quite naturally. The fact that they were both artists was a pleasant coincidence. Sam had joined the art department the year before, after graduating from Berkeley and spending six months in Paris. He lived in an apartment near the campus done entirely in gray after a *fin de siècle* poet, drove a gray Checker he had purchased from the cab company, and had his clothes made by a local tailor. Yet because he was tall and athletic, with a red beard and wavy hair, he seemed exuberant rather than precious. There was nothing bloodless or drab about Sam. After talking with her, Sam invited Dory to sign up for his design class.

Her experience would be good for the others, he said. But when Dory got to class, she discovered that at least half the people there were women in their thirties and she thought she was the only one who hadn't slept with Sam. This both pleased and depressed her.

Yet Sam was really Ben's friend. When Ben saw Sam's apartment, he said, "This is great, you never have to dust!" Sam was delighted with Ben and often went along on tour with the quartet. While Ben rehearsed, Sam would visit galleries; at night, they would have long meals together and argue about art.

Dory suspected Sam was taking her on as a graduate student, partly as a favor to Ben, and this made her feel self-conscious. There was also the fact that she knew more about him than she should. She didn't want an intimate relationship with her major professor. Ben had told her Sam's first wife left him flat while he was in graduate school, without even a farewell note. And though she didn't know why, Ben also told her Sam had not been circumcised until he was twenty-five. The operation had been extremely painful, Ben reported, and though Dory couldn't see how this related to art, it seemed relevant to her. Her feelings for Sam were an odd mix of affection, sympathy, and intimidation. She knew she would attach greater importance to his judgments than made sense.

She took down a cubist study of Ben and replaced it with an abstract canvas in blue and green. The colors fought for dominance, but there was no coherence, no logic to it. Dory was disgusted. The thought of teaching art, even in high school, seemed pretentious. How could she teach? What did she know? Yet she felt she had to, had to try anyway.

And she knew that however she felt, she couldn't possibly be that bad. If she lacked talent, how had she survived at Corcoran, at Alfred, in New York? Yet that was ten years ago, time enough for talent to erode and disappear. She had been a promising student, but little more; she had married Ben when she was only a few months out of school. And now, depending on what was wrong with Ben, she might have to support a family. She sighed and began to clean up.

Dory was washing her brushes in the sink when she heard the car in the driveway. She waited while Ben slowly descended the stairs. He looked pale and thin.

"Were you painting?" Ben asked. Dory was still touched by his interest in her work.

"For a while. I went sketching in the park and brought some leaves back, but I couldn't concentrate. This isn't the best place to work—no light, and I always feel like I just got out of the shower."

"Where are the kids?" Ben said.

"Where do you think? At school, where would they be." Then she remembered that it was odd for him to be home at this time. She smiled at him. There was a silence that seemed interminable. Finally Ben said, "The doctor says I have multiple sclerosis."

Dory felt her body go numb. "I don't know what that is," she said.

"I don't either, really. But the doctor said the tripping was part of it. He says I'm in remission now, but that it won't last."

"Are you going to be all right?"

That was the hard question, the only important question, when you came down to it. Ben looked out at the faded green plants rising out of the snow at eye level on the basement window. "It doesn't look like it," he said.

Dory felt herself shaking involuntarily. "What do you mean?"

Ben swallowed. It was as if a ball of wool had lodged in his throat. He wanted to explain everything in a way that would allow no questions, yet would satisfy Dory. "I have an incurable disease. They don't know what causes it, and they don't know, can't predict, what effect it will have on me. It's different with different people."

He saw she was crying, but it only made him angry. He was the one who should be crying, he was the one who was sick. But all he wanted to do was forget, about the damned disease and all sickness everywhere. He

47

faced the garden again. He felt like walking, hanging by his knees from the branches of the barren trees.

Then Dory's arm was on his shoulder. "It's just so sudden," she said. "You always assume it's nothing, because it always has been. You never think of anything like this."

"Happens every day," Ben said.

"Yes, but not to us."

She was right. It hadn't happened to him alone, but to all of them, even the kids, though they wouldn't realize it yet. "That's right," he said now. "Not to us." He pulled her toward him, wrapping his arms around her and squeezing, as if to reassure himself of his strength. He would make things turn out all right, he thought. He always had. But the pale green of the plants in the garden seemed to rebut him.

Dr. Richman was no more specific than Bowen. They couldn't predict the course of the disease; they would have to wait and see. Exercise might help, but even that would probably be temporary. As Ben was leaving, Richman suggested that he might want to visit someone else with the disease.

"What for?" Ben asked.

"Well, you do have something in common," Richman said. "Perhaps they could answer your questions better than I. Besides, they don't have many visitors."

Dory was against it. "It's bad enough already," she said. "It would be depressing. What's the point in seeing what might happen?"

"It depresses me not knowing anything," Ben said. "I feel like there's this invading army inside me somewhere and I can't get my hands on it. Maybe seeing some other people will make me feel better, like it's not just me. At least I'd know what I'm heading for."

"Some things it's better not to know."

"Sure, ignorance is bliss. But the disease can't be any worse than I'm imagining it is right now."

"Don't be so sure."

"That's precisely the problem: I'm not sure of anything, and I want to be. Even if I'm going to die, I want to know it."

When Ober heard about it, he was noncommittal. Now that a diagnosis had been made, he seemed almost uninterested. He sat in his chair, nodding as Ben gave his report. Then he said, "So, we'll see what happens, yes?" And they had gone to join the others at rehearsal.

The hospital was built on a hill overlooking the lake on the outskirts of Madison. There was a glassed-in veranda circling the building, and nurses attended old people in wheelchairs. Only white heads protruded above the blanketed chairs, as if the rest of their bodies had been replaced, leaving only the shrunken brows and hollow cheeks as evidence of lives lived. Ben passed a line of these shrouds and walked through the main door of the building.

Dr. Richman had given him three names, but two of the people were unavailable, and the nurse seemed hesitant.

"Are you sure you want to see Mrs. Barrow?" she said.

"If she's the only one available, yes."

"You're not a member of the family?"

"Dr. Richman said she might like a visitor."

The nurse pursed her lips. "Yes, she hasn't had many. She's very sick, you know." Ben nodded, and the nurse said, "Please follow me."

The hospital was enormous, and corridors stretched off in all directions. The air seemed close, and to each side of Ben were stretchers on large, ancient wheels, and wooden wheelchairs, standing ready. Should he feel faint, he had little doubt one would appear behind his buckling knees to gather him up and spirit him away forever.

The nurse faced resolutely forward, her white back a rebuke. As they walked, Ben looked into the dim rooms. Most were empty; some had unmade beds and a few personal articles, pictures or flowers on the bureau, a crocheted pillow on a chair. Then Ben heard a cry for help. He stopped and looked in the door of a room. An old woman lay nude on the bed; her eyes were terrified and imploring, but Ben found himself looking at her body. From the wild yellow-white hair to her slack breasts and the insubstantial tuft of pubic hair at her crotch, the woman appeared cadaverous, almost inhuman. The only clothing she wore was a pair of white support stockings pulled up to her knees.

"Can I help you?" Ben said.

The woman stared at him. Her trembling lips framed a word, but no sound came. Spittle dribbled down her chin. At last she whispered, "They're killing me. Take me home! Home!"

Ben stood transfixed, helpless. "I don't know . . . " he began, but then the nurse was at his side.

"I thought you wanted to see Mrs. Barrow," she said.

"This woman called me," Ben said. "She's afraid."

The nurse crossed the room and pulled a sheet over the woman. Then she smoothed her hair and spoke softly to her. "Everything's all right, Patty. Don't worry, no one's going to hurt you." She turned to Ben. "You've upset her, Mr. Seidler. She's afraid of strangers."

"She called out to me. She said you're killing her."

49

The nurse smiled slightly. "Will you leave now? I think she's ready to sleep."

The nurse led Ben out of the room, and they resumed their walk. Finally they arrived at a room labeled "Isolation." The nurse stopped and said, "You'll have to wear a gown."

"I thought it wasn't contagious," Ben said.

"The gown isn't to protect you, Mr. Seidler. Multiple sclerotics are very susceptible to infection; that's how we lose most of them. You might have a slight cold that would kill her."

Ben peered into the room but could see little. Suddenly he was cold with fright. He wondered if Dory hadn't been right. The nurse was not encouraging. But when she handed him the gown, he slipped it over his head and tied the mask securely. Then he entered the room.

Mrs. Barrow was lying next to the window, a sheet over her body, her head turned toward the light. "You have a visitor, Mrs. B.," the nurse said. But the woman did not reply. The nurse shrugged and said, "Ten minutes, Mr. Seidler." Then she left.

Ben stood next to Mrs. Barrow, not speaking, listening to the woman's breathing. There was a slight wheeze, but otherwise it was not labored. "Dr. Richman said I could come to see you," he said, and immediately felt foolish. It wasn't up to Richman; the woman still had rights, invalid or not. "What I mean is, he thought you might enjoy having a visitor." The woman did not give the smallest indication of having heard. Mrs. Barrow was turned on her right side; her hip was outlined in the bedclothes. It was all he saw of her body other than her head and her feet, which were encased in green plastic booties and stuck out at the foot of the bed. Ben looked at the woman's face in profile. Her skin was stretched tightly over her cheekbones and straight bony nose. He wasn't sure about her age, but he thought she probably looked older than she was. He wondered about Mrs. Barrow; she seemed alone. Ben leaned over the bed now and saw that she was crying.

"May I sit down?" he said. The woman said nothing, so he pulled a chair to the head of the bed. "I understand how you feel," he began. "You're all alone and you have a dreadful disease; it's perfectly natural that you're unhappy." He felt ridiculous, patronizing. Why had Richman sent him here anyway? How could he help this woman? It was humiliating to both of them. He didn't know how she felt at all. But what could he say that made more sense? He wanted desperately to help, to comfort her. It occurred to him that perhaps she was unable to speak. "Can you talk?" Ben asked.

50

The woman nodded.

"You can, but you'd rather not?"

She nodded again.

"Do you mind my being here? I'll leave if you want. Would you like me to leave?" The woman was silent as the grave. He stood again; it seemed unnatural to talk to the woman without looking at her. She continued to stare blankly into the light. Ben passed his hand before her eyes. There was no reaction. For a moment he was overwhelmed by the woman's condition. She couldn't walk or see, and didn't want to talk. Under the circumstances, he didn't blame her.

"I want you to know that I have multiple sclerosis, too," Ben said. Now the woman seemed to show interest. She turned her head slightly, waiting to hear more. "There isn't much else to say," Ben said. "It's just been diagnosed, but we have that much in common." The woman smiled—with some irony, Ben thought. Then she turned away again.

"If there's anything I can do to help, anything I can do for you, I'd be more than happy," he said.

For the first time, the woman spoke. Her voice was scratchy, like an old record. "No one can do anything," she said.

"I didn't mean medically," Ben said. "But if you'd like me to read to you, I'd be glad to. I'm a violinist, I could play for you. Anything you'd like to hear?"

The effort of speech seemed to have exhausted Mrs. Barrow. Ben saw her shoulders heave and knew she was crying again. He felt defeated. There was nothing he could do to help, nothing anyone could do. She was right about that. Moreover, there was nothing he could learn from her. He couldn't even imagine himself being in her condition. The doctor said it could happen; well, the doctor could also be wrong. He'd die before he'd live like this. Some things were more important than life.

He looked at Mrs. Barrow a last time. She hadn't changed her position, but now there was something immensely appealing and innocent in her expression. Impulsively he took her in his arms and hugged her to him. Her body was incredibly frail and skeletal. Ben slipped off his mask, supported her head with his hand, and kissed her on the mouth. The woman struggled for a moment, then relaxed, and to his surprise, kissed him in return. He felt her dry lips, tasted her stale breath, and held her for a long embrace before slowly releasing and lowering her to the bed again. He kissed each of her eyes shut and rose to leave.

But now Mrs. Barrow was staring at him, amazement on her face. "Why?" she croaked, flailing blindly for his arm.

"It's only that I could never resist a helpless woman," Ben said.

The woman hesitated for a moment, unbelieving, then began to laugh, uproariously, choking and wheezing on the words. "Resist," she said. "Helpless!" Then she surrendered to a series of hacking coughs which brought back the tears and left her breathless but still smiling broadly.

Ben squeezed her shoulder. "I'll be back," he said. At the door, he looked back. Mrs. Barrow was framed in late-afternoon sunlight. But now she was smiling contentedly. She looked oddly serene.

Part Two

6

Moshe stood in his doorway holding his stomach. He rarely walked outside anymore or socialized with the other shopkeepers on the block. They knew where he was, let them come if they wanted to talk. The view was not encouraging anyway. Black men and women walked by, rarely looking into his shop. Occasionally a boy would stop and point at him before running away.

Moshe's face was a grimace. The pain was so familiar by now that he was hardly aware of it. His stomach had bothered him for years, especially in the morning, when it was tender and distended. Then he would caress it gently, as if pressure would cause an explosion, spraying organs all over his shop. He groaned slightly and tasted bile. *Tsuris*, from morning to night. If not from the *schwartzes*, then from his wife. Wasn't a man entitled to peace in his old age? But things seemed to get worse all the time.

Moshe turned from the window and retreated to his sewing machine. Then he remembered he had finished the last job. It made him feel anxious. Not that he needed money. There was plenty, but he liked to sew. It kept his hands busy and stopped him from worrying. Now, with nothing to do, he was restless. Sarah was in the back, but he didn't want to talk. They would only argue; what else had they ever done? Moshe spit into the wastebasket and returned to his post at the window.

He knew he had no reason to be unhappy. When were people unhappy? When they were alone and out of work. He had a family, and business was good. "Good" was an understatement; he couldn't believe how good it was. During the war, Moshe bought four apartment houses on K Street for next to nothing. Then, with housing at a premium in Washington after the war, they had made him a wealthy man. He was building a house on Sixteenth Street, with a lot that backed on Rock Creek Park, as an investment. His tax lawyer wanted him to incorporate. He couldn't complain, he'd been luckier than anyone deserved to be.

Yet each morning it seemed more difficult to get out of bed. The mahogany bedposts loomed large, like prison watchtowers; the mattress seemed to sag, though he had replaced it. Every day he had to sit and rest for five minutes from the effort of extricating himself from sleep. There had never been much space in the small apartment upstairs, but now it seemed even smaller. The walls and ceiling pressed in on Moshe. The shop seemed less oppressive, so he had his coffee there.

Ben had been gone ten years now. They hadn't seen him or their grandchildren. Moshe hadn't been so much against the girl in the first place. He had been forced to cast his son adrift because of Sarah, and now he regretted it. Not that Moshe had any great love for *goyim*, but if the girl was willing to accept them, why should they refuse? Anyway, ten years was enough, more than enough, too much. He was getting old; he wanted to know his grandchildren. For that matter, he wanted to know his son again. Was that a crime?

He turned and marched into the back room. "Enough!" he shouted. "Enough already. I'm going to see Benjy in Wisconsin."

"A regular Marco Polo," Sarah said. "When did you get such a brilliant idea for spending our money?"

"What better way than to see our son? Better I should leave it to him?"

"And what do we do in our old age?"

"This is our old age."

Sarah shrugged. "So go, have a wonderful time. I'll get by."

A wave of guilt passed over him. "The shop will take care of itself. The super collects the rents. You can come along, too."

Sarah looked astonished. "Ha, I should go visit Benjy and his *shiksa?* No, thank you very much."

With Moshe, to think was to act. He called a friend to drive him to the airport and had Sarah pack a bag. "You'll call Benjy?"

"Why waste the money? I'll tell him when I get there."

"What if they're busy?"

"Too busy for his own father? Not Benjy. I don't need much room anyway. I can sleep with one of the boys." He was drunk with the idea of getting away. He was anxious to see Ben, but in a way, that was a pretext.

Perhaps he would simply keep on going west. See the Black Hills, the Badlands, and finally California. That was his dream. He envisioned himself high on a white horse, wearing a sombrero and chaps. He would never come back to Washington, to the darkness of the store and Sarah's carping. His friend's horn sounded out front. Moshe clasped Sarah briefly and then hurried out, with a faraway look in his eyes.

After practicing in the morning, Ben took a short nap in his study. Then he walked out along the lake path before going to lunch at the Union. He was returning to Music Hall when he saw, like a mirage, a short bald man approaching him. The man looked remarkably like his father, but Ben had experienced the sensation before. He knew it was because he missed the old man; he never imagined he saw Sarah on the street. Ben wanted to sit and play checkers and talk in the afternoon with his father. He wanted to let Moshe win.

High on Bascom Hill, the carillon was banging out a melody. Ben stopped to listen. As usual, it was out of tune. He looked back at the street; students moved past him, unseeing. The old man was closer now. The resemblance was uncanny, down to the toothless grin. Then Ben realized it really was Moshe.

As though he understood Ben's amazement, the old man yelled, "Benjy, Benjy, it's me! I'm here." Then they were hugging each other while the polite students waited to get by. Finally Ben pried Moshe's arms loose and stepped back to look at him. He was surprised by his father's strength; he was a head shorter, but had arms like an ape's. Panting and out of breath, they stood staring at each other, pleased but slightly embarrassed.

"Pop," Ben said. "I didn't know, I mean, we didn't expect . . ."

"How could you know? I didn't know myself. I was standing in my shop and suddenly it came to me: I'll go see Benjy. So here I am." Then he enfolded Ben in another bear hug.

"Here you are," Ben repeated. Then he looked around Moshe, as though, improbably, he had missed Sarah. "Is Ma here, too?"

Moshe looked apologetic, as though he was ashamed of what he had to say: "She stayed home to watch things, the shop, you know."

Ben knew. It was Dory. After all these years, it was still his wife that was locked out. To hell with her, then. He didn't care if Sarah ever came; she could rot on Seventh Street. "Look, Pop," he said. "My office is right over there." He pointed at the red roof of Music Hall. "Why don't we go over and call Dory—she can come pick us up. I walked over to campus and let her have the car."

"Pick us up? No, we'll go to her—take a cab. And I know about your office. I left my bag there. Your secretary let me in."

They walked to Music Hall, but once inside, Moshe was hesitant, following Ben by a half-step, like a small boy. The green of the grass on the hill, the stooping elms, the darkness of the music building, so different from the gloom of his tailor shop. Cool and elegant instead of lowering and oppressive. He followed his son up the stairs and waited as he unlocked his office. Ben dialed his home.

"Dory," he said. "Something remarkable has happened; my father is here."

"Your father," Dory repeated. "From Washington?"

"Sure, how many fathers do I have?"

"You mean he just walked in in the middle of office hours?"

"Not exactly, but he's here now."

Dory was silent, and Ben was disappointed with her lack of enthusiasm. "I'm sorry," she said finally. "I'm just surprised. It's been ten years."

"Ten years, ten minutes, what's the difference? He's here and I'm bringing him home to meet you and the kids. We can have lunch together."

"But, Ben," Dory said. "Nothing's ready; I mean, I don't know what he wants to eat."

Ben was astonished. "What difference does that make? He'll eat what we eat."

"But isn't he orthodox? Doesn't he need kosher food?"

"Jesus, Dory, he's Jewish but he's not from another planet. He'll make out. Don't worry about it."

Ben looked over at Moshe. The old man was looking out the window, lost in the green campus, unaware of Dory's doubts. All he wanted was for all of them to be happy together. "What do you want me to do?" he whispered. "Send him home?"

"Of course not," Dory said. "But what if we hate each other?"

"I'll still love you," Ben said. "But I think you'll like him."

"Oh, Ben, I don't know."

"Trust me," Ben said softly, and hung up the phone.

Dory's ear was hot from the pressure of the earpiece, and her hand shook as she hung up the phone. She had imagined meeting her in-laws many times, but not like this. She had thought it would approximate a summit conference, with elaborate protocols and all parties in separate hotels with a neutral meeting place. Instructions would be circulated in advance before face-to-face contact took place. Now, suddenly, Moshe was in town, in a cab on his way over. They would be here in fifteen minutes.

58

It was too much, and Ben should know it. She couldn't get over ten years of rejection in a few minutes. She couldn't just forget about it; she had spent time hating these people. And Ben's attitude annoyed her. Certainly he should know how she felt. He should protect her.

Even as she thought these things, however, Dory began to soften. She knew how much Ben had missed his father. She was making too much of the whole thing. Other people had trouble with their in-laws and survived. Why couldn't she?

Dory looked out the window for the boys. She didn't see them, and she had things to do. She should have some food ready, she thought. Jews liked to eat. And the boys had to be clean and well-dressed. She didn't want Moshe to think she was a bad mother. She was determined to be calm, not to make too much of this, but it was hard. He was like a character in a book or movie; she couldn't think of him as a real person.

The cab left Ben and Moshe in front of the house. Ben started to pick up his father's suitcase, but Moshe did not move. He stood staring straight ahead. "This is your house?" he said.

Ben was accustomed to it by now. He had almost forgotten what it was like to live in a city, pinched by the buildings and other people. His house was among the most modest on the block. Brown shingled siding, a green door, a small front yard, shrubs. Nothing fancy. "It didn't cost much," he said.

But Moshe was impressed. At the age of sixty-five, he had just built his first house. If he was lucky, he'd live long enough to move in. And here was Benjy living like a king. He shook his head and followed Ben up the stairs.

Dory, Michael, and Charles were waiting on the porch. The boys hid behind Dory. Ben stopped and pulled his father up the last stair. "Pop," he said. "I want you to meet my wife, Dorothy. Dory, this is my father."

They looked cautiously at each other. There was no sign of recognition in Moshe's face, and Dory was relieved. She smiled at him shyly. Then Moshe threw his arms around her and kissed her loudly on both cheeks. "Daughter," he said. "Welcome!"

7

Moshe sat, a glass of tea before him, looking out into the garden. He felt as if he was living in a dream. The small house on the quiet street; his son's dark, quiet wife; the two boys who called him Grandpa; all this seemed to exist in some world independent of Seventh Street.

"You okay, Pop?" Ben was standing next to him.

"Why shouldn't I be okay?"

"No reason. You were just sitting there, I don't know, looking at nothing."

"I'm fine. Sit here with me. Have some tea."

Ben took a chair and immediately felt uncomfortable. When he was growing up, he and Moshe had few conversations. He thought of his father as doing little besides working and yelling at Sarah. Now Moshe seemed docile, almost sweet. He would pat Ben on the shoulder or put his arm around him for no reason. But when he discussed it with Dory, she said, "Maybe he's just resting. After a life in the shop, he deserves it." Ben couldn't argue with that.

"So, Benjy, this music, it's turning out?"

"Sure, Pop, it's fine. I get along with the other guys all right; I like the university."

"People come to hear you?"

"Are you kidding? We haven't got enough tickets for them all."

"How many people?"

"It depends. Some halls are bigger than others. Sometimes two hundred, sometimes more, a thousand."

Moshe nodded. He was not satisfied. He sensed an underlying sadness in the house, but Ben seemed happy with his wife and job. Once or twice, he saw Ben stumble, but he didn't want to interfere, and maybe it was nothing. Still, he was curious. He sat, looking once more at the garden; then he tried again. "Your wife, a very nice person."

"You like her?" Ben was pleased.

"Very nice, I said so, didn't I? And a good mother."

Ben patted his father's arm. "That's great, Pop."

"I was wondering, Benjy . . ."

"What, something wrong?"

"Sometimes when you walk, it's like you're falling."

Ben looked away. He didn't want to discuss it with Moshe. He wanted to take care of him, impress him. "I'm fine, pop."

"Really fine?"

"What do you want, Charles Atlas? For now, I'm fine, everything's okay."

"And later? What is it? You sick, Benjy?"

Ben stretched and looked at his father. Moshe was examining him closely, his forehead a mass of wrinkles. He could lie, but the old man already knew something was wrong, so what was the point? It would be harder later, and between now and then he'd have to worry about concealing things from his father. He decided to tell Moshe the truth.

"Yeah, Pop, I'm sick. That's why I lose my balance sometimes. But there's no point in your worrying about it. I want you to relax and have a good time while you're here."

"Please, mister, let me worry about what I want. I hear my son is sick, so I'm interested. Lectures about having a good time I don't need."

"Okay, you're right. I've got a disease that gets progressively worse, but slowly, very slowly. My doctor says I'll have to quit work someday, but he can't say when. Maybe never. I feel fine now."

"But you trip, maybe you fall down?"

"Sometimes, but mostly I'm all right. I feel a little tired in the afternoons, especially in the summer when it's hot."

"Your wife, what does she say?"

"Can you stop calling her 'my wife'? She's got a name."

"Dory, sue me. What does she think of all this?"

"She's worried. About me, the family. She's in graduate school now. Maybe she'll get a job."

"Your wife is going to support you?"

"Why not, I've been supporting her for years. Anyway, I won't stop working unless I have to."

Moshe looked at his son with great sympathy. Before, he had felt like a stranger, an interloper, but the dream world seemed more recognizable now. You could get an education, go far away, have a nice family, find a good job, live on a quiet street in your own house, and it would all catch up with you anyway. Madison wasn't so different from Seventh Street after all.

"I wish you wouldn't tell Ma. She'd think God was punishing us."

"Who says he ain't?" Moshe had no great affection for his maker, but respected his power. "But I am a man. What you say to me is safe." Then, almost as an afterthought, he said, "Can I help, Benjy? You need anything, money?"

"We're fine. It's just good to have you here. I haven't talked much to anyone else. Whenever I mention it to Dory, she starts to cry."

"Why not? Do you blame her? Here she's young, happy, a mother, and her husband is a famous man. Then all of a sudden it's gone. Don't you want to cry sometimes, Benjy?"

"Sometimes it keeps me up at night and I can't think about anything except what it'll be like when I'm flat on my back in some hospital," Ben said. "But what can I do about that? I just go along doing what I've always done."

"But you won't be able to play any music then. What will you do?"

"Maybe I could still be a doctor."

"I ain't joking, Benjy."

"That's the trouble, Pop. I can't really understand that it's not a bad joke. It doesn't seem real. Ever since I was fifteen I've been out working, playing the fiddle for a living. Now a doctor tells me I'm going to be in a wheelchair the rest of my life. It doesn't seem possible."

"Maybe not, but you got to think about it like it is. Benjy, some day maybe you ain't going to be able to walk. You ain't going to sleep with your wife no more."

"Who knows what will happen for sure?" Ben snapped. "That's one thing the doctors all agree about. They don't know what will happen. Anyway, it's my problem, not yours." He got up abruptly and left the room.

After a few minutes, Moshe heard the front door open and close. For the next hour there was nothing; then Ben returned carrying a bag. He came into the dining room and said, "I bought you some pumpernickel." He went into the kitchen, then returned to the dining room. "You all right?" he said.

"What should I do, dance?"

"I told you, there's no point in worrying. If I don't think about it all the time, why should you?"

"It's different. I'm your father. I got to think."

"Okay, but I'm not a kid anymore. I've got a wife, a family."

"Them I'm thinking about too."

"I mean, it's not your responsibility. I appreciate it, but you can't solve my problems for me. You've got your own."

"What do you know about my problems?"

"Is something wrong?" Ben felt uncomfortable. "How are things, the shop, Ma?"

"Things are the same."

"Well, then are you happy?"

"I should be happy too?"

Ben sighed. "I remember once when I asked you why you and Ma stayed together you said, 'You don't make orphans.' But now I'm grown and out of the house. Why stay together?"

"Benjy," Moshe said. "Do me a favor?"

"Sure, Pop, anything."

"Good. Leave me alone."

Ben went back into his room. For an hour he worked on a Mozart trio, but he had trouble concentrating. His father had come a thousand miles to see him, and they were arguing. And why? Because Moshe had tried to help, to understand. Finally Ben put aside his fiddle and went into the dining room.

Moshe was still staring out the window. "How about a game of checkers, Pop?"

Moshe looked up, suspicious. Ben knew he was thinking about the time Ben had beaten him ten straight times. Ben had been checkers champion of the Jewish Community Center in Washington. At the age of twelve he had been ruthless. "Come on," Ben said. "I'll get the board."

Ben won the first game but lost two in a row before winning again. "Best of five," he said, but Moshe managed a triple jump to take the game. "You've improved," Ben said.

"You let me win, to humor the *alter kocker*," Moshe said. But he was pleased. Ben smiled and picked up the bread. "To the victor go the spoils. I'll make lunch," he said.

8

THE OLD MAN took to Michael immediately. Michael liked his grandfather because he was the only adult he knew who was close to his own size. He thought Moshe looked like the dwarfs in his book, but when he asked, Dory said, "Michael, you must never say that to your grandpa. It would hurt his feelings."

Moshe tried to talk to Charles too, but the younger boy was less gregarious. He preferred to stay in his room and build block skyscrapers. One day Moshe came home with a small brown bag and approached Michael. "You ever seen one of these, *bubele?*"

"It looks like a doughnut," Michael said. Ben came into the room and saw them. "Where'd you get a bagel in Madison, Pop?"

Moshe waved him off. "You want to share with me a doughnut?"

Michael shrugged. The bagel was yellow, with poppy seeds. "I've never had one like that," he said.

"I'll make you a deal," Moshe said. "We'll share. I'll take the bagel, you take the hole, okay?" Michael laughed, delighted. He knew his grandpa the dwarf would never cheat him.

Often, in the afternoon, they went fishing together. Neither Moshe nor Michael cared much about the fish, but they liked being out in the sun together, with the lake spread before them. Moshe had a folding chair and sometimes he brought along a Yiddish newspaper. But now he sat quietly on the end of the dock, his pants rolled to his knees, his feet dangling in the cool, green water. Occasionally small fish would swim between his legs, rippling the water, and Moshe would smile at them. The sun was hot, but he enjoyed the fish, sleek and swift, tracing small currents in the water.

Michael kept throwing his line and pulling it in slowly, as he had seen the old men do. His pole was made of bamboo and he had no reel, but he imitated their quick wrist-flicking casts. It was the cast he admired; he had no desire to catch fish. The only time he had hooked a catfish, it terrified him; the desperate struggle of the fish to get free was horrible to watch. The boat master had come and wrested the hook from the catfish's mouth. Then he put it on a line for Michael. But when the man returned to his shed, Michael threw the fish back into the water. Now, though he had attached a bobber to the line, there was no hook. After a while Michael tired of the game and sat down.

"Are they biting?" Moshe asked.

"The bait's no good."

Moshe nodded. He looked into the lake again.

"Grandpa, why are your feet purple?"

Moshe looked at the boy, then at his feet. They were distorted by waves and seemed small and far away. "They ain't purple. A little blue maybe. The water's cold."

"No, I mean the bumps are purple." Michael pointed to the bunions on Moshe's feet.

Now Moshe felt embarrassed, as though his secret had been discovered. He pulled his feet from the water and started putting on his socks. "Maybe when I was your age I didn't have shoes that fit," he said. "Maybe when I was twelve years old I went to work carrying heavy bags of potatoes, so maybe my feet ain't so beautiful, but so what?"

"But why, Grandpa? Why didn't you have shoes? Didn't your daddy buy you shoes?"

Moshe looked at the boy standing at his side. His eyes were so large they seemed to demand an answer. Yet what could he say? How could he tell his grandson about a place on the other side of the world where people spoke a language he couldn't understand? How could he tell Michael about his boyhood on the *shtetl* and about the small low *shul* where it was so crowded on Yom Kippur that women fainted from the heat and lack of air and called it a miracle? What could this small boy on a dock on Lake Wingra in Madison, Wisconsin, possibly know about pogroms, about his uncle who was killed or his sister who was raped? What did poverty and prejudice have to do with him? There was nothing Moshe could say.

"He was punishing me," Moshe said at last. "Because I was a bad boy.

65

Now, if you don't hurry home right now, I'll tell your mother you were a bad boy. Then when you're my age you'll have purple feet, too."

But Michael just laughed. "You wouldn't tell, Grandpa."

Moshe smiled. "You're right, *bubele*," he said. "I wouldn't tell." He took a last look at the fish, picked up his chair, and took the boy by the hand. They stood in the sunlight together, and Moshe looked down at Michael. His hair was bleached blond from the sun and his skin was lightly tanned. Moshe's own legs were thin, white, and hairless. He stooped and unrolled his pant legs. Then he stood erect and breathed deeply. He felt giddy and held Michael's shoulder for support. He had the sudden feeling he was not alone, but that his father was holding his shoulder, and his grandfather his father's, back to the beginning of time. And he was glad he had come to Wisconsin, to see Benjy and meet his grandson and form the latest link in that endless chain. He looked down and smiled again. "It's late," he said. "Let's get home for supper."

On Friday Moshe approached Ben in the yard. He was watering the begonias and the flowers lay on the ground like pieces of cloth. "Benjy, can I talk to you a minute?"

"Of course, Pop. What is it?"

"Today . . ." Moshe said, then stopped, embarrassed.

"Today?"

"I mean, today is *shabbos*." He waited, hoping Ben would understand. But Ben said nothing, so Moshe continued. "I know Dory's not Jewish. That's okay, but I . . ."

"You want to have *shabbos* tonight, we'll do it, Pop. No problem."

"I don't want to cause trouble," Moshe said. "I could stay in my room, do it there."

"Don't be silly. We'll do it in the dining room. I told you, it's no problem. The only thing is, I don't think I can remember the *broche*."

"It's been that long, Benjy?"

"I guess it has, Pop. I'm sorry."

Moshe shook his head. Then he brightened. "I remember, I'll teach you. Besides, I want the boys to hear, once anyway."

Dory was not enthusiastic. In part, she felt betrayed, as if she had been promised one thing and was now being given something else. She had asked Ben about religion before; she had been worried about raising the boys without it, worried about what they would miss.

"What they'll miss," Ben had said, "is a lot of *tsuris*, that's what they'll miss."

66

"But isn't that up to the boys to decide—later, I mean?"

"Sure, and later they'll decide to hate us for forcing them to go to *cheder*."

"They don't have to go to *cheder* any more than they have to go to Mass. They can go to the reform temple. It's just down the street."

"They'll have to go by themselves. I won't take them."

"I don't see why you're so negative. Religion is important. Some of my most moving experiences were inside a church."

"Moving?" Ben said. "It made me move out of my house when I was sixteen. Look, Dory, for years I went twice a week to *cheder* and twice to my fiddle lessons. The fifth night was *shabbos*. I didn't play baseball, I didn't have friends. I studied Hebrew and I played the violin. It was a hell of a childhood."

Dory had joined the temple anyway and even attended a few conversion classes, but Ben came only once and then left in the middle of the sermon. "They're not Jews, those people. They're like *goyim*, so why bother?"

"What do you mean?" Dory said. "They're perfectly nice. And how can you accuse them, when you don't remember the prayers yourself?"

Ben had a pained expression on his face. "That has nothing to do with it, Dory. Who gives a damn about prayers? But they aren't like my father, and they aren't like me."

Dory had to admit they weren't like Ben. They lacked his intensity, his sharpness. But they were very nice to her and the boys. They seemed anxious for them to join, pleased that a young mother was interested in converting. They were Midwesterners, that was the main thing, she thought.

It occurred to Dory that Ben might feel more comfortable in an orthodox *shul*, so one Friday night they visited one in the Greenbush section, where the first immigrants from Russia had lived fifty years before. Now most of the younger Jews had moved to the West Side, but there were still a few kosher meat markets and grocers among the decaying tenements. Black children swarmed over the streets, and the old Jews who dared the sidewalks kept to the edges, walking delicately and carrying their hats like eggs.

The *shul* was poorly maintained, and there was barely a *minyan*, but here Ben felt at home. He covered his head with an embroidered yarmulke before entering the sanctuary and was curiously reserved throughout the service, humming softly to the prayers and even davening once or twice. But they did not really belong here, either. No one in the congregation was under sixty. At last Dory admitted defeat; her experiment with Judaism had failed. Yet now Ben was telling her to prepare a Sabbath meal; to be a good Jewish wife for his father.

"I thought we agreed not to raise the children as Jews," she said.

"It's not raising them as Jews to have *shabbos* once."

She nodded. Then: "Is this why he's come? To reclaim the next generation? To rescue Michael and Charles from a Christian fate?"

"Don't be ridiculous. He was very careful about it, even offered to do it alone, in his room. Every Friday, all his life, he's had *shabbos*. Why should this one be any different?"

"You're sure that's all it is?"

"Look, Dory, we've been through all this before. I told you, I don't care if I ever go into a *shul* again in my life. But I don't see why we can't do this for Pop."

Dory softened. "You're right," she said. "It's just that I tried before. I don't want the boys to be confused, and I don't want them turned against me because I'm not Jewish."

"No one's against you. Pop's crazy about you, he told me. He said you were a good mother. To him, that's the highest praise. He's very impressed."

"He said that?" Dory was quiet for a moment. Then she said, "The only problem is, I haven't the slightest idea of what to do."

In the afternoon, Moshe took a nap. At six, he emerged from his room refreshed. He was wearing a long *tallis* with black bands, and a white yarmulke. Under the *tallis* he wore a coat and tie. His expression was peaceful, almost beatific.

Michael looked at him in awe. He was intrigued, but also afraid. He wished the old man would smile or wink. He stood to the side of the couch, hesitating before coming forward. He knew something had changed, but he wasn't sure what.

Moshe sat down and opened his small green prayer book. Then, humming softly to himself, he flipped through the pages, stopping now and then to read a passage before moving on. Charles joined Michael, and they stood together, studying their grandfather. "Come," he commanded. "Come to me, both of you."

Michael pushed Charles ahead of him. Charles climbed on Moshe's lap and started examining the *tallis*, but Michael stayed aloof. Sensing the boy's fear, Moshe said, "What you afraid of, boychik? This?" He indicated the *tallis*. "It's like a tent, to protect you if it rains."

"It's not raining, Grandpa," Charles said.

"It's always raining somewhere," Moshe said. "Anyway, it's a gift. Your grandmother gave it to me when we were married a long time ago, before you were born, before even your father was born, before you were even an idea."

"A long time ago," Charles said, and Moshe nodded. Michael laughed.

"Why did Grandma give it to you?" Charles said.

"She liked me better then."

"Doesn't she like you anymore?"

"She does and she doesn't. Sometimes when you get to know people very well, you don't like them the same. But that doesn't have anything to do with the *tallis*. Every time people get married, the woman gives the man a *tallis*. Just like when a boy is *bar-mitzvah*, his father gives him a *tallis*."

"Did Mommy give Daddy a tent?" Michael asked.

Moshe was stopped. "No, I don't think she did."

"Why not, didn't she like him?"

"She liked him fine; she still does."

"Then why didn't she give him a tent? Did she want him to get rained on?"

Moshe rocked in his chair, thinking what to say. "Now things are different," he began. "It doesn't always happen that a wife gives her husband a *tallis*. It doesn't mean anything, it's just different."

Michael took the braided fringes of the *tallis* in his hands and began tying knots with the ends. Then he said, "Can I wear the tent, Grandpa?"

Moshe looked at him critically. "But it isn't raining," he said. The boy laughed, comfortable again.

When Dory came to call them for dinner, she found Moshe reading his prayer book and Michael sitting on the couch with the enormous *tallis* draped around him, covering his entire body except for his thin legs, which extended beneath the borders of the prayer shawl. Charles was playing by himself in the corner. Moshe stood, smiled, and took the *tallis* from Michael. Then he wrapped himself in it, and with one hand on Michael's shoulder and the other around Dory's waist, they went in to dinner.

Dory had put two candles in front of her place as Ben had instructed her. Ben poured burgundy into wineglasses and sat down, leaving the head of the table for Moshe. Then everyone waited. For a moment Moshe sat looking thoughtfully at his napkin; then he turned to Ben. "You don't remember nothing, Benjy?"

"I'm sorry, Pop. You start, I think it'll come back."

Moshe nodded, resigned. Then he smiled apologetically at Dory. "Daughter, you'll please stand up and light the candles. But first I'll tell you what to say."

Dory took a match from the box at the side of her plate. "First I'll say, then you repeat, okay?" Moshe said. Dory nodded, and Moshe began: "*Boruch atoh adonai . . .*" He looked at her. "Now, light the candles and say what I just said."

69

Dory lit them carefully, her hand shaking slightly. She concentrated on the leaping flames. In a tremulous voice she repeated, "*Boruch atoh adonai.*"

"Not bad," Moshe said to Ben. "She's got an ear." Then: "*Elohainu melech ha'oholum . . .*"

Dory finished the prayer slowly, pleased with herself but aware of the vestiges of her Southern accent. "*Adonai*" sounded in her ear rather like "I don't know," and she repressed a smile. She enjoyed the candles' heat on her forehead; it seemed ecumenical. It was the first religious service of any kind she had attended in years, much less participated in. Now she knew she missed it. In the middle of the *broche*, she found herself thinking of midnight Mass in the Episcopal church in Lexington, when they lit candles and marched around the old stone building while the organ played.

Michael was entranced. His grandfather seemed to have gained in stature. The prayer shawl, the strange language he spoke, and the candles brought out a new quality in him. He seemed dignified, serene.

Ben sat back, pleased that things were going so well. Moshe started the long blessing, his eyes closed, his tongue running over the syllables, mumbling sometimes, in a trance of sound and memory. They were all together in the nimbus of candlelight, and without meaning to, Ben started singing along, humming when the words wouldn't come, following Moshe. Dory's fingers tightened around his under the table, and he heard her voice, higher than the others, uncertain of the words but attuned somehow to the sound, the spirit of his strange ancestral chant. When Ben looked at her to show his approval, though, he saw Dory's eyes were tightly closed.

9

MAY 20, 1957: When I was a little girl, nine or perhaps ten, I got a diary for my birthday. Blue leather with a gold lock and key. I remember thinking the book was sacrosanct, that I could entrust my most private thoughts to it. Then one day I came home and found the lock torn open, the leather stripped back, and my brother and two of his friends laughing over what I had written. What could it have been? The boy I was currently in love with, sometimes about my teacher or my parents? I remember being furious, feeling beytrayed, and I tore into the boys, hitting and tearing at them, until they ran away. Then I took the book and ripped out the pages one by one and burned them. I swore I would never keep a diary again.

So here I am, nearly thirty years and thousands of miles later, starting another. But this is different. This time I have no illusions. Instead of a locked diary, I am writing in a 39¢ notebook which anyone could read. I haven't the courage to say out loud the things I feel, so I will keep a journal instead. If Ben or someone else reads this, the burden will be on their shoulders, not mine. They cannot accuse me of hypocrisy, but only of discretion. In fact, I am writing to shield Ben and the boys from me, from the things I feel when I am fed up. I write out of despair, because I know there is no way to make sense out of our lives, and although Ben's disease proves every day there is no God, I want to appeal to him, anyhow, to help us, to make our lives, to make us, happy again. And since I would feel foolish saying this, even to myself, I write it down in the hope it will look less ridiculous on the page.

May 28, 1957: We took Moshe to the station today. It was a solemn occasion: Moshe wore a black coat and tie and Michael cried and tried to board the train with him. It surprises me, but I feel a real loss, though I've only just met the man. While he was here, Moshe provided an outlet for Ben, a way for him to express his feelings, to be a little boy again. It is a terrible strain for Ben to be husband and protector while being a victim. It was also good for the boys to have Moshe here, good for them to know that all their ancestors aren't dead. Before, I think they felt we had somehow been banished by our families, as if we weren't good enough to live in the East or South. I felt that way myself. But now Moshe has come and we are all right.

June 11, 1957: Even to write this makes me feel guilty, because I'm concealing things from Ben. Actually, the problem is the opposite: I don't want to keep anything from him; I want to share everything I know, feel, think, as we always have. But I am afraid, and now he shuts me out. When I come home from the studio he seldom asks about my day or work. Only why I'm late, if I'm late, or what I want for dinner, so he can put in the order with Marie. If I weren't so tired and discouraged, I would feel like the lady of the manor, with the luxury of sitting down for a drink while someone else makes dinner. But now it is only depressing. I don't want Marie in our house, in our life. I don't want anyone to see us now.

Today was Michael's birthday and he thought I had forgotten. Ben bought him a fielder's mitt, but it was for a right-handed boy. Michael didn't want to tell Ben what was wrong, but he was disappointed. "I paid fifteen bucks for that glove, and the kid cries," Ben said.

After dinner I took Michael back to the store and we exchanged the mitt for another. Then we went to the Chocolate House and a movie. When we got home, Michael hugged Ben and thanked him for the present and Ben felt better. This seems disloyal. Ben surely has more important things to remember than whether Michael is right- or left-handed. In the past I would have told him, but I don't now because I want to protect him, and the boys sense this and confide in me instead. The result is that Ben is frozen out because we try to shield him from hurt, pain, or embarrassment.

June 14, 1957: The heat is disastrous for Ben, but cold is almost as bad. We had an air conditioner for his room, but now his circulation is so poor that often he must spend a half-hour working on his hands before he can play. And he must play. That is the most important thing for him now. He must rest and exercise and practice and do what the disease will let him do as long as it will let him do anything.

Now, as I write, I can hear him breathing in bed. I am sitting on the toilet with the notebook on my knees, writing to rid myself of the sick feeling that comes at night when everyone else is asleep. His breathing is regular except for a slight wheeze that reminds me of the gate at home in Kentucky. Sometimes, if I concentrate, I can imagine I am back there and I am swinging on the gate in a starched yellow dress, waiting for my grandfather Bryan to come and take me for a ride in his car. Then I can sleep.

June 17, 1957: Tonight was the last meeting of my painting class. Sam took us all out for beer and then swimming at the Willows. I am older than most of the class, but they seem to accept me and I don't usually feel self-conscious. It is only Sam who makes me uncomfortable. He is thirty-nine— a year older than me—but he seems younger. I think he is interested in me but unsure how to go about it. He acts more self-assured with the younger girls. Of course, no one brought swimsuits to class, so most of the kids went in nude. I felt oddly Victorian swimming in my bra and panties, but even that seemed pretty daring. I swam faster than the others, pulling hard at the water as I used to back in high school, and then I was all alone, sitting on the deck of the raft, looking back into the inky water. But no one else came out, and I wondered if I had been deserted. I sat there by myself for quite a while, thinking of nothing, but enjoying the peace of the night and the sound of the ducks.

Finally Sam approached, dog-paddling and looking puny beneath me in the water, his arms and legs like antennae, small and insubstantial, foreshortened by the lake. I could see his penis clearly; he had an erection, but that looked small too, and not at all erotic. I was reminded of the times when I would give Michael a bath and he would become hard. At least Michael had the sense to smile when it felt good. Sam was very serious. Yet when Sam spoke, he was ironic: "Does your husband know you're seeing me?" he asked.

"Ben thinks you're his friend."

"I am, I was only joking."

"So was I."

He said nothing after that, and I felt bad for being sharp with him. I'm alone so much that I'm more impolite than I used to be. It is odd that in time you become accustomed to a lack of intimacy so you don't take the steps necessary to achieve it. It bothers me to think I don't need people as much anymore, don't want to call my girlfriends when I have a free afternoon, don't miss as much the long walks Ben and I used to take, or the rides in the country to look at the leaves. A part of me seems almost insensate; I am like one of those people who have an arm or leg amputated but continue to feel sensation in it, to believe it is still there.

"How is Ben?" Sam said at last.

"You know how he is. You see him, have lunch with him. You know."

"Well, how are you, then, Dory?"

It was a simple question, but for some reason I began to cry. I cried not only for Ben but for all of us. I cried because I was almost forty years old and sitting out in the middle of a lake at midnight with an attractive man and felt perfectly safe. I cried because I felt ridiculous; I cried because of the cesarean scar on my stomach and because of the blue veins that bruise whenever I brush too hard against my easel; I cried for what I was and what I had lost. Sam seemed to understand. He sat next to me and put his arm around me, and I saw that he had gone soft, but now I didn't care. There was nothing sexual about it; it was something else. I was sharing my grief with him, something I would have shared with Ben before but could no longer. We sat like that for what seemed like an hour; after a while I stopped crying, but he still held me and neither of us talked. Then we swam back to shore. The rest of the class was gone, and Sam dressed quickly. We walked to his car barefoot and didn't talk all the way back. At home, the house was dark. Sam leaned over and kissed me on the forehead, and I went upstairs to Ben. He lay on his back, his body hair and white skin forming a dim chiaroscuro on the bed. The sheet was pulled back, revealing his penis, and his right leg was perpendicular to the left, as though it had been arrested in mid-spasm. As I looked at him, it struck me that Sam was the first man I had seen naked since meeting Ben. I should have felt like a woman of the world, but it was all so chaste, so innocent. I felt warm, not lewd or even sexy. I moved to cover Ben as I would one of the boys. He groaned in his sleep and reached for me or where he thought I would be, his fingers long and thin. Finding nothing, the fingers tightened into a fist and came to rest against my pillow.

June 23, 1957: Summer school has started almost before the regular school year is over. I am taking eighteen credits and trying to put together enough of a portfolio to hang my show next year. In the morning I take art history; in the afternoon I try to see Ben and the boys; at night, when the studios are empty, I work. Already I see this is not good. I can sleep during my morning classes, but the trouble is, I feel inadequate in everything: I am neither a good enough artist nor a good enough wife and mother to justify taking time from both. I am not satisfied with being half-assed at the things I have to do, and sometimes I wonder why I try at all. Let the disease do what it will to Ben; I could simply shore up the home front and give him the love and support he needs. No one would blame me for not trying to get a teaching job. I am a young wife and mother and my primary responsibility

74

is to my family. Somehow, though, I feel obliged to exhaust myself in this effort.

Our families should take care of us, but we have no families. That is what makes me saddest. The boys have to suffer this without the benefit of loving aunts and grandparents to spoil them. They seem so small when I see them, and so pathetic. Ben has to blame me and I have to resent him, and still we have to love each other that much more because we are all we have. On nights when I am tired and it is late and I am alone, it seems too much to expect.

July 3, 1957: It is two o'clock in the afternoon and I am trying to straighten up before going to pick up Michael at the park. He is captain of his Little League baseball team and I drive them to and from games. One of the other teams is sponsored by Rennebohm's Drugstore. They get sodas when they win, so I offered Michael the same deal. Fortunately, they seldom win, but today they are playing a team with the smallest, slowest players in the league, and Michael says they will win. It costs five dollars to buy the ice cream, but it makes Michael happy, so I don't mind. I hear the humming of the air conditioner in the bedroom as I write, and I wonder about Ben. It is Ben's room; it doesn't really seem like ours anymore. We sleep there, but the room is slowly being taken over by Ben's paraphernalia. Everywhere there seem to be containers for his piss: floor, bureau tops, desk, chairs, everywhere. And all seem to be perpetually half-full. Occasionally he will empty a few of them into a large milk bottle, and I empty the milk bottle into the toilet, but we don't discuss it. We preserve the fiction that the bottles are only for convenience and nighttime, when it would be too much bother to go all the way to the bathroom. The fact is that Ben seldom leaves his room these days. The heat exhausts him and it is more comfortable to stay there. Sometimes I or the boys will join him and listen to the radio or play chess, but usually he is content to be alone. Sometimes he practices, but the air conditioner makes it hard for him to get warmed up. I think much of the time he just sits, though if I go and open the door he will have the fiddle on his shoulder and look angry at the interruption. Then, if I am not insulted, we will sit and talk and it will almost feel normal.

The nights when I am not working are best: the boys go to bed early and by nine it is cool enough for Ben to come out. Sometimes we walk to the corner to get ice cream, but usually we just stay around the house. We hold hands and talk softly, and the night hides our fear. Recently I have tried to get into the studio in the afternoon so we can have our nights together. We need all the good times we can get.

If I could know that things would get no worse than this, I think I could live with it. But it is the opposite; our only certainty is that things will

75

get much worse, but we don't know when. Not knowing when, we can pretend it won't ever happen, but this gets harder as the days go by. Sometimes I think I will burst with the strain of knowing. I feel then that we must talk, plan for the future. But I realize that our only chance is not to talk, to act as if nothing is wrong; to simply live our lives as best we can. Without talking, it's hard to remain intimate, but we try. We touch, and we hold hands, and sometimes when Ben is up to it, we make love. That is not enough, but it is something.

July 18, 1957: Because of Ben's bladder we have a small glass jar in the glove compartment of the car. When we are driving, he sometimes has to use it in a hurry. When he is finished, he throws it out the window. The boys laugh and it is good that to them it is still a joke. Today, as we drove home from the beach with Janie Bachman and her boy, Janie noticed something dripping from the glove compartment. Not content to ignore it, she put her finger to the leak and smelled. "It's urine," she said. "Sherlock Holmes," I said. "How could it be?" "It is," Janie insisted. "I know what urine smells like." I was going to ask whether she goes around smelling other people's glove compartments, but then I became aware of Michael's sudden silence. I looked in the rearview mirror and saw his face pinched with shame. It made me mad that we should have to explain ourselves to Janie. It was childish, I know, but I got mad and denied everything. There was no urine, I didn't care what she smelled. Janie was put off, but Michael was relieved. Let her think what she wants, but I don't want the kids to feel more self-conscious than they already do.

August 5, 1957: Sam is avoiding me. At first I thought I was being paranoid, that we were simply working different hours. But tonight he came in ready to work but then left abruptly when he saw me. No one else noticed, but it makes me feel like a schoolgirl. It's as if I should feel guilty about the night at the Willows. At the same time, I understand how he feels. Sam knows things are different between us now, and he's not sure he likes that. I have to talk about Ben, but I can't blame people who don't want to listen. It's a lot to dump on a guy who just wants to get laid. Is that fair to Sam? Is Sam fair to me? I don't think he really likes women, as friends, I mean. His new paintings are very violent, showing women in garter belts carrying submachine guns and bloody knives. That's how he sees us: castrating Dianas to be feared and avoided; fucked and left. But his women have left him instead. What right does he have to blame me? To hell with him. Why do I want him to come to the studio at night?

August 27, 1957: I surprise myself. I have made it through the summer and nothing awful has happened. Ben seems happy, or happier, with his music; the boys are fine; I got all A's in summer school. I start teaching in the fall. I will be doing two jobs—one course at the university and full-time at a junior high school—but I'm confident I can do it. Sam has gone to France on a Fulbright, and I'm glad he's gone. Ben has adjusted to his new routine and I have gotten used to the pee bottles. You can get used to anything, I find. Michael pitched a no-hitter and got his name in the paper, so Ben promptly got twenty-five copies and sent clippings to all his relatives in the East. God knows what they thought of that. Charles is content to be alone with his chess set. It is bad to be hopeful—it is so easy for things to go wrong—but now it seems possible that we will make it, that we can stay together and be happy. That doesn't seem unreasonable, unless to hope at all is unreasonable. I am tempted to say we've all done very well. We managed to go on, loving each other and our boys, accepting the changes in our life. For now. That is enough.

10

BEN HEARD something pop as Jack stretched his leg. "Jesus," he said, "take it easy."

"Got to get you in shape," Jack said, pressing down on Ben's right knee with his fist. "Got to handle pain."

"All I want to do is be able to walk out of here; I'm not in training for the Olympics."

"I'm going to have you running the two-twenty," Jack said, and shifted his attention to Ben's calves.

"Sadist," Ben said. But Jack just smiled.

Ben visited the hospital twice a week for physical therapy, and it had become an important part of his life. To Jack, he was simply a problem in rehabilitation, a network of muscles to be revived and maintained. Jack was not moved by the pathos of his situation, and that was fine with Ben. On the days when he had no physical therapy, he swam in the armory pool or worked out on a mat in his bedroom. At Jack's suggestion, he had dieted and lost fifteen pounds, down to a svelte 160. Despite his efforts, however, he knew he was becoming weaker. Yet his strength varied, depending on the weather. On a humid summer day he lacked the energy to leave his room. But if it was cool, he could walk a mile, come home, practice, and feel fine. The doctor said he could hold off the disease for another five years by moving to a drier climate, but Ben was skeptical. He would stay and fight it out here.

Jack sat back and looked at his client. "You keeping your weight down?"

"I'm practically starving to death," Ben said.

"How about your exercises at home?"

"Can't you tell? I'm a regular Adonis. I'll be the most beautiful corpse in the graveyard."

Jack nodded. "Good. It's going pretty good, so far. But we've got to keep working, keep the muscles limber. Once they're gone, they're gone."

Ben said nothing. He looked down at his legs, thin and hairy in white gym shorts. They had never mattered to him before; now they were the key to his ability to continue working.

"I was thinking maybe we should move to three a week," Jack said.

"My wife might get suspicious," Ben said.

"Let's take a chance," said Jack, and stood up. "See you Friday."

Ben took a leisurely shower and then left the hospital. It was more than a mile to the house, and he planned to stop to rest at Mickies. He would have lunch, read the papers, take a break from his exertions. But it was four blocks to the restaurant, and Ben felt it in his legs. Walking, too, had become part of his physical regimen, rather than simple recreation. He was more conscious now of technique, careful to lift his feet and avoid cracks and rocks. He walked with the upright posture of a man on stilts, swinging his arms to gather momentum, his carriage erect as a cadet's at West Point.

Ben had always had a place like Mickies. He tried to explain to Dory, but she didn't see why it was better to go out than to have coffee and Danish at home. For Ben it was not only better but also vital. He felt the need to get out in the world, to lift his head and look around, to make sure he wasn't missing something. Mickies satisfied him. It wasn't much, Ben would admit—a combination of grocery, restaurant, and newsstand—but it was as close to a deli as one could find in Madison.

He walked in, took a seat at the fountain, and looked around. Norm waved from the cigar counter, and Rose, the waitress, appeared from nowhere to take his order. "The usual, Mr. Seidler?" Ben nodded, and she brought him black coffee and an apricot Danish. Order descended on him.

As he ate, Ben looked around the room. The walls were painted light green and the counter and stools were cherry red. A large sign read: "Please, for your convenience and ours, PAY WHEN SERVED." Sitting next to Ben was a mechanic from the Lincoln-Mercury dealer next door. The man was dressed in coveralls and wore a grimy cap to protect his hair. Mickies welcomed all kinds: students, teachers, coaches from the stadium across the street, and small businessmen. In an alcove was a magazine rack where three adolescent boys furtively inspected girlie magazines. A sign read: "Adults Only."

Now Norm joined Ben. "Hot enough for you?"

"It's always hot enough for me. How are things?"

"Can't complain." Rose brought coffee for Norm, but he would never sit down. He kept one foot pointing toward the cash register, always on the lookout for customers. "Who you like in the Series?"

"The Yankees, of course. I'm a New Yorker."

Norm smiled thinly. "Give you odds. Braves in six."

"I wouldn't take your money, Norm."

"Think it over," Norm said, and walked back to his post.

Ben felt renewed by the conversation, as he always did when he saw Norm. He was over sixty, yet his hair remained jet black and he stood erect despite killing hours at the store. When they talked, it was about baseball or the fights or the weather. Small talk, not really important, Ben knew, but somehow necessary. It was what he had liked about touring, the only thing he liked about orchestras. And it was what he missed with the others in the quartet. They knew each other too well to have superficial relationships. Everything became too intense between them, and so they avoided each other entirely. He was convinced that Norm, who never inquired about his health, cared more about him than his colleagues did, and they asked every day, or so it seemed. The problem was that Ben knew little more than they did about the course of the disease. He had authorized Bowen to keep Ober informed, yet there was little to report except the obvious: Ben was weaker than before. But he could still keep up with the others and he felt he was playing better than ever. He felt a growing coldness in Heinz, but he didn't mention it to Ober. Perhaps it was only his imagination. Why make something out of nothing?

Ben drained his coffee, left a quarter for Rose, and walked home. The front porch was cluttered with sports paraphernalia. There were baseball bats and gloves; a football, helmet, and shoulder pads; a basketball; and three pairs of ice skates on the floor. Ben picked up a hockey stick on which was printed: "Mike Seidler."

Mike. Ben had never called him that, nor had Dory. But he was glad his son insisted on the diminutive among his friends. Ben thought names were important. He traced his own social awkwardness to his childhood, when the other kids made fun of his name. "Benjamin" was bad enough, but that hadn't been his real name. Moshe had called him Baruch, after his grandfather.

Ben walked through the house, calling out for Dory and the boys, but no one was at home. In the kitchen he found a note:

80

Ben,
    I took the boys to the zoo. Ober called and wants you to contact him. Back by five.

Dory

Ben tried Ober first at home and then at his office, but with no luck. It was unusual for Heinz to call; he disliked Dory and avoided talking to her if possible. Before Ben had married, he and Heinz played chess and had lunch together every week. But now they seldom got together socially. Since Ben's fall, Heinz had seemed even more remote. Although he had been the one who insisted on Ben seeing a doctor, Heinz had shown only the most casual interest in the matter afterward. Ben had no intention of resigning from the quartet. There was nothing wrong with his arms; if it came to that, he could play in a wheelchair. Occasionally he thought of Mrs. Barrow, whom he had visited that day at the hospital, but who could tell if the disease would affect him the same way? Anyway, there was no point in worrying about that now.

Still, as a hedge, Ben had started taking courses toward his degree at the university. He had transferred credits from George Washington and lacked a year's work. René Meyer, a French composer, was in residence and had suggested that Ben study composition with him. Already Ben had written two concertos. Meyer loved his work, and Ben saw a new career opening before him. Another concerto, two quartets, and a duo followed, but in time Ben began to question his mentor. Finally he wrote a sonata so difficult he couldn't play it himself and left the piece in Meyer's mailbox. Three days later he found a note from the composer. "Ben, this is superb, your best so far. May I take it with me when I go to New York?"

Ben confronted Meyer in his office. "As far as I'm concerned, this sonata is unplayable," he said. "Anyway, I can't play it. What's so damned superb about it?"

The Frenchman was delighted. He laughed and said, "How American of you, Ben. This I like very much in you, very, very much. Yes, of course it is unplayable. What of it? It is a brilliantly imaginative work all the same. You are thinking only of what man can do now, with our technical limitations. But an artist of your vision should not limit himself. In ten years or twenty, with the development of computers, there will be nothing that is unplayable. And even if there is, is that a reason to accept defeat? Let your mind run free, and don't worry about practicality. That should be the farthest thing from your mind."

None of this entirely assuaged the anxiety Ben felt, but it helped. If he was forced to give up performing, he could continue to teach. He could

81

churn out unplayable sonatas forever, or write criticism. And lately he had been studying the stock market. He had little extra cash, but he was interested in a book he had seen called *How I Made a Million—In My Spare Time*. If the disease got worse, Ben would have plenty of spare time.

Dory did not share Ben's optimism, and she was annoyed by his money-making schemes. When he mentioned the stock market, she flared up. "Ben, be realistic," she said. "We've got nothing in the bank, and a mortgage. We have trouble making ends meet now, and if you can't work, I don't know what we'll do."

"You're in graduate school. You'll find a job. And I plan to work. I'll find something."

"Fine, but not in the stock market, please."

"I think I'll ask my father to lend me a few thousand dollars," Ben said. "He's always been willing to give me money."

"For the stock market?"

Ben shrugged. "It's none of his business what it's for."

Dory smiled. "Oh, Ben, what are we going to do? Neither of us is any good at making plans."

"Just wait and see," Ben said. "Just wait and see."

Dory sat on a park bench, the remains of a picnic lunch spread out on the grass in front of her. The boys had grown tired of the zoo and were throwing a football back and forth in the park. The afternoon was unusually warm for October, and Dory had taken off her sweater. If she closed her eyes it was possible to pretend that it was summer and that she had nothing more to worry about than her family. As it was, the time she could spend with her sons had become vital. She wanted both to prepare the boys for what was coming and to succor them. She didn't really know how much they knew; at the same time, she shrank from telling them.

Now Michael came back to the bench by himself. Charles remained in the field, kicking the ball and then running after it, apparently content with his game. "Don't you want to play anymore?" Dory said.

Michael lay at her feet in the sun. "Charlie's no good," he said.

"He's just younger than you are. You should give him a chance," Dory said.

"Mom," Michael said. "Charlie was telling some other kids about Dad, you know, that he's sick."

Dory nodded. It didn't surprise her. Charles was precocious, beating old men at the chess club regularly and impressing his teachers. He had probably overheard them talking one night and made his own conclusions.

Yet the news of Ben's illness did not seem to bother Charles as it did Michael. The boy was more stolid. He was big for his age and had long black hair which was straight and thick and lay on his neck like a scarf. Since he was a baby Dory had been aware of Charles's independence, his inner strength.

"About Dad. I didn't know he was sick, I mean, really sick," Michael continued.

"Didn't you see him fall down?"

"Sure, but lots of people fall down. Charles said Dad might die someday."

"Everything dies, Michael, you know that."

"I know, but I mean not that long from now."

Michael was looking intently at Dory. "I don't know what Charles meant by that, Michael. No one knows when Daddy is going to die, or *if* he's going to. He is sick, but he still goes to work and walks to the university every day."

"You mean he's not really sick," Michael said, victory in his voice.

"No, I don't mean that," Dory said. "We're just going to have to wait and see how sick he is."

"Well, when will we know?" Michael said.

Dory understood the question: When can we stop worrying about this? She resented the intrusion of the disease into her marriage, her family. It was hard to explain to an eight-year-old boy that no one could put a limit on frustration, on illness. That no one could chart his life with any certainty.

"When I was younger I used to worry about dying, too," she said. "But the longer I live, the more I see it takes a long time to live your life, that there is really as much time as you need. Your daddy is sick—he has a disease that will make him weaker as it goes on, and after a while he'll have to be in a wheelchair. But he won't stop being your father and he won't stop loving you. You'll still be able to see him and talk to him and spend time with him. In fact, he'll want to spend a lot more time with you. I don't think he's going to die for a long, long time, and I don't want you to worry about it anymore. You're much too young to be thinking about death, Michael."

Michael got up and sat on the bench. He put his head on Dory's shoulder and held her hand. "I don't want you ever to die, Mom," he said.

Dory looked out at the field where her other son played. He ran and kicked and laughed at himself and his game. "I don't want anyone to die, Michael," Dory said.

11

THE SUN SHONE through the streaked and dirty windows of the practice room, warming and mesmerizing Ben. He had spent a recent afternoon listening to a lecture on the deleterious effects of sun spots on the earth's climate, but the speckled glare seemed benign, even beneficial. He stretched his hands, feeling the stiffness recede. Ober's voice broke through his reverie: "Finger exercises, Ben?"

"Sorry. My mind wandered. Where were we?"

"Of course, it is quite all right," Heinz said. "We were beginning over the Schubert. On second thought, however, perhaps the Schubert is not so bad."

"When you decide what you want to do, let us know," Richler said. "First Ben's daydreaming, now you're off someplace else."

"Very good, Ernst. You are absolutely right," Ober said. "I apologize. Next, we will do the Berg."

Richler grunted and picked up his cello, but his mood did not lighten. Yet he was only the most vocal of the quartet; the others felt the same way. They were all tired of practicing, anxious for the tour to begin, but Ober would not let up in his demands for more rehearsals. The quartet's contract with the university required them to perform an eighteen-week season in Wisconsin, but there was time left for a short national tour during intersession.

Generally they started in Boston, then played New York, Philadelphia,

Washington, Cleveland, and finished in Chicago. Since this was their only opportunity to reach a national audience and maintain their reputation, it was the most important part of the year for Ober. Their concerts were reviewed by critics for the major newspapers, occasionally they recorded in New York, and they renewed friendships with people who assumed Wisconsin was part of the Northwest Territories. For the most part Ober's strategy was successful: under his leadership the Casa Bella had become one of the most acclaimed American string quartets. Yet even this did not satisfy Ober. Now he wanted to tour Europe and the Far East.

They went through the Berg in a desultory manner. During the break, Ober approached Richler as he sat smoking a cigar, his feet stretched out on a coffee table. "Ernst," Ober began, "I have been thinking of all the cellists I have known. I can think of no one who is your equal."

Richler was suspicious. He associated praise with lying. "Of course," he said. "Does that surprise you?"

"Surprise? Nonsense. It is foolish to talk about ranking artists, but everyone knows you are among the finest cellists in the world."

Richler waited. Sooner or later Ober would get to the point.

"I was only thinking of a man I once knew in Basel," Heinz said.

Richler drew heavily on his cigar and then blew smoke at the ceiling. "Go on," he said.

"Oh, it is nothing. I did not mean to disturb you. The fact is, he was a terrible cellist. I am really ashamed to mention him in your presence. But there was one area in which he was a master. Pizzicato. It seems that when he was a small boy he found an old cello without a bow. All he could do was pluck the strings, you see, and that is why he was so bad. Even after he received formal instruction and had an adequate instrument, pizzicato remained his obsession. He was absolutely devoted to it, and no one could persuade him to practice other aspects of his instrument, so of course he was severely limited as a musician. It was a small tragedy, if one was inclined to see it.

"But his pizzicato. Ah, that was wonderful to hear. When he plucked the strings, it sounded like a great bell. I'll never forget it; I can hear it still. The resonance was fantastic. It was hard to believe such a sound could come from a stringed instrument. And his speed! It was incredible, but he could pluck a string faster than most people can finger." Ober sighed. "But one can't expect such skill from even the greatest artist. He was a freak, like a juggler or a sword swallower. Pizzicato is a trick, and art does not consist of tricks." Now Ober lit a cigar. "You understand, Ernst, that I would not dream of criticizing your pizzicato."

The next day Richler appeared at rehearsal with adhesive tape on his right index finger. Grimly he removed the bandage, revealing raw, blistered skin.

"Ernst, what happened?" Ober said. "You must be more careful with your hands."

"You know what happened, you bastard, you know damned well what happened." Richler began the Berg with the pizzicato.

Ben was astonished by the change. The heavy notes vibrated with a sharpness and force that set the other instruments humming. Richler played with an intensity Ben had never seen in him before, his eyes boring into the score, his jaw set, denying the pain.

At the break, Ben took Ober aside. "If that's how pizzicato can sound, I'd like to hear your friend from Basel," he said.

"Basel?" Ober said. Then: "Oh, yes, Basel." He smiled to himself. "Of course. Basel."

Though Richler and Beaulieu had resisted Ober at first, his imprint was now unmistakable. They complained among themselves, but Ober's habits had become theirs, his ideas the ideas they imagined they had had all their lives. Ben had expected Heinz to be demanding, but he had not known how demanding the older man would be. Ober's first assumption was that he had an indisputable lien on all his musicians' time. There were rehearsals morning and afternoon, on weekends and holidays, even sometimes after a concert if Ober decided it was necessary. He disdained the American tendency to take vacations and holidays. "This is a country of amateurs, passionate about their hobbies," he said. "Work is my hobby, art is my hobby; now it must also be yours. Art cannot be a half-time proposition, suspended because of Columbus Day or the Fourth of July."

So they practiced endlessly, seamlessly, practiced pieces they had no plans to play or had only played years before, practiced when they had no upcoming concerts and the tour was six months off. They practiced, Ober said, so that when it came time to go onstage it would seem utterly natural, a part of them, and not some special occasion. "Art is either easy or impossible," Ober said. And after weeks and months of practice, Ben found it was true: the most difficult piece yielded to him with ease, and then he was profoundly grateful to Ober.

Yet while Ober's dominance was unquestioned, Casa Bella, the beautiful house, was plagued by dissension. Ober had more difficulty with the others than with Ben, both because they were older and because they were European. Richler and Beaulieu had concertized with the quartet for years before Ober came along, and they resented him still. Since they abhorred each other, however, they could not overrule him. Ober needed Ben's support to tip the balance.

Their quarreling was often unrelated to music. Antoine had a favorite hotel in Cincinnati, and Ernst, out of principle, refused to stay there. Ernst, who was afraid to fly, would want to take the train, but Antoine would object because of the resultant delays. If they needed an accompanist, one or the other would complain about the pianist and piano chosen. Whatever practice room Ober arranged for would be faulty in some way.

Ober came from wealthy Jewish stock and looked down on Richler, whose Viennese family had been lower-middle-class; Richler, who was six feet tall and a socialist, disdained Ober as a bourgeois dandy; Beaulieu was an anti-Semite cursed with three Jewish colleagues; Richler complained that Beaulieu's cologne could not subdue his body odor, that the real stench was spiritual; all three Europeans were contemptuous of Ben, the lone American among them, who took the blame for the many shortcomings of his native land.

Yet in time, grudging alliances had formed. Richler told Ben Yiddish stories; Ober cultivated Beaulieu, in part because he knew it infuriated Richler; and all of them had lunch together once a month. They grew closer without meaning to, because their shared displacement in Madison made them co-conspirators; it was as if they alone possessed the secrets of a long-dead civilization and could keep it alive only through their continued association. No one else, they knew, understood them or their music. All shared a contempt for their colleagues in the School of Music, which was exceeded only by their despair with the Wisconsin audiences.

Even when Ben had been healthy, he hated the tour. They always got in late at night and left early in the morning. The rooms were either overheated or not warm enough. The food was mediocre if they were lucky, abominable otherwise. Occasionally they were in town long enough to catch up on sleep and get their laundry done, but usually they arrived one day and left the next. By the time he got home, Ben was usually five pounds heavier and on the verge of pneumonia.

Still, there were preparations he could make. He saw himself as a general in charge of a beleaguered army and drove his body relentlessly. Continuing the exercise program he had begun at the hospital, he also rode an Exercycle and took daily walks. He napped each afternoon and ate vitamins and wheat germ. Dory added lecithin to his morning cereal. Ben was like an athlete in training, except that for him the conditioning was not seasonal. What the disease took away it would never relinquish; Ben could not afford to let up.

When the tour began in December, Ben weighed 155 and felt stronger than ever. If he allowed himself the illusion, it was nearly possible to believe the remission was total.

On tour, he kept to his routine, trying to sleep on planes and trains, having his meals brought to his rooms, not exhausting himself unnecessarily. If there was a nearby pool, he swam; if not, he did his exercises in his hotel room. He read science fiction, listened to records, and wrote letters home to Dory. At night he slept untroubled. He had done what he could.

On the whole, things went well. The quartet played creditably, the reviews were good, and no one remarked on Ben's illness. Boston, New York, Cleveland, all passed as if in a dream. He remembered little of the concerts, less of the cities themselves. Then they were on their way to Chicago, and only one concert remained. On the train, Ober dropped from nowhere to sit beside Ben as they passed Gary. Factories bleached then blackened the sky with smoke, but Heinz, wearing a turtleneck sweater and tweed jacket, seemed cheerful.

"So, Benjy, everything is all right, yes?"

"Fine, never felt better."

Heinz looked puzzled. "I see," he said.

"Just a figure of speech, Heinz. Don't take it literally."

"Ah, yes, the American idiom is so rich, sometimes it escapes me. A pity. But the reason I stopped was that I have been struck by your playing lately. It is really much better now than before. There was something, I don't know, thin, in your tone when you joined us. Year by year it has become richer, and now I think you have matured completely as an artist. It is really quite dramatic."

Ben was touched. "I hadn't noticed anything," he said. "It seems the same to me."

"Of course, but it isn't. It is never the same. Just as life is constantly changing, so is music. Perhaps better, maybe worse, but never the same." Heinz rose, patted Ben on the shoulder, and made his way toward the back of the car.

Ben looked out the window, thinking of what Heinz had said. He resisted compliments, even from his peers. But this was different. Heinz had sought him out privately. He wanted nothing, there was nothing Ben could give him. The tour was nearly over. For a moment Ben allowed himself to feel pleased; then the city rose suddenly around him, closing off the sky, blotting out the corn husks that stuck out of the snowdrifts, and making optimism difficult. As they pulled into the station, the brakes squealed, metal on metal, and people clogged the aisle looking for their baggage. The euphoria of five minutes before was a distant memory.

The orchestra sat tuning and improvising, enjoying their anarchy and extending as long as possible the time they had alone onstage. The cadenzas of the flutes, the snorting contrabassoon, the shrill piccolos sounded like animal calls within a strange articulate jungle. As Ben stood offstage listening, the sound reached out encircling him and overwhelming his thoughts. The sounds of the instruments took him out of himself; as they had done for twenty years. Listening to the musicians tuning up, he felt immortal.

The concertmaster, a fat red-faced man, strode onstage and bowed deeply. He was white-haired and proud of his position. Ben had seen dozens of men like him. He had begun perhaps at Juilliard thinking himself destined for a career as a soloist. Then he had met a fourteen-year-old boy who made him sound like an accompanist at a square dance. A freak, the man thought, until he met another boy better than the first, and still another who made them all look like amateurs. Discouraged, the man had joined a minor orchestra, Cincinnati perhaps, or San Francisco. He had married, and because he was a talented, if limited, musician, he had moved up. To Minneapolis or Pittsburgh, or even Boston. Now at the height of his career, he was concertmaster of an excellent orchestra in Chicago. Any member of the audience would revere and call him maestro. At times the concertmaster would congratulate himself on a long and distinguished career, but deep down he considered himself a failure. Ben could see it in the man's enjoyment of his lonely bow, his tyranny over the other musicians. Because Ben knew, the man would hate Ben, as he would also resent Ober and Richler and Beaulieu.

Now Ben studied Ober in profile. He seemed absolutely self-possessed, calm, breathing easily. As usual, he was elegantly barbered, not a hair out of place. His fiddle rested in the crook of his arm, loose but secure. But on his throat Ober bore the brand of the serious violinist: the little red mark which comes from constant contact of the neck with the fiddle. It takes years to acquire, but when the mark appears, it remains, a permanent disfigurement, like numbers on the wrist.

The mark comforted Ben. It made Ober seem vulnerable. He fingered his own throat, where he knew there was an octagonal blotch of red. Heinz wore a variety of scarves and neckties to disguise the mark, and had lately taken to turtleneck sweaters. In concert, he draped a heavy white handkerchief over his violin to protect his neck, but the damage had been done. Now Ben saw the deep maroon smear ringing Ober's tight white collar and spreading upward to the base of his jaw. Tonight it seemed particularly intense.

89

A slight rumble of protest rose from the audience. For the last time, Ben reviewed the program. First Weber, then Schumann, Respighi, Wagner, and an unknown American composer, Richards. The Brahms Double was last. Ben wondered why Ober had included Richards. A local boy perhaps? If so, Heinz would have mentioned it and the composer would have been invited to take a bow or maybe even conduct. Still, Ben was grateful for the generally uninspired selection. Except for the Brahms, the pieces were not particularly challenging, and that was fine with him.

At last the orchestra was silent. Ober waited for the audience to settle; then he led the others onstage. He nodded to the conductor, shook hands with the concertmaster, and waved to the orchestra. The quartet took their places, and Ober gave the signal to begin.

When Ober played, his strong, lined face was young. His eyes were shut tight, his expression was earnest, but his whole aspect radiated contentment. He would lean first toward one, then another of the quartet as their melody merged with his, so that it seemed almost as if they were lovers and that the quartet itself was a single instrument of various inflections rather than four distinct voices. At first Ben had resisted this, but the older man was persuasive, seductive, and before long he had been pulled along, like a minor planet in some huge galaxy. In fact, Ober's long hours of practice were intended specifically to weed out any idiosyncratic tendencies his musicians might have had. Interpretation was between Ober and the composer, and the composer was usually safely dead.

Ben was able at times to experience the concert as both artist and spectator. He was aware of the excellence of the orchestra, of Ober's brilliance, even of his own competence. Yet this ability to distance himself from what he was doing bothered him. He felt he should be completely involved in the performance, and he leaned toward Heinz now, trying to absorb some of the older man's intensity.

Ten o'clock. They had finished the first half of the concert and waited in the wings for the short intermission to end. Heinz smoked a cigarette and accepted congratulations from the concertmaster. For him, the tour was over, and the thought made Ben feel stronger. Only the Brahms remained. Then he could let down his guard, forget his exercises for a while, and go home to Dory. As if in recognition of this, he felt a loosening of his chest and stomach, as if a weight had been lifted from him. He was able to breathe again.

The orchestra was ready. Ober looked at Ben and smiled. Ben nodded, confident now. Then he followed Ernst onstage. They stood and bowed to the audience. Then they took their seats. The conductor signaled the oboe.

Ben tuned his fiddle with a series of deft tappings. Ernst plucked his strings. They were ready.

The conductor glared to the left, then to the right. Then he became a scarecrow, arms lifted high for a long moment, before he brought them down with all his strength. The sound was startling, physical in its authority, and the conductor seemed to stagger. He continued beating his baton at the orchestra, but it overpowered him easily. Then an impossibly large voice silenced the orchestra. The deepest bass of Richler's cello began the warning notes of the long cadenza. Ernst was large in every sense, and when he played, he grunted his exertion. On some recordings, one could hear his voice under the music. When the recording engineer had complained, Ernst said, "I breathe loudly when I play. It means something to me. Those who love music will listen to my playing, not my breathing."

"But, Mr. Richler, these sounds are not in the music."

"They are indeed in the music. All kinds of awful things are in the music. Wailing, gnashing of teeth, tearing of hair, things you can't even imagine, are in the music. Music can be ugly and vulgar, because music is life. I can show you a quartet by Haydn that is supposed to sound like farting."

Ernst had, of course, prevailed. Yet now the grunting seemed subordinate to the demands of the Brahms. He played, his eyes shut, his head leaning against the giant scroll of the cello, whose black pegs were buried like nails in his gray hair. Ernst struggled with each note, wringing from it everything the instrument would yield, his face alternately pained and sneering, until at last he finished the cadenza and leaned back in his chair, exhausted.

The orchestra was silent except for the woodwind choir. Richler listened without seeming to hear, staring straight ahead while Ben made his entrance. As if imitating his deepest fears, the first notes were tentative, unsure of their validity. Then, passionately, Ben displaced the melody with a sudden burst of exuberance, seeming to assert himself at last, to deny what others saw, or thought they saw, in him. He surprised Richler with his sudden self-assurance. The shrill power of the fiddle dominated the auditorium; the notes, meticulously clean, shot into the air whole and perfect, only to be replaced immediately by others still more brilliant. The torpor of the first part of the concert was gone; now that Ober had left the stage, Ben's mind was clear and focused on the music.

Ernst was attentive, watching Ben with respect as he waited his turn. Then round and round they went, pursuing one another through the music in ever smaller concentric circles while still avoiding the inevitable collision. Sparks flew between the two partners and antagonists as the fiddle fought the larger cello for dominance. They sat inches apart, oblivious of the orchestra, the audience, even each other as distinct from their instruments and the music. Ben felt as if he was inside it, controlling the flow as he was carried along by it. He was riding a wave of enormous dimensions, yet instead of crashing down, the sound kept building, enlarging itself, as if it were impossible to contain.

Then they were in the hush of the andante. The orchestra could hardly be heard, yet they sustained and supported the soloists, who supplanted then yielded for each other. The struggle of the cadenza was forgotten: the effortless melody of the slow movement seemed to render it irrelevant. Even the flying dance of the last movement seemed to move with the steady pulse of prayer. Ernst and Ben approached the end of the concerto, hurrying headlong toward the climax. The somnolent audience, pricked by their excitement, leaned forward together, anticipating the conclusion.

Incredibly, however, the violin faltered and was silent. The intricate passagework and interplay, robbed of the guiding melody, left Richler alone, his face red and contorted, his eyes furious. The bald accompaniment seesawed back and forth, idiotic without the anchor. When Ben resumed his part, it was with a subtle change of inflection, suggesting that the silence, after all, had been intentional and was part of the concerto.

In those moments, Ben had missed only a handful of notes. Five perhaps, ten at the outside. He had hardly realized what was happening, and his recovery was instinctive. But neither the grace with which he covered his mistake nor the concentration he maintained for the rest of the piece could hide his lapse. Of the audience that night, perhaps a dozen people knew what had happened—another violinist or musicologist familiar with the Brahms; perhaps the assistant conductor or an aficionado following with the score; Ober and Beaulieu; and of course, Ernst.

The musicians gave no sign they had noticed. Why should they? They had only partial scores. The conductor was absorbed in making delicate pincerlike movements with thumb and forefinger. He bowed gracefully from side to side, humming a private tune. If Ben had been able to see, he would have noticed the concertmaster smiling to himself.

Richler was furious. His face was blotched with anger and his eyes cut through the space between them, dark and menacing in their concentration. The camaraderie, the brotherhood, was gone now, and the music took into its natural charm an implacable, ugly rhythm, relentless and unforgiving. Ben, conscious of his mistake, refused to give in to it. He fought harder than before to focus his energy on the music and command the audience. He played as though it was his last chance.

The ovation was immediate and interminable. Now they were standing, the women daintily placing their purses on their seats, the men jamming programs into their armpits and beating hell out of their hands. Ben wanted to get away from the hall, out of Chicago; he wanted to go home. Yet he also wished the applause would go on forever, for he knew Ober was waiting and he wanted to put off the confrontation. The night he fell was embarrassing, but this was worse. Then he had played perfectly; only his legs had disobeyed Ober's commands.

Ernst towered over Ben, their elbows almost touching. Yet they might as well have been across the room from each other. A woman in the front row caught Ben's eye. She was tall, blond, and slightly drunk. Everything about her seemed overdone: her nose and lips were large and fleshy; red lipstick blotted out her mouth. Most striking was the stupid grin on her face as she shook her head back and forth and clapped. Ben wondered what she saw in them, in the music.

But if he had learned nothing else in twenty years, he knew she cared, they all did; it was no act.

At last the ovation began to subside, and Ernst made his getaway. Ben followed, moving slower, prolonging the journey to the artists' room. He was in no hurry to face Ernst and Ober and Beaulieu. Let them wait; maybe they'd get tired and leave him alone. The stage crew was cleaning up, and Ben stopped to watch. He preferred them to the other people he would have to see tonight. They reminded him of his father and the men he remembered from his childhood in Washington. How nice to have nothing more to worry about than sweeping a stage and taking care of props. He walked down the long corridor, which was now strangely empty.

The door of the artists' room was ajar. Richler sat facing away, polishing his cello with swift, savage punches; Ober and Beaulieu weren't there yet. Ben approached Richler's chair. "Ernst, I'm sorry. I'm a putz."

"You said it, boy. You fucked up good."

Richler's saying it made Ben mad. "I said I'm sorry. Is it that big a deal?"

"Go fuck yourself." Richler spoke in an undertone of disgust, as if he wasn't even talking to Ben but only thinking aloud. He polished the cello with large circular strokes, rubbing the red polish into the wood, his eyes never leaving the instrument. Ben sighed and walked away.

He didn't know what to say; maybe there was nothing he could say. But he wasn't really worried about Ernst. He would get over it in time. The thing to do was give him room. Ben pulled out the strings on his violin. He changed them every week, and though it wasn't yet time, it gave him something to do. He disengaged the G string and began dissolving the pattern of old rosin which lay spread on the fingerboard like a sneer. He didn't blame Ernst; probably he would have felt the same way. They were like mountain climbers dependent on the same rope. What bothered him was that he was closest to Ernst; he didn't want to lose his only friend in the quartet. He looked, but Richler was still turned away from him. To hell with it, Ben thought. Let him cool off; they'd talk later.

Ober came in, calm, unperturbed, even smiling slightly. He sat down carefully, his legs crossed neatly over a handkerchief. Ben wished he would scream at him and get it over with, but of course silence was much more effective. In time it would come out through ironic remarks at rehearsal about his training or his American upbringing or in some comment about all the books he hadn't read. His mistake tonight was a reflection of the poverty of American culture; he could see it all.

For the first time, Ben considered his lapse. He had missed notes before, everyone did, but this was different. His mind had gone blank, as if someone had wiped it clean, a damp cloth swabbing down his psychic blackboard, and without a score to refer to, there was nothing he could do about it. He thought of his first instructor, a Hebrew teacher, who used to cut his toenails while Ben practiced scales. What was it he used to say? To learn fast, practice slow. The melamed and Ober would have been suited to each other. But it was true, and Ben had always practiced slowly, learning every piece note by note, bar by bar, phrase by phrase, until he knew it perfectly and forever. Forever, that is, until now. What happened when a thread was pulled from the fabric? Did the whole thing come apart, or could it be repaired?

Suddenly he was surrounded by concertgoers. They circled warily around him, their voices full of smoke and praise, the ladies' perfume mixing pleasantly with the acrid smell of the alcohol he used to treat his fiddle.

"Wonderful, Mr. Seidler, marvelous."

"And you did it all without music, from memory."

"Do you always play without music, Mr. Seidler?"

"Brilliant, superb."

The voices filtered down to Ben as though he were at the bottom of a tank, but the effect was not unpleasant. It was only that he could not bring himself to look at them. A man with a red nose was trying to get his attention. The man held a fiddle under his arm, like a kid taking his mitt to the ball game in hopes of catching a home run.

"I play myself," the man was saying. For a moment Ben thought the guy was going to audition right there. But he just smiled and said, "Not as good as you, of course, I'm not a professional. But I enjoy it. I'm retired, you see."

Ben felt a wave of sympathy. What a nice man. They had something in common; why shouldn't he bring his fiddle backstage? "That's very nice," he said. "I'm glad, and thanks for coming by."

Then the man was gone, and Ben was looking down a row of tits. They were uniform, enormous, like racks of beef. Could they all have belonged to one woman? But there wasn't a nipple in the bunch, nothing sensual about them at all. He wondered if he was hallucinating.

"How long does it take, Mr. Seidler, to learn . . ." Take, mistake, take, mistake, the words beat a singsong tattoo on his brain. There was nowhere to turn. They were everywhere with their goddamned questions. Matrons, golden-agers out of the nursing home for the night, teens in the high-school orchestra, bored fathers or husbands, all assaulted him with attention. Yet he knew it was their right. They paid good money to belong to some club and come backstage and meet the artists. It was part of the job. Okay, but not tonight. He stood suddenly, pushing several of them roughly aside. Then Andreson, the conductor, was in front of him, pumping his hand and embracing him.

"Marvelous, Benjy, wonderful. Never better, my boy." Was it possible the conductor hadn't noticed? Maybe it hadn't really happened. Ernst was only in his usual rotten mood. The five notes had been played. How could he help but play them? He was no artist, he was a machine, finely tuned but still a machine. But now his stomach told him there was no mistake; it was only that no one else had noticed. He felt weak, dizzy from the smoke, the talk, the press of the crowd. He made an excuse to Andreson, grabbed his fiddle, and started working his way through his admirers, who yielded grudgingly but let him by. He pushed open the stage door and was in an alley. Not knowing where to go, he stopped to orient himself. Then he heard the door open again behind him and turned to see Ober walking toward him.

"Where the hell are we?" Ben said. "I'm lost."

"Come, I'll show you. We can walk back together."

"Don't you have to go to the reception?"

"I don't think Maestro Andreson will object if we let him entertain the public tonight."

They followed the alley to the street and then walked toward the lake and the Hilton. The air revived Ben; the dizzy feeling was gone. He felt like walking all night. But he knew Ober wanted to talk about the concert.

"I think I have never heard the Brahms done as well as you and Ernst played it tonight," Ober said. "If only . . ."

"I'm sorry. I told Ernst I'm sorry. I don't know what happened. It was like watching a movie, and suddenly you look up and the screen's blank but the soundtrack goes on."

"You mean you kept on hearing the music?"

"Not really, but I felt it, I felt how it should be, but my fingers wouldn't go along."

"You were weak?"

This annoyed Ben. "No, it wasn't that, I was fine, but my mind was a blank. I don't know how to explain it better than that. Didn't that ever happen to you?" He knew it hadn't. Ober never missed anything.

"Not exactly," Heinz said. "I was wondering whether perhaps the cumulative effect of the tour might simply have worn you down. It is human, after all, for exhaustion to take its toll. You wouldn't be the first."

Ben was noncommittal.

"Ben, I would be the last to suggest you are incapable of doing whatever you want, but you must admit it is possible that what happened tonight was a manifestation of your illness."

"The disease is in my legs, Heinz, not my hands. My reflexes are terrific. Ask my doctor—rather, your doctor. I just made a mistake, that's all."

"I don't mean to argue, I was only suggesting—"

"You were just telling me on the train how wonderful I sound, how well I've been playing on tour."

"It's true," Ober admitted. "Yes, you are at the top of your form."

"But I'm still not perfect; I made a mistake. It's not that unusual to miss a few notes; guys do it all the time. Hell, there was a guy in New York who missed his entrance for the slow movement, missed the whole goddamned entrance, and no one noticed."

Now Ober's voice took on an edge. "We are not talking about your friends in New York and we are not concerned with the audience noticing. Do we play only as well as an audience expects? Do we pattern our playing for people in Chicago as opposed to those in Clear Lake, Wisconsin?"

"We play different programs."

"I think you know what I mean. We play for ourselves, always; whatever we are playing, we play for one another and for ourselves. Do you honestly think that everything is all right if only the audience doesn't notice?"

"I didn't mean that," Ben said weakly.

"All right, fine, I know, you have had a hard night. It has been a long tour. But your friend, whoever he is, does not play for me. You do not make such mistakes, we do not. We have never tolerated such things and we will not begin now. You understand, Ben?"

"Sure, I know. I was just saying it was me, not the disease."

"To what extent are any of us distinct from our bodies?"

"For Christ's sake, Heinz," Ben pleaded. "I told you it was simply a mental lapse. It could happen to anyone."

They had reached an impasse: Ben was making an argument he didn't believe himself. He knew it could never happen to Heinz, or even to Ernst or Beaulieu.

But Heinz was feeling conciliatory. He patted Ben on the shoulder and said, "It's true; we all fail from time to time. Unavoidable. But there is no point in discussing it further."

They stood facing each other in front of the hotel. It was unseasonably warm; snow melted in the gutters, and a mild breeze was coming off the lake. Ben heard the lowing of ships out on the water and saw little red lights heading for the Michigan shore.

"Come, I'll buy you a nightcap," Heinz said.

But Ben demurred. "I think I'll walk some more," he said. "It's a nice night and I can use the exercise."

He started up Michigan Avenue, still replaying the concert. Five notes; picayune but essential, like a minute fault in the side of a mountain. For an instant his playing had ceased, but how could he get it back, not the moment, but his confidence?

The doctor had said his arms were still unaffected and the brain always went last. But the doctor might have lied. Now Ben started running. It had been years, but his strides were effortless; he seemed to float, his heels only occasionally in contact with the pavement. His breath came in sobs, and his eyes teared. His chest was hot but his mind was clear. There was nothing to what Heinz said. There was no connection with the disease, there couldn't be. He felt fine. It was all in his legs, and his legs were strong.

97

12

AFTER VISITING BEN AND DORY, Moshe had little desire to return to Washington. Rather, he continued west to California. All his life he had worked unceasingly, worked without questioning it, worked because he believed work was salvation, the foundation of life. He had never taken a real vacation before, and seldom even took days off. On Sundays he went in a little later and cleaned up. The rest of the week he came at seven and left at eight. Work provided the rhythm of his life; he had always expected to die in the shop.

Now it occurred to him that he could change his life. Ben and his children were provided for; from the apartments and savings there was enough money for him and Sarah for the rest of their lives. There was no reason for him to go back to work. Thinking of Sarah provided a momentary twinge of regret. But he knew she would survive; she would prosper. For once, he would worry about himself. Moshe wrote Sarah a letter: he was prolonging his trip, she shouldn't worry. He would keep in touch; he didn't know when he would return. After putting the letter in the mail, he wondered if he would be able to get along without his work, without his wife. But what was done was done.

Moshe need not have worried. Once released from his various responsibilities, he was delighted to find he didn't miss the routine at all. He enjoyed sleeping late in the morning, awaking in a strange room and trying to remember what town he was in. He liked reading the paper in the hotel coffee shop with no fear of interruption, and walking idly through the city.

At night he read paperback novels he found in the bureau in his room. At first he had trouble with the vocabulary, but in time his reading improved and he branched out. Sex novels didn't hold his interest; Americans seemed more interested in gymnastics than love. But he read westerns, mysteries, and adventure stories with relish. When he tired of whatever city he was visiting, he would move on. He was drunk on his new freedom, and except for a short visit to Washington to close up his shop, he spent little time with Sarah. When he walked in the door, she cried, "A *dank fer avek gehen!*" Thanks for going away! To oblige her, Moshe left again as soon as possible.

Sarah did not understand the change in her husband. What had happened to the docile, obedient Moshe? Where had these crazy ideas come from? Had Ben's *shiksa* wife given him this disease; was this God's punishment for defying his laws? Nothing would surprise Sarah in that connection. Hadn't she warned Ben, warned Moshe? And had they listened? She had given up wishing Ben would come to his senses, but she worried about Moshe spending all their money and abandoning her to a nursing home. She thought he was deranged when he sold the shop, but hoped it would pass. She moved in with her sister Sophy in Silver Spring to wait. When she saw the *mishegass* was not temporary, she went to her cousin Joey, who was a lawyer. Joey and Moshe negotiated a settlement. There would be no divorce. Sarah was guaranteed a lifelong income. She moved to Miami, where she shared an apartment with a friend whose husband had died. Sarah considered herself a widow too.

For Moshe, it was an ideal arrangement. The apartment houses alone supported Sarah. He sold the house he had built on Sixteenth Street to a black lawyer and invested the money along with the proceeds from the sale of the shop. He lived on the interest. His needs were simple; he had freedom, and that was priceless.

Ben and Dory were drinking coffee in the dining room when Moshe arrived on one of the first warm mornings of summer. Dory had never gotten used to the fact that there was no spring in Wisconsin, or at least not one that was recognizable from late winter. In May the boys were still bundled in their parkas. Yet there was her father-in-law wearing a lilac sport shirt, open at the neck, smiling beatifically and calling her daughter. More than a year had passed since Moshe's first visit, a year in which their lives had begun to change, but Moshe did not seem in the least different. She wondered how much he knew about Ben's illness, how much Ben had told him. Whenever

Moshe called, she left the room, thinking Ben would want to speak to his father in private. But whenever she asked what they talked about, Ben would only say, "The usual, he asked about the boys. He sends his love."

"So," Moshe said now, looking around the room. "Living the life of Riley."

"Pop, why don't you ever call us first, to let us know when you're coming?"

"What, your father isn't welcome?"

"Don't be silly. But we could come and pick you up at the station, save you the cab fare."

"I want it to be a surprise. Anyway, I took the bus. Now, wait here; in a minute I'll be back."

Moshe took his suitcase into the other room. When he returned he was wearing a cowboy hat that slid down around his ears and a western shirt with silver spurs embroidered over the pockets. In his hands were two six-guns with plastic handles. "Put up your hands," Moshe ordered.

"Tom Mix."

"None other, potner, only a little taller maybe."

Moshe twirled the guns, but one spun off his finger and hit the floor. The boys had come in during his act and stood frozen at the door. Michael remembered his grandfather, but not like this. He had been a little man in baggy pants, not a cowboy. But Charles liked Moshe's outfit and smiled at him. "Come, Chaim," Moshe said, gesturing toward the boy. "And you too, *bubele*," he said to Michael. "I got something for you." Now the boys came into the room and accepted their grandfather's hugs. Moshe opened his suitcase again and took out a large package. Michael held it in his arms tentatively. Then he shook it. Finally he opened the box. Inside were matching outfits: boots, chaps, shirts and string ties, and holsters with cap guns. For a moment Michael seemed stunned by his new treasure. Then he hugged Moshe again and ran off to try on his clothes. Charles stayed behind for a moment. Then he gathered up what Michael had left for him and packed his gifts carefully in the box. He looked first at Dory and Ben as if he needed permission; then he approached Moshe. "Thank you, Grandpa," he said.

Moshe beamed. "Such a boy," he said to Ben. Then he patted Charles on the behind. "Go catch your brother," he said, and pushed him out of the room.

Dory got Moshe a glass of tea and they all sat at the table. "So, how was the wild west?" Ben asked.

Moshe sipped his tea and considered his answer. "Benjy," he said, "how long I been here? Forty, fifty years, something like that? You remem-

100

ber all those times in Washington when you were home and we'd go to the movies on Saturday and see cowboys and Indians shooting each other?"

"Sure, Pop, I remember. Triple features for a dime."

Moshe leaned forward and spoke in a whisper. "All that time, I thought it was a lie, *goyishe* nonsense. But it's true. With my own eyes, I saw it. I stayed in Laramie, Wyoming, and in the morning I wake up and there's men riding on horses through the backyard, men with guns and hats like I gave Chaim. And Indians? Everywhere you look, in the town, on the street, everywhere. Here, I'll show you." Moshe produced a picture of himself astride an enormous black horse in front of a banner that read "Wild West Days."

Ben laughed. "So now you're buying a ranch?"

"Don't laugh so hard, but I got to think it over."

Moshe stayed four days before leaving for Boston. He wanted to see the Freedom Trail, and it was crowded in the summer. Ben drove Moshe to the airport and they had breakfast in the restaurant. They watched planes land and take off silently. Moshe recited the names of the airlines like a litany, but he often emphasized the wrong syllables. "*Ozark*," he said. "Not so good. I rode it once to St. Louis. All the way there I thought we'd hit a tree they flew so low." Ben nodded. His father the aviation expert. "North Central," Moshe said. "Not bad, but bumpy. For breakfast they give us eggs, and by the time we land, the ceiling is yellow. But safe, I give them that. I read in the paper they never have accidents, so a little bumpy is okay."

When Ben had come to Madison the airport was a quonset hut salvaged from the Air Force. Cornfields had ringed the tarmac. Now the fields were gone. In their place were hangars and strips of concrete that stretched out to meet the horizon. Private planes and commercial carriers seemed to be arriving constantly. Madison was becoming a big city.

"You remember when I was here before, Benjy, what we talked about?"

"We talked about a lot of things, Pop."

"About your, what you call it, when you fall."

Ben flushed involuntarily. "Yeah, I remember."

"So, how is it?"

"Almost the same. It hasn't been that long, only a year. I suppose there are some changes. Why, do I seem worse?"

The question made Moshe uncomfortable. He had noticed Ben didn't go out as much and that he had gained weight. Still, what did he know? He didn't want to hurt Ben's feelings. "To me you're fine," he said. "I was only wondering, is that a crime?"

"Of course not. I appreciate it."

They sat together, unable to get past the disease. Finally Moshe said, "Benjy, did I ever tell you about Succoth, in the old country, I mean?"

Ben was puzzled. "I don't think so, why?"

"It's a nice story is all. You'll like it. You know Succoth is only a few days after Yom Kippur and it lasts a week, a little longer, eight days maybe. So the eighth day is Simchat Torah. Now, Simchat Torah is a very joyous holiday. The tradition tells you to let yourself go, even drink too much if you want. On Simchat Torah it's okay.

"So I was about Chaim's age, a little older, and my father was, like me, a tailor. But I had a friend whose father used to treat the whole town on Simchat Torah. The man had a dry-goods store and was tall and handsome and had a full head of white hair, even though he wasn't old. All year long, whenever we'd go in the house, my friend's father would tell us to be quiet or ask us why we weren't studying. A good man, but strict, you didn't talk back to him. But on Simchat Torah he had a smile for everyone; he was a different man. I remember he would order huge sponge cakes from this wonderful Jewish bakery, which were cut into little squares. Even on the holiday my friend's father didn't believe in having too much. Then they took the cakes to the *shul* and served them with vodka the night before Simchat Torah. My friend's father used to water the vodka so everyone would stay sober, but the Jews came in hundreds, from *shtetls* all over the place. People you never saw the rest of the year, you saw then. They would shake hands with my friend's father and wish him well, and the women would kiss us and tell us how much we'd grown. I'd stand there with my friends, just like one of the family, and when no one was looking, we'd take a little pinch of cake or drink a little vodka. I can still see it: my friend's father standing tall over our heads, his watch chain dangling from his belt, shaking hands. And everyone so happy, even if they were poor, their eyes sparkling, their cheeks flushed with wine and vodka. It was a happy time."

Moshe was smiling. He gazed up at the ceiling while Ben waited for him to make his point. "That's a nice story, Pop," he said.

"Yeah," Moshe said. "I thought you'd like it. But the thing is, Benjy, for me it's like a dream, because I started out poor like my father and now I'm like my friend's father, not rich, but I got some extra. Except I got no community to invite in for sponge cake. All I got is my family. You and your mother, and she don't need me."

"I see what you're saying, Pop, and I appreciate it, but—"

"Don't give me no buts. All I'm saying is that when you need, all you got to do is ask, and when you do, it won't be me doing you a favor. You'll be doing me the favor. A man should help his children; all I want is to help."

"I've got a job, Pop."

"Sure, but for later."

"When I can't work, you mean?"

"Maybe then."

"If I need money, I'll call you. Anyway, how do you know there'll be anything left after your world travels?"

"You're a smart boy. Maybe I should come live with you."

"You're always welcome."

"You should first ask your wife. But I appreciate it."

They embraced, and when they separated, Ben saw Moshe was crying. Helplessly, Moshe punched Ben's arm, his small fist hardly making an impression. "Sue me, I just want the best for you," he said. Then he turned and went to the plane.

Part Three

13

JUNE 23, 1958: Ben has changed. I don't know how or when it happened exactly, but he is different. Always before he denied the disease and refused to believe it would cripple him. Who knows what will happen? he'd say. It affects different people in different ways. Now he's scared. He doesn't say anything, but it's palpable, so real I can reach out and hold it. He doesn't do his exercises anymore, and he even takes the car to Mickies. If the boys play when he's practicing, he yells at them for breaking his concentration and I have to take them out for a walk. He says sleep is the only thing that does any good, but at night he tosses continually, and if we make the slightest noise during his afternoon nap, he says we're robbing him of his strength, what little he has. He is difficult even with his doctors. None of them know anything, he says, and he's right—no one does know much about this disease—but it's no reflection on them. Still, he is driving me crazy with the articles he reads about miracle cures and new treatments. He wants to go to New Jersey, where some man claims an 80-percent cure rate with vitamin therapy. We did drive to Indiana, where a doctor opened a clinic specializing in treating multiple sclerosis. Yet once we were there, the man could tell us little more than we already knew. He gave Ben some new drug and sent us home. Our cleaning lady Marie, prays for Ben; and for all the wonders of modern science, I can't see that her solution is any worse than anyone else's. The trouble is, I understand Ben's frustration, his need for an answer, a miracle, because it is so hard to live with this disease, with the way it dominates every aspect of our lives. If we take a vacation, we must first think of how strong Ben is, of whether the weather would make him weaker. Yet the thinking and planning don't seem to make Ben feel more sure of himself; his desperation is really a sign that he's given up, like a man in bankruptcy playing the lottery. It hurts me to see him like this. The problem is that there are pity and hate and fear and resentment mixed in with the love and sympathy and respect, which is confusing. God, we all need support so badly.

I'm also worried about Michael. Ben's rages terrify him. He cries and says he hates his father, and at night I have to tuck him in and wait until he goes to sleep before leaving. In the morning he'll sit in Ben's lap at the breakfast table and they both feel bad for fighting. Michael has always been nervous, but lately he's been going through this ritual of touching all the corners of the door before going from one room to the other. Outside, he jumps over cracks and touches trees. His eyes are dark with fear and he cries more than a nine-year-old should. I think he is too sensitive to live with this disease. I wish I could send him to his grandfather, but Moshe doesn't live anywhere anymore. It would be good if Moshe would buy a ranch; he and Michael could ride horses together.

Charles is better, or worse, depending on how you look at it. He seems indifferent to the disease, almost anesthetized. He follows Ben's orders without seeming to think about them. I worry about him, too. Is it normal for an eight-year-old to be a stoic? I suspect he says nothing but sees everything.

June 25, 1958: It is ten o'clock and Ben is still practicing. This used to be our time. We would go to the movies or take long walks after the children were in bed. But now he practices, even though the season is still six months off. He keeps going over the Brahms, as if playing it endlessly could erase Chicago. I wish he would play Mozart or Beethoven or Debussy, or best, nothing at all. How nice it would be to have the house quiet again! I feel for him and sometimes I want to go to his room, to be with him as he plays. But if I go in he stops and glares at me as if I'm an intruder. If I say I just like to listen, he becomes self-conscious. Once he would walk around the house with the fiddle balanced between chin and shoulder serenading me, asking whether I liked a phrase better this way or that. Now he is in seclusion.

Maybe I was wrong not to go to Chicago to meet him. When he arrived early the next morning, ahead of the quartet, I knew something had happened, but he wouldn't say what. Even now, he won't tell me everything. I know he missed some notes, and even though he didn't say what Ober said or how Richler reacted, I know he was crushed. Ben is still arrogant, but there is a hollowness to it; his confidence is gone. Now he is tentative, fragile, afraid of being rejected. The quality that dominates is fear. We are all afraid.

The oddest thing, though, is that sometimes things seem the same. Sunday mornings Ben will make breakfast before I get up and then sit at the table drinking coffee and joking with the boys. It is wonderful that they can forgive him so easily. Thursday nights Ben takes Charles to play chess and they go to the Cuba Club for dinner. Last week he took Michael to the baseball game in Milwaukee. He is extravagant with me, as always, insisting that we go out to eat or to a movie or to buy clothes I don't really need. At times like this the tension and anger are distant memories and it seems to me that the bravest thing we can do is simply to go on trying.

July 10, 1958: It is raining, which suits my mood. The sky is gray and a low fog covers the ground, so even though I know there are bright summer flowers in the yard, I can't see them. On days like this, everything seems hopeless. Now it is ten o'clock in the morning, but with the boys away at camp, the days run together and time loses its rhythm. Last night the air conditioner broke down and Ben was uncomfortable. He thrashed back and forth, sweating and swearing at the heat. Then in the dark he knocked over one of the bottles of piss and that made him even madder. It was too much. I got up and went into Michael's room to sleep. I sit here amid baseball cards and pictures of Hopalong Cassidy, unable to face my husband. It seems prophetic, as though he were saying, "Get away, get away now, when you can!" So I did, but I will return before long.

July 16, 1958: We are still sleeping apart. We say it is because of the heat, but the truth is, we haven't really slept together for a long time. We do have sex, but it's forced, as if to prove to each other that we still can. But it is important to Ben, so every week or so, he mounts me and we make love. I always feel that I am draining him of precious fluids, strength that he needs for other, more important things. Yet what is more important than this? I want to scream sometimes: I am a young woman! I am entitled to love, to sex, to my husband! But of course I never really scream at all. I remember instead how delighted Ben was with me, with my body; how he would sit for hours looking at me nude in bed, running his hand gently down my shoulder to my breasts and from there onto my stomach, tracing the line of my legs from my vagina to my heel, but always gently, as if he was worshiping some deity. We spent whole days lying in bed, making love, sleeping, and then just talking softly and holding each other. I remember when I was having trouble getting pregnant. We went to a gynecologist and the man asked how often we made love. Ben said ten to twelve times a week and the man just laughed. You've got to give the sperm some time to mature, he said. Slow down. What we do now seems to have no relation to all that; the play is out of it. Sometimes I just get tired. I want to be away from the house, away from Ben, away from the disease. I feel like Gulliver among the Lilliputians, held down by myriad pieces of rope, attached to hundreds of tiny stakes. It is the quantity of things, not their dimension, that exhausts me. Ben needs ankle braces and special shoes, and I have to go and pick them up. We need a handrail in front of the house. He is in the process of trying out a variety of canes, and none of them seem right. The truth is, he doesn't want a cane and would reject anything.

The worst thing is the uncertainty, the fact that we don't know what we are in for. We don't know whether Ben will be able to go on playing for another year or five years; if he will be flat on his back in ten years or still walking. If he stays like this, or close to it, we can go on living as we are. If not, I will have to decide at some point whether or not to leave him in a home or keep the family together. Yet now there are no choices to be made; instead I sit and think of a future when such decisions might have to be made. I am a young woman and this is my only life! But I can't leave him, can't even think of it now without feeling guilty. This is what tears at me, so that I feel an actual pain in my abdomen, a burning sensation, as if to remind me of my fecundity and my fading youth.

July 17, 1958: The air conditioner has been fixed and I moved back to the bedroom. Last night Ben came to me, and today, with the boys gone, we had breakfast in bed. It seems incredible now that I could have written the things I did yesterday. Of course our situation is uncertain, but isn't life? Who can ever know when we go out in the morning that we will return? Things could be worse. When I am not depressed, I am an unreasonable optimist. Since I don't know what will happen, what point is there in worrying?

The house is bright and sunny. I've washed the dishes and weeded the garden. I sit now in the dining room watching the snapdragons trying to keep their heads above the wildly growing grass. I am wearing only a shift. The floor is cool and rough against my bare feet. I hear Ben playing Mozart and I think it is nice that my husband is a musician. I remember when I first went to his concerts, how proud I was to see him onstage, how pleased I was that people sat and listened to him. It seemed amazing that I knew such a man. Today I feel that way again. Nothing has changed.

14

BEN STOPPED to rest before attempting the stairs. It had been months since he had been to the second floor of Music Hall, and he did not relish the climb. He tried to avoid buildings without elevators now, but that was impossible in this case: Ober had called him and he had to go. His right leg jerked uncontrollably, and not knowing what else to do, Ben hit it sharply with his fist. To his surprise, the spasm stopped. Encouraged, he began his ascent. Left leg first, then pull the right after it, and then the left again. Slowly he made his way.

Ober's office door was open, and Ben saw him sitting, facing away, looking out at the lake. Ben paused to catch his breath and studied Heinz. He looked much as he had when they first met. He was still lean and fit; his clothes remained impeccable; his bearing was as erect as ever. Time did not seem to touch Ober. Ben knocked on the doorjamb, and Heinz swung around to greet him.

"Ben," he said. "Please, come in." He rose and brought a chair over from the wall.

Though they had not been close for years, Ben remained fond of Ober. Before he married Dory, Heniz had practically been a father to him, telling him where to live, what to eat, and what clothes to wear. And Ben had welcomed Ober's interest, for the most part. But Dory came between them, or at least Heinz saw it that way. He had never been able to forgive Ben for letting his family take up so much of his time. But he understood. He knew what a woman could do to a man.

111

"I'm sorry I'm late," Ben said. "I had trouble parking, and then the stairs . . ."

"It is nothing, nothing at all. I am here anyway." Then Ober lapsed into thought. "Do you remember, Ben," he said finally, "how you would come here to this very office when you first joined the quartet, and we would talk the afternoon away?" He sighed. "It's been a long time since we've gotten together, just the two of us."

Ben nodded. He was waiting for Ober to tell him why he had been summoned. At last he said, "What was it you wanted to see me about, Heinz?"

"Must I have a reason? Isn't it enough to call an old friend, a colleague, to ask that we get together to talk?"

"Sure, but I thought it might have something to do with next year's tour."

Ober waved his right arm to brush such thoughts away. "Later, there is time for all that later on. I wanted to talk about you, Ben. How are you feeling? Is it any better?"

"Actually, it's always a little worse in the summer, because of the heat. But I'm all right. I got up to your office, didn't I?"

Ober smiled. "Indeed you did. But I was wondering if there is any new treatment you are taking, any physical therapy?"

"Any hope, you mean? I'm afraid not. I've been to New York, California, Chicago, and some hospital out in the middle of Indiana. I've tried special diets, exercises, baths, medicines—nothing seems to work. I even visited a faith healer in New Jersey."

"Ah, your faith was insufficient?"

"Maybe. Anyway, it didn't help."

"It's odd. Your playing is better than ever. But on the other hand, this makes sense; you are older, more mature, now you understand something of life. I am tired of these young virtuosi who can do anything, but understand nothing." Ober shook his head to rid himself of the idea. "But what about your walking? You have some pain now?"

"I've never had much pain; it's not that kind of disease. But it's hard for me to walk. I try to avoid stairs; I take taxis; I tire easily. But that has nothing to do with my playing. My arms are fine."

"Of course," Ober said quickly. "It's only that there are people who don't understand this, don't know anything about the disease and why you stumble and fall."

"What am I supposed to do, put out a press release?"

Ober smiled thinly. "I'm not sure that would help, Ben. Unfortunately, some people don't care about your difficulties. You know, you haven't

112

exactly gone out of your way to ingratiate yourself with the music faculty."

"None of us have. I'm no better or worse than Ernst or Antoine or you, Heinz."

"True, but now we are vulnerable. The novelty has worn off; many schools have string quartets. We are no longer unique."

"What does this have to do with me?"

"Oh, you know some of it and sense the rest, I think. At first, when you had the accident with the fireplug, some fools thought you were a drunkard. That was easily taken care of; if it had stopped there, we would have had no problem. But later, when it became known that you were sick, some questioned your ability to carry on. Of course, that is nonsense; with one hand you could surpass any of them, but you get the idea."

Ben nodded. "You're right. I knew about the rumors and I know the music school isn't crazy about me. But what are you trying to tell me, Heinz?"

"I? Nothing. It's only that there have been suggestions that perhaps you could use a rest. I know how tiring the tour is for you."

"A permanent rest?"

"I should certainly hope not! Something might happen, you may improve."

"And if I don't, as I probably won't? What then, Heinz?"

Ober was flustered, his face red. He turned away. "I don't know. Don't you see I'm in an impossible situation? There is a great deal of pressure on me. I must think not only of you or me, but of the whole quartet."

"Pressure? To do what? Get rid of Seidler and bring in someone new? What the hell, he's a pain in the ass anyway. Let's hire a fiddler the piano teachers can get along with, a man who'll come to the Christmas sing. Is that it, Heinz? Dumping me will help you with them? Sure, and everyone will understand. Who can knock you for it? It's brilliant. Too bad for Seidler, but we can't have cripples on the state payroll; this is a university, not a nursing home. Tough about his wife and kids, but that's life. Am I getting your drift?"

"Not at all. You're getting overly excited, and there's no cause for it."

"No cause? No cause my ass. You bring me in here and tell me you're going to replace me because those morons in the School of Music are putting pressure on you and there's no reason for me to be upset? You're holding me hostage for the goddamned quartet and I shouldn't be mad? Be serious, Heinz." Ben stood up, making an effort not to shake.

"Ben, please, sit down. No one is getting rid of you. I am only telling you what they said."

"Thanks, I can take it standing up. Am I fired?"

"Of course not. As I told you, a leave of absence. It is only temporary."

"And how do I feed my family temporarily?"

"Of course your faculty salary will continue for the year. This is only a sabbatical. I thought you'd be pleased."

Ben ignored this. "What happens after the year?"

"Am I psychic? I can't predict the future."

"I think I can," Ben said. "A year goes by and, predictably, I'm in worse shape than before, especially since I haven't been playing. With one foot out the door, it's easier to make my leave permanent. Who could blame you? You paid me for a year while you waited for the disease to cure itself. Now, regrettably, you must let me go. Everyone is very sorry. Well, let me tell you something, Heinz. I don't need your goddamned money that badly. I'm quitting, effective immediately. No salary, no severance pay, no nothing. And I think I'll call the newspapers and tell them. Why not be honest, after all?"

Ober was sullen. "You misunderstand me entirely, and willfully. I never intended anything like this."

"All right," Ben said. "Let's forget the whole thing, then. The sabbatical, the money. I'll just stay on."

"I'd like that, but I'm afraid it's impossible."

"That's what I thought. I'll be seeing you."

"Ben!" Ober's voice was sharp now. "There's no point in beating your breast over this."

Now Ben smiled. "That's always been a problem, hasn't it? I'm just too uncouth and don't know how to behave in public. Haven't read the right books, don't dress well. I understand, Heinz. It wouldn't be dignified to call the papers and tell them you're firing invalids, would it? And what good would it do? Self-pitying, lacking grace, all that. I should have the old stiff upper lip, I know. Okay, Heinz, I'll think it over." He turned and walked out the door, steadying himself against the frame, then the staircase as he went downstairs. At the bottom, he stopped to rest. He heard Ober come out of his office and walk halfway down.

"Ben," he said softly, worried lest others should overhear. "Come back, so we can talk this over in a civil way. . . . Ben," Ober hissed. "Please!"

"Go to hell," Ben said, and lurched out the door.

15

WHEN BEN LEFT MUSIC HALL, he went to the corner drugstore, shut himself into a phone booth, and made three calls. First he called Jimmy Shapiro in New York. Then an old friend from Curtis who was in San Francisco. Finally he phoned Dory and told her he had quit his job.

"Quit?" Dory said, her voice hollow in his ear. "What do you mean?"

"They were going to fire me anyway," Ben said.

"Well, which was it? Did they fire you or did you quit?"

"I quit because I knew they were going to fire me."

"When?"

"Next year, but I wasn't going to stay around and be humiliated."

"Humiliated? Are you crazy, Ben? Are we going to live off your pride now?"

"Relax," Ben said, conscious that a few minutes before, Ober had been telling him the same thing. "It's going to be all right. I've got another job."

"Already?"

"I work fast. I called Jimmy Shapiro and he's got a friend in Tulsa. That'll show those bastards."

"Oh, God," Dory said. "You mean we've all got to move to Tulsa? I don't even know what state it's in."

Dory's questions made Ben feel less sure of himself. "Look, Dory, don't get hysterical. It'll all work out."

"Sure," she said. "Things are wonderful. It's not bad enough you're sick and I'm trying to get my degree in one year. Now you quit your job because you don't want to be humiliated and call to say we're moving to Tulsa. I can think of very few situations in which hysteria would be more appropriate."

"Calm down," he said.

"Tulsa, that's great."

"Look," Ben said. "I know how you feel. I'm not crazy about it either. But I didn't really have a choice. Ober wanted me to take the year off and then reevaluate things. If I took a year off, I wouldn't be able to play at all. Then they'd have a reason to fire me. If I'm going to be any kind of musician, I have to keep on playing, even in a third-rate place like Tulsa."

"I know," Dory said softly. "But the boys are happy here, and I'm in school. I wasn't even thinking about moving."

"We don't have to. The season is only twenty weeks long. I'll go down there by myself; you can stay here with the kids."

"I don't know. Can you live by yourself?"

"Why not? If I need help, I'll get a housekeeper or something."

"Are you sure you want to do this, Ben?"

"I have to."

"And what happens after Tulsa?" The edge was off Dory's anger now; she had begun to accept Ben's decision.

"I called Ray Burrows, too."

She waited.

"Well, Ray says he thinks I can get a job in San Francisco. But they've got a six-month waiting period. I'd have to go out there and establish residency to join the union."

"Drop us a postcard."

"Don't tell me you wouldn't move to San Francisco?"

"It does sound better than Tulsa," Dory said.

"You see. When have I ever let you down?"

"I'm just worried about a new trend."

Ben laughed into the phone. "I'll talk to you when I get home," he said, and hung up.

He walked over to the low soda counter and sat down. There was a newspaper on the seat next to him, but the headlines didn't make sense. The letters seemed blotted, indistinct, abstract. The girl came to get his order and Ben asked for coffee. She set a small container of cream beside the cup. As Ben lifted it, he noticed his fingers were shaking, spilling the cream. He tried to steady his hand by an act of will, but a large dollop of it stained the coffee a murky brown. He put the cream down. It was only nerves. It

116

was understandable, considering what he had been through. He lifted the coffeecup to his lips, but his hand shook so badly that the coffee surged onto the counter. He put the cup down in a clatter of china. The girl looked at him.

"Is anything wrong, sir?" she asked.

Everything, he thought. He stood up to go. "Nothing, except I forgot an appointment. What do I owe you?"

Dory was out when he got home, but there was a note saying Jimmy Shapiro had called. Ben dialed Jimmy's number.

"You can have the Tulsa job, if you want it," Jimmy said. "I talked to my friend, he's the concertmaster. He couldn't believe you were interested. Personally, if it was me, I'd come back here. You could pick up lots of jobs in New York. Madison is bad enough, Tulsa is really nowhere."

"I've got a family," Ben said. "I can't go back to New York and record the March of Time again. Anyway, they don't have those newsreels anymore."

"You could teach, you could do lots of things. You go to Tulsa, you'll never get back. They've got Indians out there."

Jimmy was right: if he had any future, surely it was in New York. But that was the problem. He had no future to speak of. At least there was something for Dory in Wisconsin. She could finish her degree and work. It seemed safer to him. "What are they paying in Tulsa?" he asked.

"My friend thought six, maybe six-five."

"It's not bad for five months. What do I have to do for that?"

"Not much. Show up, mainly. Oh, and you've got to live there."

"I'll call you back when I decide," Ben said.

"Sure," Jimmy said. "Take your time."

"It won't be long," Ben said. "And thanks, Jim, thanks a lot. You're a friend."

"Some friend. I send you to Tulsa," Jimmy said.

The season started in October, and Ben didn't have much time to make arrangements. Ober called a few times to ask him to reconsider, but Ben refused to speak to him. After a while Dory came to see his point. Ober should stay with him out of loyalty. Couldn't he expect that much after ten years? A year as a lame duck wouldn't make Ben more attractive to anyone. They would all want to know what happened in Wisconsin. This way at least he could stay in shape.

After Tulsa, Ben would go to San Francisco. He could stay with Bur-

117

rows until he got a room. After six months he would audition for the orchestra. Dory approved of the plan. She didn't know how long Ben could go on playing, but she liked the idea of moving to California; it awakened some pioneer instinct in her. Her father had gone to Colorado when he was eighteen to work in the mines. Now they would go west, too.

The second week in October, Dory and the boys took Ben to the train station. Ben hugged each of his sons and shook their hands with mock solemnity. Charles was eight, Michael ten. He looked into Michael's large brown eyes and said gravely, "You're the man in the family now. I want you to take care of Charles and Mother while I'm away."

Michael nodded. He didn't seem especially unhappy, but he was very serious. Too serious, Ben thought. "I will, Daddy," Michael said.

"Good boy." Ben bent and kissed his son. Then he and Dory walked a short distance away and stood abreast of the last car in the train. Dory was crying. The tears ran down her cheeks in a steady stream, and she made no effort to stanch them. Her crying always made Ben feel guilty, as though he had failed her.

"Cheer up," he said. "Think of all the parties you can have now. You can stay up all night with those young kids and go for midnight swims."

Dory blew her nose and looked away.

Ben took her in his arms and kissed her eyes. "Dory, Dory. You're making it worse than it is."

"I don't think that's possible," she said.

"It won't be that long," he said. "Five, six months, and I'll be back. It'll be like nothing, you'll see."

"Five or six months," she said, backing away. "Nothing?" She shook her head. "Don't you remember when you didn't want to leave us for two weeks to tour with the quartet? When you refused to go to Australia because you'd have to be away for the summer? Now you're saying it's nothing to go off for six months? What's happened to you, Ben? What's happened to us?"

He felt awful. "What can we do? I've got to go to Tulsa. It's a job, and I need a job. There's no other way. Before, I could say no; now I've got no choice. All we can do is try to make the best of it."

She fell into his arms again. "Oh, I know, I know you don't want to go, but this whole situation is so hard, so . . . I don't know, tragic."

Ben smiled now. In a professorial tone he said, "I'm surprised at you, Mrs. Seidler. Tragedy needs intent. This is merely an unfortunate accident." Then he dropped his voice. "Anyway, we'll be together soon. This is only for a year. I'm not going to spend my life away from you and the boys."

Dory took out a handkerchief and wiped her face. Then she smiled slightly. "Well, take care of yourself, then. Get enough rest—you know how important that is. And play well."

"I always play well, I can't help it."

Dory laughed, glad to hear Ben arrogant again. He held her tightly and kissed her, and then Ben was gone down the platform toward the passenger cars. Dory stood alone, watching him. The conductor was at the door of the car taking tickets. As Ben climbed up, he stumbled over the short step and had to grab wildly for the conductor's hand.

Dory cried, "Ben, watch out!"

Ben looked up, startled by Dory's voice. He seemed embarrassed by her fear and turned to say something to the conductor. "I just slipped. There was some grease on the step," he called out, smiling down at his family. Then he climbed into the car and was gone.

16

DORY STOOD in a corner of the sculpture studio surrounded by her work. There were five slabs of metal pushed into vaguely recognizable forms. None were finished, most hardly begun. Time was not the problem; since Ben left, she had too much free time. She took the boys skating and to the movies, but when she was alone she felt a mixture of boredom and anxiety. The house was a record of projects she had taken up, then abandoned: the bathroom was half paint, half tile; the storm windows were on in front but not in back; the living room was littered with novels she had opened and put aside.

At work she seemed to float through the day; she knew she appeared absentminded to her colleagues. She tried to concentrate, but everything reminded her of Ben. She thought of him constantly, worried about him. What if he fell and there was no one to help him? Had the doctors in Tulsa ever heard of m.s.? Where could he get strings in Oklahoma?

Meanwhile, the boys needed winter coats and she had to prepare her graduate show. There was really a great deal to do, but she was able to attack it only fitfully. For all his demands, Ben had provided Dory with a stable emotional base. Now that he was gone, things seemed out of control.

She appraised a figure of a naked woman she had painted, who carried on her shoulder what would be a hawk, if Dory ever finished the bird. What was the hawk doing there? she wondered. Dory didn't know. When she started the piece, it had seemed right. Along with the woman were a ghostly ship with skeletal masts, a small bird recumbent in death, a large rectangular mass of indeterminate identity, and a mother and child, the baby sucking a breast the size of a cantaloupe.

She had been working on the mother, but now she stopped, torch held high, the blue-red-orange flame incinerating the dusty air. It was eight o'clock at night, and her shoulder ached from the weight of the torch. The metals course had begun to absorb more of her time than she had to give. Dory had only taken it because Sam Matthews had urged her to, but she had become fascinated with welding. She knew she should return to painting, but there was something in the cold abstemious blackness of the metal that attracted her. She welcomed the physical aspect too; welding was hard work, it made her use her body in new ways, draining off some of the tension she felt.

She sighed and turned off the torch. Then she stepped back to examine her work. The welds were still brittle and amateurish. She would never make her name as a craftsman, that was sure.

Dory heard someone enter, knew it was Sam, and knew she had been waiting for him. Still, she was embarrassed by her gray smock and bib overalls. She was embarrassed too because she wanted his approval. It was ridiculous that she, a mother of two children, should still be here when the regular students had gone home.

Sam was also wearing a smock, but on him it looked more fashionable. Beneath it he wore a rust turtleneck, light gray flannel pants, and brown suede shoes. He looked at the mother, then he reached forward, smiled, and chucked the baby under the chin. "Cootchy-cootchy-coo," he said.

"That's just because you don't have children," Dory said.

Sam laughed. "Ah, a Freudian. My failure to reproduce is childish self-indulgence, right?"

"Not exactly, but you don't understand," Dory said. "It's really very beautiful."

"Perhaps so, but this isn't." He inspected the other pieces, ending with the undefined mass, which seemed to interest him most. "It looks like a flayed pig," he said. "Is it?"

"I don't know what it is," Dory said.

"Ah, perhaps it is an expressionist piece, then?"

"Maybe." She didn't know, didn't care. But Sam was enjoying his cross-examination.

"I hate expressionism," he said. "It is a fraudulent concept, and yet students can't get enough of it, which, when you think about it, makes sense. If something lacks form or meaning, we say it is expressionist, and there can be no objection. But students have nothing interesting to express, or more precisely, they do not yet have the expertise to render their innermost feelings about life and form in interesting ways. Lack of form, lack of coherence, this becomes expressionism. Farts, belches, are thus the matrices of expressionism as we see it here; it is lavatory art."

Sam paused, pleased with himself. He had never articulated his ideas as succinctly before. But Dory wasn't impressed. Sam might be right, but she didn't want to be badgered. "Is that the end of the lecture?" she said.

Sam ignored her, looking more closely at the ship, then pulling apart the rickety mast and sails. "These welds are awful. If I had a three-year-old daughter, she would do better."

"Haven't they improved at all?"

"A little better perhaps. But better than what? Before, they were terrible. Now they are merely awful. You must see it. Look." Sam picked away at the latticework of the mast that had occupied Dory for a week. "Now," he said. "The boat will do, but I want you to redo the mast. It's a disgrace."

"I'm going home, Sam. I have two kids to feed."

"Of course, but fix the mast first. It won't take long. I'll wait to see how you do."

"It took me five days to do what you just picked apart. I'm going home."

Sam was enjoying her rebellion. "You will stay and finish your work," he said.

Dory was amazed. The man was a sadist. Sam didn't care about her sculpture, he was a painter. He was only teaching the course because Klaus Steinmetz was on leave. It had been years since he had shown sculpture himself, and then it hadn't been good, or at least not up to his painting and prints. Why should she listen to him? Why had she listened when he told her to take the course? It had all been a plot calculated to put her in a submissive position, to give him the opportunity to humiliate her. She breathed deeply and said, "Look, Sam, to you this is some kind of game, a battle of wills or something. Maybe it works with the other students, but I've been on my feet all day. I'm exhausted and dirty and my two kids are waiting for me. I'm going."

She packed her things, pulled a sweater over the coveralls, and walked toward the door. As she opened it, she heard Sam's mocking laugh. "If you leave, I can't guarantee you an A."

She turned, furious that he'd threaten her with a grade. "As far as I'm concerned, you can take your goddamned A and stick it up your ass," she said.

122

Sam was speechless. He wasn't accustomed to students swearing at him. He encouraged a casual, relaxed atmosphere in class, extending at times to a friendly beer in the Rathskeller afterward, but this was too much. This was insubordination. He decided to put off his anger.

He raised his hand instead, in a sardonic salute. "As you wish," he said. "Have a nice supper."

17

Dearest Dory,

Thanks for sending the halvah. God knows where I could get any out here. Do you think G&S would send it direct if you asked? At this rate, I'll need a pound a month.

I'm terribly sorry you have to work so hard and that Matthews is such a bastard. Some men seem to take pleasure in lording it over women; of course I suspect he is secretly in love with you, but that doesn't help much, I know.

I am all right. The rehearsals are nothing; we stop all the time because neither the musicians nor the conductor is any good. Jimmy's friend Bobby Fireman is the only one I respect. Bob found me a first-floor apartment near the center of town and I bought a Ford that will just get to the concert hall and back. Except for the fact that you aren't here and I'm always exhausted, things are fine.

I worry about you and the boys. It's bad enough for me to be sick, but I don't want it to affect all of you more than necessary. I don't want the boys to think of me only as an invalid, but as their father, someone they can talk to, look up to, ask advice of, all the things a father should be. When I think back, it seems I did little besides yell the last six months I was home. I don't

124

want my sons to be afraid of me. I'm enclosing letters for both of them.

Well, there isn't much more to say, sweetie. Except that I love you, think about you all the time, and wish we were together. I'd give anything just to be able to look at you, but I really feel lucky to have landed on my feet, even if it's in Tulsa. Ah, well. Perhaps you could come to visit over Christmas? Write soon.

Love and kisses,

Ben

Dear Charles,

P.QB4. Now it's your turn to make a move. I have discovered postal chess and have three games going, one with a man in Maryland, one in Minneapolis, and one with a friend of mine in New York. Now we can play too.

Mother tells me that you got straight A's in school and that you are almost as tall as she is. Of course she isn't very tall, but what happens when you're as big as me? I hope you won't beat me up.

You asked in your letter how I'm feeling. I'm about the same. When it rains and is hot I feel very weak, but usually I'm able to get around quite well. Some of the men in the orchestra come around and play chess with me on Fridays and sometimes I'm invited out to eat. Tulsa is about the same size as Madison, but not as pretty. Maybe you can come visit.

Well, I'll close now. Study hard and be a good boy.

Love,

Daddy

Dear Michael,

How is my big, gargantuan boy? I hope you are taking care of everything around the house for me. I'm enclosing two articles from the Tulsa newspaper about Willie Mays and Mickey Mantle. Did you know Mantle comes from Oklahoma?

Mother tells me you're on the basketball team and come home late for dinner and fall right into bed. I'm glad you enjoy sports, but don't forget to study, as this is really much more important. It always amazes me that in America grown men earn a living for running after a little ball. Of course, Grandpa used to say the same thing about playing the fiddle. The main thing is that you not practice so hard that you forget to have fun.

125

The Giants have spring training near here, in Arizona. If you're a good boy, maybe you can come see me then and we can go to a game. In the meantime, write me another letter.

Love,

Daddy

November 23, 1958

Dear Ben,

Happy birthday! We will call you, of course, but I wanted to write since long-distance calls always seem so hurried. I miss you very much. What I miss most is just having you here to talk to when I come home from work. The boys are very good and try awfully hard, but it isn't the same. Marie is wonderful but not much of a companion. I would never have thought so when I was a young mother, but one of the best things about marriage is that you have a friend. Or at least I do. Now you're far away and I'm without a lover or a friend.

Don't worry about Sam. I think much of the time he's only kidding. He's really all right, and sends you his best. What's more, he likes my paintings and gave me permission to hang my show in the spring. Maybe I'll get the damned degree after all.

Work is draining. I have classes all day at the junior high, then go two nights a week to teach at the university. When I'm not teaching, I work in the studio. I miss seeing the boys, but on weekends we usually do something together. Last week I took them to see Wisconsin play Minnesota, and after that they dragged me to a Pat Boone movie. You'd never be persuaded to see such dreck, but I'm a pushover. I feel I neglect them in other, more important ways. It doesn't seem to matter much to Charles, but Michael is more upset. His teacher called to say he'd been fighting with other kids and neglecting his homework. And last night he asked if you were ever coming home. I tried to convince him you were, but reassurances are not always reassuring.

But don't worry about us on your birthday. We'll get along. I asked Mr. Stein at the kosher grocery to send you another brick of halvah. He is sending along a surprise of his own to wish you a happy birthday. I think he is still pleased because the last time I was there I wished him gut yontiff. It takes so little to please people that I wonder why we don't try to do it more often.

Now it is eleven and I must get up at 6:30, so I'll close. Please take care of yourself and get enough rest. That's the most important thing. I'm hoping to come visit over Christmas, but I really don't know how we can afford it, as we'd have to make arrangements for the boys. We'll see. Write me a nice long letter. I love you.

Your,

Dory

18

Dory got out of bed, threw a robe around her shoulders, and half-asleep, made her way to the bedroom door, dimly aware of pressure in her bladder. She opened the door and moved slowly down the hallway, past the boys' room, to the toilet.

She had been dreaming of Ben. He was suspended in a cage, unable to hear her cries for help. He only stared off into space. She shook her head to rid herself of the memory.

The bathroom was dark, though slats of moonlight slipped through the blinds; it was the half-light of five o'clock in the morning. Dory hadn't bothered to turn on the overhead before sitting on the toilet because she didn't want to become fully awake. She patted herself dry and looked dully at the window. Slowly she became aware of a peculiar quality in the darkness: the center of her field of vision was almost entirely black, but on the periphery she saw clothes, books, magazines.

Dory rose and flushed the toilet. Then she walked deliberately to the wall and switched on the light. It was as if she were looking into a shadow box: light bordered the velvety blackness of the room. She stood dumbly with her hand on the switch. She expected it somehow to make sense, to change, but nothing happened. She thought she would suddenly see a pattern, that the curtain would lift as at the theater. But as the seconds went by, no pattern emerged, no light illuminated the room. It was as if she was looking at something through an enormous tree; the center had simply been blacked out.

At first, she felt only mild curiosity. She blinked her eyes, held her hand in front of her, and marveled at the disappearance of the middle fingers. Then the terror began to build. Her chest constricted involuntarily and her knees felt weak. She slid to the floor, her robe bunched beneath her like a beach towel, and screamed a wild, keening yell that she hardly recognized as her own. Then she was quiet again. She sat hunched on the floor, both hands over her face.

For a moment she seemed to black out; at least she was not aware of the passage of time. When she came to, both boys were standing over her in the doorway. Michael had his arm draped protectively around his younger brother's shoulder. Instinctively Dory thought first of her nakedness and pulled her robe around her to cover herself. "Go back to bed," she said. "I'm all right." But the boys seemed rooted. Dory got up and pushed past them to her bedroom. She picked up the telephone book, then remembered she couldn't read it. She got Dr. Sykes's number from the operator, but when she tried to dial, the numbers evaded her. She moved her head from right to left, then tried to dial by touch. Nothing worked.

"I can do it," Michael said. She hadn't heard him enter, but now he stood at her side, Charles just behind him.

"I told you to go to bed," Dory said. "You have to get up for school in the morning, in just a few hours." She didn't know what time it was; she couldn't read the clock. The room was lighter, though, gray with dawn.

Michael didn't move. "Why are you crying, Mama?"

"I'm not crying."

"Yes you are, and before, you screamed. You woke me up."

She looked at her sons now; Charles hadn't said a word, but his eyes were wide with fear. Michael trembled slightly as he stood before her. "I'll be all right," Dory said. "I'm just nervous."

"You shouldn't worry so much, Mama," Michael said.

"You sound just like your father."

Michael sat next to her on the bed and began to stroke her back. Dory stretched out her arms to Charles and held him to her. They were so small, she thought, so defenseless. She wanted to protect them, to hide her feelings, but she needed to talk so badly, and there was no one to talk to. Then she remembered what she had been about to do.

"Will you dial Dr. Sykes's number for me, Michael?"

For once the boy didn't ask questions. The number was written on a pad. Michael dialed quickly; Dory kissed him on the forehead and hunched forward to listen. The phone rang seven times, which surprised her. Wouldn't a doctor have an extension beside his bed? Finally Sykes answered the phone. Dory couldn't tell whether he had been asleep or not.

129

"Dr. Sykes? It's Dorothy Seidler. I'm sorry to wake you at this hour."

"It's perfectly all right, Mrs. Seidler. What's the problem?" Dory thought it was odd that he was so formal. She knew his wife through the League. Of course, she hadn't called him Bob.

"Something peculiar has happened."

"Can you be more specific?"

"I think I'm going blind. I can't see anything, except around the edges."

She had expected a reaction, but Sykes was calm. "When did you first notice this?" he asked.

"When I woke up to go to the bathroom."

"In the dark?"

It was a logical question, but Sykes's attitude annoyed Dory. "It wasn't completely dark. Then I turned on the light."

"And has it changed at all, become better or worse?"

"I don't think so. How would it change?"

"Oh, that depends."

"On what?"

"A number of things. There's really no point in talking about it now, Mrs. Seidler. What I want you to do is take a sleeping pill and go back to bed. In the morning, if you're still having trouble, come down to the office. I'll fit you in."

"Dr. Sykes, I don't think you understand. I have two young children, and my husband is in Oklahoma. I have to go to work in four hours. I need help. I thought you'd come over."

"I don't think that's necessary," Sykes said. "There isn't much I could do anyway. We'll see what develops."

"Doctor, blindness is the first symptom of m.s. Ben went blind in the beginning too."

"Of course that would occur to you, Mrs. Seidler, but it's extremely unlikely that you would also have multiple sclerosis. I can't be certain, but what you're experiencing is probably hysterical blindness. It's fairly common and it will go away in time. All I could do is give you something to relax."

"Doctor, I was relaxed. I was asleep—you can't get more relaxed than that. I wasn't in the least hysterical."

"It's a medical term, Mrs. Seidler. It doesn't mean you were yelling and screaming; you might not have been aware of being upset at all. It does tend to come on suddenly."

"I want to see you now."

"I'm afraid that's impossible," Sykes said.

"Then I'll get another doctor."

"As you wish. But if you change your mind, I'd be happy to see you in the morning. As I said, it's nothing to worry about, unless it continues."

The phone went dead, and Dory was alone. But now her anxiety had been replaced by a hard, cold hatred of Sykes. It wasn't that she doubted the doctor's medical judgment. He was probably right about the blindness. She hated him for not being the kind of man she admired. It was impossible to imagine Ben or her father or grandfather, even Moshe, not coming if a friend had called in similar circumstances. But this went beyond friendship. It was a matter of simple humanity.

It took Dory fifteen minutes to dial Sam's number, but the response was immediate. "I'll be there in ten minutes," he said.

Dory knew she should change clothes and brush her hair, but she lacked the energy. When Sam rang the doorbell, she was still sitting on the bed in her robe.

It didn't matter. Sam wrapped Dory in a quilt and put her on the couch in the living room. He showed the boys how to stack wood for a fire and put them to work feeding the flames. Then he took a bottle of cognac out of his coat and poured a glass for Dory. After that, he went into the kitchen and started making breakfast. The flurry of activity made Dory forget what had started it all. Where had Sam gotten the wood? But soon the fire was warming the room and Sam was back with eggs, bacon, and orange juice. The terror seemed remote now; instead, she felt sleepy.

"Feeling better?"

"I didn't know you could build fires."

"I used to be an eagle scout," Sam said. "The town I grew up in was so small that we didn't have a Boy Scout troop, so I had to write the national office to start one." He still sounded proud of it.

"Well, you've done a good job. This is nearly equal to helping an old lady across the street."

Sam laughed and went to pick out a record. Then he sat with Dory on the sofa and watched the fire. In a moment the Pathétique sonata moved around the room, warming them much as the fire had. Dory closed her eyes. They might as well be closed. The cognac burned slowly in her stomach, and she felt immensely grateful to Sam.

Dory's forehead was pleasantly scorched. A curtain of red burned beneath her eyelids. Charles wriggled closer, and she felt his hot hand in hers. At first she struggled against exhaustion to stay awake. It wasn't right to fall asleep in her bathrobe in front of Sam. But he was so kind, so giving, and he was Ben's friend. She could trust him.

131

When Dory awoke, sun was streaming in the window. She could see: a miracle. The next thing she knew Sam was coming in the room with a pot of coffee. "What time is it?" she asked.

"Ten. I thought you needed the sleep. I sent the kids to school and called in sick for you."

"But I have things I have to do, Sam. I was right in the middle of something at school."

"It'll wait," he said, and smiled. He handed her a mug of coffee and sat down.

Dory took the cup, but she felt confused. During the night she had been scared, panicky, grateful to Sam for coming. Now, looking at him in the morning light, she realized she wanted him there for other reasons. He looked tired but enormously attractive. His thick red hair was disheveled, but Dory wanted to run her hands through it, and she felt her body tense in response to her feelings. She drank the coffee too fast and scalded her tongue. Then she put the cup down on the floor. She would simply get up and get dressed, and everything would be fine. But as she was about to rise, Sam put his hand on her shoulder, and suddenly she was in his arms, kissing him, stroking his neck with her fingers. As he lowered her to the sofa Sam said, "It's okay, Dory. Everything is okay now."

19

BEN MADE his way along the darkened corridor of pavement between the garage and door of his duplex. He carried a cane, flicking it back and forth like a blind man assessing the terrain. God only knew what lay in wait. Toys, bicycles, even a garden hose would be enough to leave him helpless on the ground.

He walked with a stiff, upright carriage, accentuated because of the clamp on his penis and the raging sea of urine that demanded to be let free. He wondered if it was possible for the dam to burst, for his skin to simply give way under the pressure. The pain was bad enough now; if he fell, it would be unbearable.

Ben's bladder problems had developed as the disease progressed, on schedule, as promised. At first, it had merely been a frequent urgent summons to the men's room. In the middle of rehearsal, he would drop his fiddle and hurry out, clutching his groin. It was embarrassing but manageable. Then things got worse. Occasionally he didn't make it to the lavatory in time. The urine would spurt out uncontrollably then, staining his trousers and running down his legs like warm syrup before turning cold as ice.

Doctors had proposed a number of solutions. It was clearly intolerable for a well-known concert artist to wet his pants in public. He could wear rubber pants with thick cotton linings, but the padding was bulky and it was hard to maintain a sense of dignity in rubber pants. There were various urinary devices, but most were impractical or uncomfortable, or both. All of them leaked, leaving telltale pools of urine wherever Ben sat.

The most successful of the lot joined a condom with a long tube running the length of Ben's leg to a rubber sack, which bulged just above his right ankle. Another rubber tube ran to his cuff. A detachable screw served to drain the bag. Ben tried to gauge the tumescence of the sack and fasten the screw tightly, but his hands were not as strong as before. Often he would look down to see his shoes gleaming. His colleagues had learned to keep their distance.

Ben hated all of the devices; they made him feel inhuman, like a malfunctioning machine of some sort. Moreover, they didn't attack the basic problem: how to keep the urine in until it was called forth. He wanted something to hold it, that was all, but the muscles were gone, taken by the disease. Finally he found a small rubber clamp which could be fastened around his penis. The clamp was uncomfortable, but it allowed Ben to feel relatively normal.

At last he made it to the steel banister that ran along the porch and hoisted himself up the stairs, one leg at a time. He fished in his pocket for the key, hoping his landlady wouldn't hear him. She was a season ticket-holder and thrilled to have a virtuoso, as she called him, in her house. The woman was nice enough, but how could he tell her they couldn't talk until he had a chance to piss?

The key appeared magically in his hand. Ben opened the door, slammed it behind him, and swung from table to chair, hand over hand, like the Ape Man, to the bathroom, where with the greatest imaginable relief he unfastened his pants, let his penis hang free, unclamped the rubber harness, and watched with satisfaction as the yellow fluid rushed out in a steady stream.

Ben's urethra burned, but the pain was so slight in comparison to what he felt before that it seemed almost pleasant. Then, finished, he replaced his penis, put the clamp in his pocket, and zipped his trousers. As he reached for the bathroom light, Ben saw himself in the mirror and hesitated. His face had become fuller, fleshy, because of the drugs he was taking, and his hair was streaked with gray. He was only forty, but he knew he looked older. It had been two years since he fell onstage, but it seemed like ten. He had gone from being strong and healthy to a near-invalid; from a solid family man to an unwilling bachelor; from Wisconsin to Oklahoma; from Casa Bella to the Tulsa Philharmonic. It was a long way to go in two years, and he regretted the trip. Recently he had seen a book called *Life Begins at Forty* and considered buying it. Now he nodded to himself in the mirror. "Here's to reincarnation," Ben said, and turned off the light.

134

He opened the refrigerator door. Three wieners sat on the shelf. There was a small container of frozen orange juice, three-quarters of a pound of butter, a quart of milk, a jar of mustard, and a loaf of white bread that had gone to mold. In the side panel was a jar of green cocktail olives. Ben unscrewed the top, reached in, his fingers pinched by the cylindrical jar, and extracted four olives. He was licking the salty brine off his fingers when he heard a knock on the door.

He knew practically no one in Tulsa, and he didn't want to make friends. He would be leaving soon, and besides, people would want to talk about music. It was hard to avoid arguments. Life was difficult enough without that. Another knock. Ben replaced the olives. It was his landlady, he thought. Perhaps she would invite him for dinner.

Ben opened the door, but at first he saw no one. His eyes weren't used to the dark. "Who is it?" he said.

"Joe," a voice said. "I almost gave up on you. Ever hear of lights? I almost broke my neck coming up here."

Joe the bootlegger. "What's the password?" Ben said.

"I got no time for games."

"On the contrary," Ben said. "Games are the only thing you should make time for."

"I got other customers'll take the booze."

"Ah, that's no joking matter. Come in." Ben opened the door. Joe was thin and laconic, with a long nose and a mouth which seemed to hang open in perpetual astonishment. He rarely entered the apartment beyond the foyer, preferring to stand in the hall in his overcoat, like a bill collector. As a rule, Ben didn't mind, but tonight he felt companionable.

"Please, come in," he said. "It's funny, I was just thinking I would like a martini, and here you are with the gin."

"It's Thursday. I come on Thursdays."

"That's true. Well, will you join me?"

"I'm late. I got other customers." Joe thought the guy was stalling. He didn't want to pay.

"Of course," Ben said, pulling Joe into the room. "But you can take a few minutes. Here, sit and relax."

In the light, Joe seemed older but less seedy. His face was deeply lined, as though he had worked outside most of his life, and his clothes, though shabby were clean. Ben had once imagined Joe was linked with organized crime, but he realized there was nothing romantic about bootlegging in Oklahoma. Joe was probably moonlighting from another job to put his son through college. As though he read Ben's mind, Joe said, "Okay, but just one. I got a wife and kid."

135

Ben went into the kitchen with the liquor, and Joe sat on the sofa, still in his overcoat. "Did you get Gordon's?"

"You got eyes. Look," Joe said.

Ben mixed drinks, dropped two olives in each, and carried them in on a small tray. He took a glass himself and gestured toward the other. Joe took a white handkerchief out of his pocket and wiped the bottom of his glass dry before setting it on his knee. He turned to Ben. He wondered what his excuse was.

To Joe's surprise, Ben reached for his wallet and gave him a ten-dollar bill. "You only owe eight," Joe said.

"Keep the change," Ben said. "I appreciate the service. It's hard for me to get around." He enjoyed drinking with Joe, mixing camaraderie and anonymity. He didn't feel self-conscious about the damp spots beneath his fly; there was no need to explain anything. They would never be friends. It was nice simply to have someone else in the apartment for a while.

Joe put the bill in his pocket, and they sat quietly, each man taken up with his own thoughts. Then Joe said, "You sick or something? The cane, I mean."

"I have multiple sclerosis," Ben said. The way he said it, it sounded like an honorary degree.

"Too bad," Joe said. He'd never heard of the disease.

Ben nodded and took a sip of his drink.

"They got a cure?" Joe asked.

"No, and it gets worse."

"You married?" Joe looked around the room for evidence, but the tables were clear of pictures.

"My wife and sons are in Wisconsin," Ben said. "I'm a musician. I'm just out here for a few months."

Joe appraised Ben. He thought he was a Jew; it was the bald dome and the nose. He could have been a wop or a Greek—but Joe thought he was a Jew. The Greeks he knew didn't throw money around, and the wops didn't have any. The funny thing, though, was that the guy didn't act like being sick fazed him. It was like he'd said he had brown hair. "How long you had this . . . what you call it, multiple. . . ?"

"I've known about it for two years."

"How'd you know?" Joe asked, just to make conversation.

"First I went blind. Then that cured itself. Then I had trouble walking, tripped a lot. That went away too, but it came back. So I went to the doctor. He said I have m.s."

"But you can still work?"

"If you call it working."

136

"I mean, you're out here."

"Yes."

"And you're not laid up?"

"No, I'm not laid up."

"And you can still do most things."

Ben nodded.

"So it's not that bad?"

"It's great, I love it."

Joe sat back and sipped his drink. He was dissatisfied. Ben's buoyancy bothered him. Sick people should act sick. He began to feel the effects of the long day. He had driven to Texas in the morning, then back over the line, and this was his fifth stop, with two more to follow.

Ben went into the kitchen. When he returned, he had two more drinks. "I said I only had time for one," Joe said.

Ben shrugged and put the second martini on the table. Joe drained his glass. His forehead burned now, and his right eye was fluttering involuntarily. He closed it and sat like a Cyclops, eyeing Ben. He didn't like to get involved with customers. But the gin made them co-conspirators.

"Your wife," Joe said. "Everything okay there?"

"What do you mean?"

"You know. You're a young guy, got a young wife. You get sick . . ." He didn't finish the sentence.

"You're asking if our sex life has been affected by my illness?" Ben said.

"Hey, I didn't mean anything."

"It's all right. It's a natural question."

Joe felt as if he'd trespassed on sacred ground. "Do me a favor," he said. "Just forget I ever said it."

Ben ignored him. "I worried about it a great deal at first," he said. "Not that I doubted my ability, but I'm not as strong as I used to be, and my wife is young and attractive."

Joe thought Ben sounded like a professor. It was as if the whole thing had nothing to do with him.

"There's a story," Ben continued, "about an eighty-year-old man who marries a twenty-year-old girl and his friends come to him and say, 'Look, you're an old man, you should get a boarder so your wife will be happy.' The old man says, 'I'll think about it.' A few months later, the friend sees the old man and says, 'Did you take my advice and get a boarder?' The old man replies, 'As a matter of fact, I did, and my wife is pregnant.' 'That's terrific,' says the friend. 'What about the boarder?' 'Oh,' the old man says, 'she's pregnant too.' "

Joe laughed. "So you got a boarder?"

"Oh, no, I just thought of the story. But I wanted to do the right thing, for both of us. What will I do if things get worse, I thought, knowing they almost certainly would. I needed help. In time, I would become completely immobile. What if I couldn't move at all?"

"You're not there yet."

"No, but it's always best to plan for the future."

"So what did you do?" Joe's head was clear now.

"Well, I considered every option, including boarders. I couldn't bring myself to do it. Then I realized I wasn't impotent, far from it. My problem was mobility, that was all. Then it hit me, the perfect solution. I hired a man."

"For what? You said you didn't want a boarder."

"He's not."

"Then what. . . ?"

"To start with, he's enormous. Six feet five inches tall, two hundred and thirty pounds. A mountain of a man. Originally I hired him to do yard work and shovel the sidewalk, but when I had this idea, I knew he would be perfect. He's Latvian, about sixty, doesn't speak much English, and he's nearsighted."

"He sounds like a prize."

"You have a way with words, Joe. For my purposes, he is a prize. You see, I've hired him to lift me up and down."

"You've hired him for what?"

"You heard me. My problem was mobility. Now I have it. That is, Janowicz has. He lifts me like a toy and can hold me as long as necessary. Right to left, back and forth, I can go at any speed, any elevation. Our sex life is better than ever."

"You're putting me on." Suddenly Joe felt nauseous. He rose to his feet, spilling his drink on the rug. "That's the most disgusting thing I've ever heard," he said.

"It's not disgusting, it's funny," Ben said. "But you're too sentimental to see the humor in it."

"It's not funny at all. It's sick."

"Oh, that's very interesting. You come in here and ask me the most intimate questions. That is acceptable. That is normal. Invalids are legitimate objects of curiosity, after all. How do we feed ourselves, how do we dress, bathe, shit—all this is information we should cheerfully share with the public. But if I tell you a rather harmless story, this is sick."

Ben got out of his chair and walked across the room to lean on the windowsill. "*You* want me to confide in *you*, confess my most desperate fears,

138

not because it matters a damn to *you*, but because it makes *you* feel strong and magnanimous. Well, let me tell *you*, mister, I don't need *your* pity or *your* approval, and I don't want *your* help. If you don't like my sense of humor, it's too goddamned bad, but don't come here telling me how to behave."

Ben gestured as he spoke, thrusting his glass forward, then to the side. The bootlegger looked scared, uncomprehending, as if he thought Ben had been driven crazy by the disease. "I've got to go now," Joe said, edging for the door.

"Go to hell," Ben said.

The door slammed and Ben returned to the window. In a moment, Joe appeared and hurried to his car. The lights went on, the engine roared, and with a squeal of tires he was gone. Ben stood watching the street. A pulse raced in his throat, and he leaned forward, his eyebrows pressed against the cool glass.

Standing in the middle of his living room, a thousand miles from Dory and the boys, he suddenly felt desperately alone and frightened. For a moment he thought he would lose control, crack up. But then he became aware of the dull throb in his groin. The moment had passed, the nervous breakdown would have to wait; right now he had to go to the bathroom.

20

THE HOTEL ELEVATOR was out of order, so Dory climbed the stairs to the second floor and peered down the corridor looking for the room. The brown runner was worn and the floor tilted slightly to the side. Behind the doors she passed, Dory heard vague music and muffled voices. Finally she stood in front of number 235. She considered knocking, then decided against it and boldly pushed the door open. Sam Matthews sat on the bed reading a newspaper.

The room was neat but dowdy, like the hotel. The faded green wallpaper was flaking and there was a bare bulb hanging from the ceiling. Sam was smiling at her.

"What a dump," Dory said. "I have a new respect for your talents if this is where you make your conquests."

"What do you want? It's clean, discreet, and fireproof. All for two dollars and sixty-five cents a night."

"Next time, I'm bringing my own sheets," Dory said.

"Come here," said Sam.

They had been lovers since the night Sam came over and made breakfast. Dr. Sykes had been right. The blindness had not returned. She did not have m.s. But that did not change Dory's feelings for Sykes, or for Sam. Sykes had failed her as a man, while Sam came to her rescue. Yet more than Dory's attitude had changed. Where in the past Sam had been suave, cruel, and distant, he now seemed vulnerable, warm, and caring. He bought Dory small gifts and found things to praise in even her most awkward efforts in the studio. The boys accepted Sam eagerly. Michael asked Sam to take him to the father-and-son banquet at school. Charles invited him to his birthday party. Sam reciprocated by taking the boys to the circus.

Dory justified this by telling herself it was important that her sons have a man around the house. But when he saw Sam in corduroys sitting in front of the fire, playing checkers with Charles, Dory felt sorry for him. This kind of life suited him best; his reputation as a rake, while no doubt earned, misrepresented him seriously. Perhaps it was only that no one had given him the chance to be generous before. Having no choice, she had called on Sam to help, and he had responded. But most of the time Dory didn't worry about it. She was grateful for Sam's presence that winter, whatever his reasons were for being with them.

They had agreed, however, not to meet in public, and Sam had never stayed overnight at the house. It wasn't fair to the boys, Dory said. And as long as they confined their affair to hotel rooms, she could pretend it wasn't really happening, that it wasn't a threat to her marriage. Two or three times a week they spent the afternoon together. Sam brought wine and Dory a picnic lunch. Once they drove to Spring Green to look at Frank Lloyd Wright's home and school, but that was all. It was winter, a good time to stay indoors.

Dory didn't know if she loved Sam or was simply grateful to him, but she wanted to find out. Ben had been outraged when she told him about Dr. Sykes, but when he offered to quit the orchestra and come home, Dory had discouraged him, and she knew Sam was part of the reason. She didn't feel the excitement with Sam that she had with Ben, but rather something more sedate. She was content with Sam, happy when they were together, relaxed when they were apart. She looked forward to seeing him, liked making love with him, but mostly she enjoyed being able to talk openly again with another adult. She told Sam everything about Ben and didn't worry about his betraying her confidence. They passed books back and forth and talked about art. Sam wanted to go to New York in the spring to see the new shows, and Dory imagined visiting galleries with someone who would see them as she did. They could stay at the Chelsea and walk uptown together. She still knew people in New York, of course, but it didn't matter. New York was a safe place to have an affair; people almost expected it of you.

On Valentine's Day, Sam arrived for dinner with a bunch of yellow roses, a box of candy, and a bottle of brandy. After dinner, when the boys had gone to bed, they sat in front of the fire and talked in a desultory way about her show. Then, rather abruptly Dory thought, Sam asked, "When's Ben coming home?"

"The season ends in March."

"What happens with us then?"

"I don't know. What do you think should happen?"

"It isn't up to me, Dory. You know how I feel."

"I guess you two could fight over me."

"I couldn't take advantage of a sick man. Anyway, Ben's my friend."

"He's my friend, too, Sam."

Sam nodded and got to his feet. He walked over to the bookcase, removed a novel and read the flyleaf. Then he replaced it and poured himself more brandy. "Is he still going to California?"

"I don't know. He hasn't said anything about it in his letters."

"What about Tulsa? Could he go back there?"

"It's hard to imagine Ben staying in Oklahoma for good." Dory smiled. "The man just can't hold a job."

"He's kept you."

"I guess he has. Was that a question?"

"I already knew the answer," Sam said. "The trouble is, I like both of you too much just to forget about this."

"Don't."

"What are you talking about? We can't go back to the way things were before, before we were involved."

"We were always involved, Sam. From the first time I met you I was interested; Ben's being away was only the catalyst."

"You mean you faked the blindness?"

Dory laughed, then was serious again. "That isn't what I meant. I just don't want you to think I fell into this because my husband's sick. It isn't a casual affair. I used to think about you all the time; what you thought of my painting, what you thought of me, if I was as attractive as the other women in the class. I used to write about you in my diary, for God's sake."

Sam was pleased by the idea. He returned to the couch and put his arm around Dory. "Your diary? Does it have a lock and key?"

"I don't need one," Dory said. "Ben trusts me. That's part of the problem. I'm too old-fashioned to be able to deceive my husband."

"We could be honest with him."

"Why? He'd be furious and hit you, or try, and then what would you do? I'd only be telling him because I felt guilty."

"Well, what about me, then?" Sam had a hurt expression on his face. He looked like a little boy.

"What do you mean?"

142

"Just what I said. Okay, you've got the disease and your career to worry about, but you can handle that. You've also got Ben, the kids, your home. What do I have? Now I've got you, sort of. When Ben gets back, I'll have nothing."

Dory wanted to laugh. "Sam Matthews lonely?" she said. "What about the legions of art students that are always after you? What about the faculty wives you have to drive from your door? You're a legend, Sam. I'm just part of the parade."

"Come on, Dory, that's not the same. You know that."

"Yes, I guess I do," she said slowly. "You've been wonderful this winter, not just to me, but to the boys. We couldn't have made it without you. I don't want it to end. If it was just sex, it wouldn't have to, but I'm probably falling in love with you, and that's not fair to Ben. He's got enough to contend with; I just can't do it to him. Besides, I love him, too." She laughed suddenly. "I feel like a character in a soap opera."

Sam sat looking at the rug. Then he stood and pulled on his coat. "I think I'll go for a walk in the snow."

"You'll be back?"

"I don't know, but I'll be around. Don't get up; I can let myself out."

Dory waited on the open platform for Ben's train. It was March, and March in Wisconsin did not leave much hope for spring. The train was late, and now Dory stamped her feet on the concrete. She debated going inside to wait, but she might not hear the announcement then. It was better that she wait than Ben. She knew from his last letters that things had not gone well. He had fallen again, though not onstage this time, and he was discouraged. Oddly, she did not feel as worried about their future as she had before. The year had given her time to think, to plan ahead. She would get her degree this spring, and she would find a job. They would get along. She was grateful to Ben for having gone on working, even in Tulsa.

First she saw the smoke; then she heard the train. Then it was there in the station and conductors were coming out of the cars, putting stepstools on the platform for the passengers. But Ben was nowhere in sight. She positioned herself in the middle of the platform so she would see him, and was suddenly grateful the boys were in school. She didn't want to explain Ben's condition to them now. When all the other passengers had gotten off the train, she approached the conductor. "Was there a man with a cane inside?" she asked.

The conductor looked down at her and nodded. Then she saw Ben above her in the doorway. She smiled, happy to see him, but she was shocked by the change. He was older, grayer, and though his face was

143

fleshy, he seemed to have lost weight. Now Ben descended the stairs, kicking his feet out to avoid slipping, his jaw taut with the effort. Finally he stood on the platform, leaning on his cane. "George," he said to the conductor. "I'd like you to meet my wife."

But Dory was in Ben's arms. "Oh, Ben, it's good to have you home."

Ben held her and kissed her ear. "I'm going to hold you to that," he said, and squeezed her again. Then they walked arm-in-arm down the platform together to the car.

At first it seemed to Dory that little had changed. Ben was weaker, that was obvious, but otherwise he appeared the same. He was gone every winter on tour; this was only a longer version. The blindness, Sykes, Sam—all were vague memories now, like part of some dimly recalled movie. She felt cheated in a way, as if she had been deprived of hard-won emotions, of anger and love and fear. But she knew too that life had a way of being less dramatic than one hoped or expected. And in time she could see that things were not as they seemed, that Ben had changed.

He was always distant at first after returning from a trip. Some internal grounding device had to be satisfied before he settled into his old routine. But now he was more so, almost secretive. Often he was in bed when Dory got home at night; and he had apparently developed the habit in Tulsa of rising at dawn. The birds woke him, he said, but even robins weren't around yet. He stayed away from the School of Music and his old friends, but whenever Dory came home at noon to surprise him, Marie said he was having lunch out. Was Ben having an affair? But Dory quickly dismissed the idea. He was only having trouble adjusting to being home. It was the first time he had lived in Madison and not been in the quartet. Madison could be a small town if you didn't work at the university.

It was mid-April before Dory found out what was really bothering Ben. She came home early one afternoon, thinking she would make roast beef for him, and found an envelope leaning against the mirror on her dresser.

1:30

Dory,

I am going to the Belmont Hotel. We both know why. The reason I have delayed this long is I didn't want the children to suffer unnecessarily, but some pain is inevitable in life, I guess. You will want to call and talk me out of this. Don't bother, as my mind is made up and we have nothing to discuss. In fact, don't call at all. If I need to, I'll call you.

Ben

Dory read the note again, and then a third time. Ben was wrong. She didn't feel like talking him out of leaving, but she did want to scream at

144

him, throw books, tear at his clothes. She wanted a good fight at least if she was going to lose her husband. Frustrated, Dory threw her coat on the couch and went into the kitchen. For once, she felt like doing housework, and started piling dishes in the sink. She was crying, but she wasn't as much sad as angry. What did Ben mean, walking out like this? What was she supposed to tell the boys? She had to work and go to school; she was too busy for domestic crises. She took a large pot encrusted with the scorched remnants of last night's lasagna and began to scrub it with steel wool. Damn him, she thought, damn him to hell. He can go to the Belmont, and he can rot there.

Yet in time the scrubbing absorbed some of her anger. Dory finished the lasagna pot and started on a large cast-iron skillet. In her mind, she went over Ben's note again. There were hints at a reconciliation, on his terms. If he wanted to be alone, for example, why tell her where he was going? And if he had really known about Sam, why had he delayed so long before leaving? He had mentioned pain and suffering, and Dory knew the pain was real. Ben was worse than before; she didn't deny that. Maybe Tulsa had been harder for him than she realized. Even in her anger, it hurt her to think of him struggling with the disease alone in some hotel room. Who would get things for him? Who would carry his suitcase? Still, there was little she could do. The last line of the note was the giveaway. He was in control now: Don't call us, we'll call you.

Dory finished the dishes and drained the sink. Then she made dinner. When the boys came home, she sat with them, but she wasn't hungry.

"Where's Dad?" Michael asked.

"He had to go away for a while."

"Did he go back to Oklahoma?"

"No, I don't think so. But he'll be calling to talk to you. Maybe you can ask him then."

The phone rang at nine, and Charles answered. He spoke to Ben for a while, mostly saying "yes," though Dory had no idea what the questions were. She took the receiver from his hand when he was finished. "Ben," she said. "We have to talk. You must know that." Ben's voice was high, with a slight wheeze in it. "There's nothing to say," he said. "Please get Michael."

Dory knew there was no point in arguing with him, so she went to find her elder son. Michael was in his room winding a spool of black tape around the handle of his baseball bat. He looked at her inquisitively. Dory sat down next to him on the bed. "Your father's on the phone. He wants to speak to you."

Michael hesitated, as if he sensed loyalty was involved here. "What about?" he said. Dory put her arm around his head and pressed it against

145

her chest. It comforted her still, after all these years. She remembered how she had loved nursing Michael and how she hated to wean him. Charles had weaned himself, but Michael had cried and cried, and she had always felt slightly guilty, as if she should have recognized his greater need and nursed him longer. Now she disengaged herself. "Go on," she said, and gently pushed Michael's head away from her breast.

While Michael and Ben talked, Dory sat on the bed and took stock. She was a part-time high-school art teacher of forty with less than two thousand dollars in the bank. Her husband had walked out on her and she had already dismissed her lover. With luck she would complete her degree this spring, but what would she do then, and with whom? Would Ben get a lawyer and fight her for custody, dragging them all through a courtroom battle? She imagined the headlines: "ART TEACHER TAKES LOVER, CRIPPLE TAKES KIDS."

The thought made her smile. She was as irrational as Ben. She thought of herself as being helpless at the hands of cruel fate, yet the fault was hers. Hadn't she invited Sam into their home, into her bed, in the first place? She could have asked Ben not to go to Tulsa or insisted harder when he said he had to go. She could have taken the boys to Oklahoma for the holidays. She knew she had been attracted to Sam from the start. A love affair with another man, a healthy man, an artist, was in some way necessary to her. She needed to feel desirable again, and that her staying with Ben represented a choice rather than an inevitability. Michael came back into the room. "Did you have a nice talk?" Dory asked.

"It was okay." The boy didn't seem upset. "Daddy said he'll take me to a game in Milwaukee for my birthday."

Dory was grateful that Ben hadn't tried to turn the boys against her. "Did he say anything else?"

Michael was taping his bat again. "Are you mad at Daddy?"

Dory reached for Michael and held him to her. "Is that what he said?"

"No. I just wondered. Why did Daddy go away, then?"

"Sometimes it's a good idea to go away for a while if you're upset about something."

"Why is Daddy upset?"

"I don't know exactly. Anyway, sometimes he just has to go away, you know that."

"Like when he went to Oklahoma before?"

"Yes, like that."

Michael nodded, satisfied with Dory's answer. "But he'll come home later?"

"Yes," Dory said, hoping she wasn't lying. "He'll be home soon. But now it's time for bed."

"It's only nine o'clock," Michael protested.

"Nine-fifteen. I'm going downstairs to get Charles, but I'll come back in a minute and tuck you in."

Dory found Charles on the porch drawing on a large white pad. She admired the colored arrows for a minute before sending him to bed. Then she went into the kitchen to phone her father-in-law.

All of Moshe's visits were linked in Dory's mind. No matter how many times he came, she thought of him as he had looked that first day: a little man in baggy pants, with a shy smile and an armful of presents. This time was no different, though Moshe now wore a golf shirt with his initials monogrammed on the pocket. He sat with the boys while they ate. Then he played checkers with Charles and let Michael show him his trains. No one mentioned Ben. It was as if Moshe had dropped in while he was away on tour.

When the boys had gone to bed, Moshe joined Dory in the kitchen. "Would you like some tea?"

"Later, maybe. Here, sit." He patted the chair next to his. "Tell me. What's this all about? What's the matter?"

Dory started to speak, then stopped. What could she say that would make him see her point of view? He was Ben's father. She felt isolated, and the hopelessness of her situation bore in upon her. She started to cry, and Moshe put his arms around her. He smoothed her hair and gave her a handkerchief from his pocket. "Go on. It's good, you'll feel better. Cry."

Dory did feel better, but she was embarrassed, too. "I'm sorry," she said. "I don't know why I started crying."

"It's so awful? Your husband walks out the door. Why shouldn't you cry?"

"It's just that it's my fault. He left because of me."

"It's never all one person's fault. Benjy ain't so easy to get along with. If I know anything, I know that."

"It's not Ben, Pop," Dory said. "The reason he left is that I had an affair with another man this winter when he was in Oklahoma. It's over now, but Ben found out about it and that's why he went to the hotel."

Moshe looked away, then down at the floor. He was embarrassed for Dory, for himself, that they had to be together talking like this. They had never discussed sex. Why would they? He wasn't her father. Where were her people, her friends? "Why did you call me?"

147

Dory took a deep breath. "Because I thought you might understand, and I knew Ben would listen to you."

"I ain't so sure," Moshe said.

"I just want to talk to Ben. I don't expect you to solve our problems and I know you don't approve of me; I don't approve of myself right now."

Moshe looked at her critically. "You sure you want Benjy back?"

"What do you mean? Of course I do. Do you think this is easy for me?"

"Easy, hard, I don't know. All I'm saying is, think it over. Your husband is a sick man, getting sicker all the time."

"Ben is your son."

"That's why I'm saying it. He's hurt now, hurt real bad. Otherwise he wouldn't go away and leave you here with the boys. Maybe he'll come back if I talk to him, and maybe not. But I don't want him here unless you do. Don't do me no favors. You're feeling guilty maybe? Don't. I'll hire a nurse, I can afford it. Benjy and me can live together again, and we'll get along fine. You don't have to worry."

Moshe's voice was harsh now, and Dory noticed his big hands, cut and scarred by years of work at his sewing machine. His shoulders were large and his veins were like rope. She believed him. He could probably take better care of Ben than she.

"It's not that, really."

"You're a young woman. What happened this winter, it could happen again, and I wouldn't even blame you. Approve, don't approve, who cares? I ain't a rabbi, I don't make the laws. All I ask is that you think carefully about this, about Benjy. If you're sure, I'll do what I can."

"I'm sure," Dory said. "I thought about it before I called you. Before Ben even came home, I knew what I wanted to do. Don't you think I know about my age and Ben's condition? I don't want my husband back because I'm Florence Nightingale. I love Ben."

Dory only realized how loud her voice had been when she stopped talking and heard once again the hum of the refrigerator. "I'm sorry, Pop," she said. "I didn't mean to shout."

"It's good," Moshe said. "Now I know you give a damn. That's enough for me; Benjy, I don't know. But it's no good breaking up families. The boys need a father and a mother too; one ain't enough. I'll go talk to him."

"That's wonderful, Pop."

"Thank me when I do something," Moshe said.

21

BEN'S ROOM at the Belmont looked as if he was preparing for a siege. On the night table was a pile of paperback mysteries. The morning paper lay on the bed. On the desk were two cans of sardines, one of mixed nuts, a bag of apples, a jar of pickled herring, a gallon of California wine, a package of halvah, and a box of assorted Wisconsin cheeses. Ben stood at the window looking across Capitol Park at the white stone building. He held his fiddle in the crook of his arm, but now he set it down. He couldn't concentrate on music; there was no point in trying. His body was taut, expectant, but everything was over now. He was too late.

Since his return, Ben had suspected Dory. She was erratic in her behavior, effusive one minute, then almost indifferent the next. When they made love, she tried too hard to please him, and when, as sometimes happened, he became impotent, she seemed to blame herself too readily. Then there was the fact that Sam didn't come by to see him. After a week, Ben had called to suggest they have lunch. Sam was tied up, he said. When Ben suggested an alternate date, Sam was evasive. He'd check and get back to Ben. But he had never called.

One day Ben and Michael went to the zoo and had lunch. Michael mentioned that Sam had taken him there during the winter, and as they talked, it became obvious that Sam had taken him many places. When Ben asked, Michael said Sam had also been at the house frequently. Furious, Ben went to the university to have it out with Sam, but the artist had taken

149

his class to Chicago on a field trip. The secretary explained that from there Professor Matthews was going to New York. The next week was Easter vacation.

Sam's absence answered Ben's questions. At first he intended to get out of town. But where to go? He had supported himself since adolescence, but now he was struck by self-doubt. He couldn't go back to Tulsa, and, except for Jimmy, he no longer had any contacts in New York. He needed to think, but his mind was full of Dory and Sam. He had lurid visions of them in bed together, coupling in various exotic ways; it was hard to think rationally of his future. Finally he did what he had always done: he went to a delicatessen and bought enough food to feed an army. Fat boys never change, he thought. When you're scared, angry, or frustrated, just stick something in your mouth and you'll feel better. Now he sat at the desk and plucked the fiddle's strings. Out of tune. No wonder he sounded so lousy.

There was a knock at the door. "Come in," Ben yelled. He was expecting the boy from the drugstore with cigars.

"Looks like you're staying awhile," Moshe said.

Ben jerked around in his chair. His father upset his thoughts of alienation and lonely nights. "Pop, what are you doing here?"

"Every time I come, you ask. Maybe I'm not welcome?"

Actually, he was right. Ben would have preferred to break the news to his parents in his own way, in his own time. He felt awkward, as if he should explain himself, the situation. "Of course not. I wasn't expecting you, is all."

"I was passing through. It's okay if I sit? I'm a little tired. I was eight hours on the plane."

"Sure, there, on the bed. Would you like some cheese?"

Moshe waved him away. "I ain't hungry. But go ahead yourself."

"Were you at the house?" Then: "Of course, how would you know I was here otherwise."

"I know all about it," said Moshe. "I talked to your wife."

"Then you don't know all about it," Ben snapped. "You know her side is all."

"Sides? What do I care?" Moshe shrugged, raising his eyebrows. "I'm no referee like in a baseball game."

"Umpire, Pop," Ben said, unable to resist correcting his father. "In baseball, they're umpires."

"Okay, professor, whatever you say."

They were silent for a moment, Ben's eyes working the room, avoiding Moshe. Finally he said, "Did she tell you why I left?"

Moshe nodded. "Some."

"And do you blame me?"

"I'm too old to blame, Benjy. What you do, you do. You're a grown man, a father."

"Well, what would you have done, then?" Though the old man said nothing, Ben felt he was being led somewhere.

"Why ask me? My life is such a picture? But if you want to know, there was plenty of times when you was a little boy that I wanted to walk out the door. Times I thought I couldn't stand for one more minute your mother screaming and calling me a schlemiel that wasn't good enough for her family."

"So why didn't you leave?"

"You know why. I told you before. You don't make orphans. You know what else, Benjy? I'm glad now I stayed. Glad. Even with the *tsuris*, I don't regret it for a minute. You're grown up and doing fine. That I'm proud of, proud that I helped you. Working all my life making suits for *schvartzes* ain't so great, but I got one good boy. That's something."

"Was it worth it? Giving up thirty years of your life for me?"

"To me it was. Anyway, your mother ain't so bad."

"Why aren't you with her now, then?"

"Now's different. For her, for me. Anyway, I want to try it, living alone for a while. It's wonderful to wake up in the morning with nothing to do, no one to talk to. Sometimes I get lonely, and then I come to see you. But lots of times I just sit in the morning and listen to nothing. And you know, Benjy, it sounds beautiful."

"I'll bet Ma doesn't think it's so beautiful."

"She'll try it too," Moshe said. "But you're not fair to your mother. I never got a divorce from her, and I never will. You know what else? Sometimes when I'm lonely, I'll call her up on the long-distance telephone and we'll argue a little, and then I feel better. It sounds crazy, but when I'm gone too long I miss the *tsuris*. Your mother is an interesting woman. I never met no one else like her."

Ben smiled at his father. Moshe had never talked about his marriage before. Always it had been the solitary oath accompanied by a hand on his stomach. In recent years, when he had been away from Sarah, he had seemed blissfully relaxed. Who would have thought he missed her?

"Whatever else Ma might have done," Ben said, "at least she was faithful to you."

"I think so. But to tell you the truth, Benjy, if it would have made my life easier, I wish she could have had ten lovers, all at once if she wanted.

151

There was nothing like that between us for years now. What difference would it make?"

"You can say that because it never happened."

"Maybe so. You got a point. No one can say what he'd do until something happens." Moshe looked toward the window, and Ben studied his shoes, both suddenly embarrassed.

"Did Dory send you?" Ben asked.

"No one has to send. I come when I feel like it."

"Sure," Ben said, ashamed of himself. How could he question Moshe's motives when his own were so muddled? "I'm sorry, Pop. It's funny, though. When I married Dory, you disowned me. Ma called her a whore; she still hasn't accepted the marriage or the existence of her grandchildren. Now that Dory's actually done what Ma said she'd do, you sound like you're defending her."

"I ain't defending no one. Go ask her, she'll tell you if I think what she did is so wonderful. But your mother's a foolish old woman. That girl's no whore, and you know it. Don't talk crazy, Benjy. What's done is done. Don't make it worse than it is."

"It can't be any worse for me," Ben said, rising. "You know how I felt when I found out? I felt like killing both of them, like blowing their heads off, like some goddamned maniac, that's how I felt. Here I was in Oklahoma working my ass off for six months trying to earn a living, and back home my wife's fucking my best friend. You can say it's over, what's done is done. And maybe it is done for now, maybe this one is over with. But how do I know there won't be someone else next year or the year after that?"

"How do I know when I go to bed the sun will come up the next morning? There ain't no guarantees in life, Benjy. You sound a little like your mother. She's still mad at the Russians for kicking her father out of Kiev. You can't think that way; you'll get sick. You want the truth? The truth is, you don't know if your wife is going to be happy. You're a sick man, going to get sicker, I can see why you worry. You got a right to be mad. But she's a good person. And you got two little boys. Lots of people who ain't sick get divorced."

"That's different."

"Sure. They're them and you're you. But it's the same, too. People want to walk away from their problems; it's easier that way, I'll admit. One thing I give your wife credit for, she ain't afraid to fight. She wants you back home."

"If you can believe her."

"So go ask yourself. Anyway, if she didn't want you home, why did she call and ask me to fly a thousand miles? For my health?"

"I thought she didn't send you, that you were just passing through."

"I told a lie. I should burn in hell."

Ben laughed and looked away again. What Moshe said moved him. He enjoyed talking to his father, and regretted it too. Did it take this for them to be open with each other? Why did it always have to be some crisis; what was wrong with fathers and sons loving each other on a daily basis? Despite himself, he was impressed, too, with Dory, with her efforts at reconciliation. But thinking about the future scared him. Whatever else had gone wrong, his marriage had always been solid, the firmament of his life. The possibility of losing Dory, as he was losing the strength in his legs, had made him panic. But he couldn't stay in hotels forever. Moshe was right: there were no guarantees.

"I don't know, Pop," he said.

"Benjy, at least talk to her. Be a *mensch.*"

"I wouldn't know what to say." It was the truth. The thought of Dory in the room made him intensely uncomfortable. Should he clean up first? They were like strangers now.

"You'll think of something," Moshe said. "The girl's miserable. She cries so much she can't talk. You'll see."

It hurt Ben to think of it. He wanted to comfort her, to fix her life, to fix his own. But then he thought of Matthews. "It just makes me mad as hell to even think of it, Pop. How could she do it?"

Moshe shrugged. "Ask her."

For a moment Ben was silent, thinking. Then he said, "Okay, Pop. I'll talk to her."

Dory stood on Pinckney Street trying to collect herself. She didn't feel ready to face Ben. Would she ever? It hadn't occurred to her until now, but the Belmont and the Madison Hotel faced each other across a corner of the square. An unintentional irony, she was sure. How could Ben have known where she and Sam had gone? Unless Sam had bragged of his other affairs, which was a possibility. She would have expected Ben to stay in one of the railroad hotels, though. The Washington or the Cardinal. The Belmont seemed an odd choice. Of course, Ben had not been himself; he was upset, he was still, and she was too. That was why she was here.

Dory looked at her watch. They had agreed to meet at two, after lunch, and she was late, but still she hesitated. Moshe had come home full of assurances. He knew his son. Ben was hurt, but who wouldn't be? And now he was just waiting for her to come and apologize. "Don't worry about the boys," Moshe had said. "We'll make out fine." In fact, the boys were doing very well. Since Moshe had arrived they had spent most of their time in toy stores and restaurants. They seemed bored with the domestic drama, anxious to be rid of their parents so they could take advantage of their grandfather in peace.

Dory was grateful to Moshe but felt he didn't really understand. He seemed to be waiting for her to ratify the treaty he had negotiated with Ben. Moshe could come home and command her to "Go to your husband!" But it was a new role for her. Devoted wife, young mother, even aspiring artist—all those were familiar enough. But she had never even considered adultery before Sam. Even when she was in his arms, she hadn't thought of it that way. Sam had nurtured her, and she needed that. Only later had she felt guilty, and then it was too late. Unfaithful? She had never lost faith in Ben. Faith wasn't part of the equation, but she had only the clichés of a thousand movies to guide her.

Her anxiety annoyed her. Why couldn't she walk over to the hotel and have it out with Ben? They were both adults. These things happened; they weren't innocent; they knew. Why couldn't she act like a woman of the world if she was going to be treated like one? She couldn't even smoke in a sophisticated way; she always started coughing. How would Garbo handle this, she wondered, or Bette Davis. With scorn, she decided, and no apologies. This is my life, take it or leave it. But this was no movie. There was a real chance Ben would reject her, whatever Moshe said. She had to think about it seriously.

Tell him what you told me, Moshe had said. But they were so different. Moshe personified acceptance, invited confidences, while Ben was brittle and proud. Of course, no one could be more generous than Ben, but there was Sam between them now. Don't justify yourself, Dory thought. Don't argue. It's not a debate; you can't win. Admit you were wrong and ask him to forgive you. Dory took a deep breath and crossed the street to the hotel.

Ben answered her knock almost immediately. He stood aside to let her enter the room, and Dory walked in. Ben was dressed in a suit and tie and seemed smaller to her. Appearing to list slightly to the left, he leaned momentarily against the doorjamb. Then he pushed off and stood between the bed and the door. The desk and windowsill were piled high with books and papers, but the one chair was empty, as if it had been cleared for her. Dory sat down and looked across at the Capitol. "Nice view," she said.

"I hadn't noticed," Ben said. He didn't mention the time, but offered fruit and nuts, which Dory refused. Then he sat on the bed, holding his right knee with both hands and rocking slowly back on his hips. His face seemed longer now, sadder and more expressive. Dory didn't know what to say. Finally Ben broke the silence. "So. Pop said you wanted to talk."

"You knew that," Dory said, turning toward him. "I told you over the phone."

Ben nodded but said nothing. It was up to her to begin.

Dory stood and walked across the room. Then she turned again to face Ben. He was looking away, but sitting on the bed, he seemed pathetically vulnerable. She wanted to hold him, to love him. She thought of New York, when they were young. She couldn't have imagined then ever being in such a situation. She walked over to the bed and put her hand on his shoulder. "Oh, Ben," she said. "I'm so sorry. It was stupid of me and it didn't mean anything, and it's over. It was over before you came home; it was really over before it started."

"You make it sound like it never happened." Ben was still looking away.

"That's because I wish it hadn't. But it did. I'm sorry I hurt you. I'd give anything to take it back, but I can't. Can you forgive me?"

Now Ben rose and walked to the window. He wanted distance. "Why didn't you tell me before?" he said. "Why did I have to wait and hear from other people? Do you know what it feels like to come home and imagine all your friends are saying, 'Look at the asshole'? Well, for me it was worse. It was 'Look at the crippled asshole. Poor bastard.' I not only had to suffer contempt, but pity, and I didn't even realize it at first."

"You never used to care about other people."

"I never had to. I was the big shot. No matter how much people in the School of Music hated me, no one ever pitied me before."

"Ben, I'm sorry. I don't know what else to say."

"I just don't see how you could do it, how Sam could. What were you thinking about, Dory?"

"Ourselves, I guess," Dory said. "I don't know. We didn't want to hurt you. Both of us regretted that part of it. But I was alone, Ben. I was scared and lonely, and Sam helped me."

Ben laughed sharply. "I'll say."

Suddenly Dory was angry. Why should she have to take all the blame? Why couldn't he be more understanding? "Look, Ben, I said I'm sorry, and I am. I want you to come home, but I'm not going to wear sackcloth and ashes for the rest of my life over this. It isn't the way you make it out to be. Sam was pretty decent to me in his own way, and it meant a lot. I had a hard winter, and your being away didn't make things easier."

"I had to go, you know that."

"Like hell. You went because you were too proud to stay at the university. You could have spent the whole year on sabbatical at full pay. You went to Tulsa for yourself, to show Heinz you didn't need him. Well, that's fine for you. I hope you feel a lot better. But you never thought about me and how I'd manage by myself. I was working and in school, and with the kids there was almost more than I could handle. Of course I needed a man, someone to talk to sometimes. What did you expect to happen when you went away for six months?"

Ben looked as if he had been hit. "You don't mean to say you were justified in doing this, do you?"

"Not exactly, but I didn't come to renounce my past life either. I said I was sorry; I am, but for the effect it had on you, not for doing what I did. I said I wish it hadn't happened; I do. But I wish a lot of things. I wish you had never gotten sick and left the university, that I didn't have to go out and find a job to support all of us, that we could always be young and healthy and in love. I wish life were easier. But I'm also old enough to know that you can't always have what you wish for. I wish things had worked out differently, but I'm not suicidal with remorse. I want you to come home, but I'll survive if you don't. I learned that this year. Maybe you don't understand what anxiety really is, what it's like to try to reassure two small children about the future when you're so scared you can't eat. Where the hell were you then? Where were you when I went blind?"

"I did what I could. I called my doctor. I offered to fly home."

"What good would that have done? I didn't need someone for a few days or a week, Ben. I was alone and scared as hell. Would you have come home permanently? Would you have quit the orchestra?"

"I don't know."

"I do. You wouldn't have, you couldn't. It was too important. And that's the point, Ben. It was important only to you. Not to me and not to the boys. You didn't have to prove anything to us. Having you here was everything, and you were gone for a very long time. Sam came when we needed him. The rest, the sex, that was almost nothing."

"I'll bet it was something to Sam."

"Not really. It wasn't very good for either of us. He was really a better friend than lover." Dory was worn out by her speech. She hadn't intended to lose her temper. She had planned to apologize. She had only meant to clear the air. "I am sorry," she said.

"I wish you'd stop saying that. You're right. I wasn't thinking about you or the boys or anyone but myself. It seemed critical to me, a turning point or something. Big deal. What did it accomplish? I don't think Ober gives a shit, and I made you miserable. God knows how it affected the kids."

156

"What about you, Ben?"

Ben had been avoiding her, but now he looked into Dory's eyes. "It was the worst time of my life. Terrible. I didn't know anyone in Tulsa and I didn't want to know anyone. I couldn't play, but it didn't matter because the orchestra was so lousy they didn't know what music should sound like. No one but me knew how bad I was, and that was humiliating. It got so I hated to pick up my fiddle. I'd skip rehearsals and come at the last moment for concerts. And when they'd ask why, I'd beg off because of the disease. I was, am, weaker, God knows, but the irony is that I went to Oklahoma in the first place to show Ober I was the same as before. I guess I really showed him."

Dory crossed the room to Ben, her arms enfolding him. They didn't seem to fit at first, as awkward as new lovers, but then they relaxed and stood holding each other in the middle of the room for a long time. When they separated, they continued to hold hands.

"I want to be with you and the boys," Ben said. "But I don't want you to stay around out of some sense of duty. What hurt most about all this was I knew it made sense for you to find someone else. Why ruin two lives? Sam's a good artist; he'd probably be a good father. A good provider. That's more than I can promise. I've done my best to hate the bastard, and for a while I really did, but not anymore. We always said he was my friend more than yours."

"Sam will be relieved to hear that. But 'duty' isn't the right word, not really. It's true that I wouldn't feel right leaving you, but it's not because you're sick. I'm not dedicating my life to nursing the disabled. I love you, Ben. That's why I turned Sam down. You can't desert people just because things are hard. It isn't the way I was brought up."

"Thank God for a Christian childhood," Ben said, and sat down.

"You think it's funny, but the truth is, I grew up in a house full of invalids," Dory said. "My grandmother had involutional melancholia; my Uncle Alfred was mongoloid; there was an anemic aunt who stayed with us off and on."

"God, what a gene pool. If I had known, I might have hesitated before having children with you."

"Well, it was a large family. But the point is, my grandfather considered them all his responsibility, and they each gave us something in return. Uncle Alfred licked envelopes in his office. Grandmother supervised the gardener, and Aunt Mildred played the piano."

"So what do I give you, Dory? Now, I mean?"

"Everything. You're the one who encouraged me in my artwork from the beginning. It's terribly hard for me to go off to the university every day to work; it helps to know that you're here, that you believe in me. That's much more important than a paycheck."

Ben looked seriously at Dory; then he smiled. "Considering the circumstances, it's lucky for me you feel that way."

"Of course, you could always learn to cook," Dory said.

"A man in my condition?" Ben said, and they laughed together.

Ben looked carefully at Dory. There were new wrinkles in her forehead, and her eyes were bloodshot. The season hadn't been easy for either of them, but at least they were together again. Now she leaned down to kiss him, and he put his hand on the small of her back.

"It's been a while since I've had a good-looking woman in my hotel room," he said. Then he slowly pulled his wife down on top of him.

The season in Tulsa marked an end to Ben's career as a concert artist. He knew he couldn't go to San Francisco, but both he and Dory wanted to leave Madison. Moshe offered to buy them a house wherever they wanted to live and advance them as much money as they needed until they got settled. But Dory wanted to work. After graduation one of her professors recommended her for a position in Milwaukee. The university was small and lacked Madison's reputation, but Dory took it eagerly. She was older than most of her classmates, and a woman. She was in no position to turn anything down. In July she and Ben drove to Milwaukee to look for an apartment. They found a small place near the campus, not far from Lake Michigan, and were pleased to discover that rents were considerably lower than in Madison.

At the end of the summer they followed the moving van down Route 30 to their new home. Dory had the almost tangible sensation of extricating herself from the quicksand of binding relationships that had accumulated over twelve years. At first, Madison had seemed ideal, but the last two years had been hell. Dory carried her world around inside her most of the time. She had so much to explain to so many people, that the very thought exhausted her. She lacked energy to begin. It was easier just to move.

They would make a new start, away from the School of Music, the old neighborhood, the League, the Democratic party, the Unitarian church, away from Sam. She had seen him just once since Ben's return, and they had hardly talked. It was at the opening of her graduate show, but he kept his distance and left early. It bothered Dory. She wanted to tell him that they could all be friends again.

She was grateful to Sam. Without his criticism and encouragement she would have been no more than a dilettante painting pretty pictures in the basement while her kids were in school. He had made her into a professional, an artist. Whatever else had happened, she wanted to thank him for that.

The week before they left, she called him.

"I heard you were leaving. I was going to get in touch," Sam said. "But I always figured Ben would pick up the phone."

"I know," Dory said. "It's all right. I just wanted to say good-bye."

"It's great about the job. Are you happy?"

"I'm happy anyone wants to hire a middle-aged woman with two kids and a sick husband, I guess."

"Come on. Forty isn't old, not anymore. Will they let you teach anything interesting?"

"Not at first, but what do you expect? Freshman survey, basic drawing, the usual. But really, Sam, I'm grateful to have it."

Sam hesitated, and Dory heard music in the background. She wondered if he had someone in his room, someone new. But when he spoke, Sam's voice was low and serious. "I'm going to miss you, Dory. I'm going to miss you a lot. In fact, I'll miss all of you. For a while it was almost like having a family of my own."

"The boys still ask why you don't come over anymore. I never know what to say."

"I'm sorry about that. Maybe I could adopt them or get visiting rights or something."

Dory laughed. "Oh, Sam, I wish you could. You were wonderful with them. But don't be sorry, don't be sorry about anything. It wasn't your fault."

"Sure it was," Sam said. "I never wanted anything more in my life."

There was silence between them. Dory looked out the door of the phone booth and watched the shoppers moving in and out of the A&P. How could they just go on with their lives like that? she wondered, and she began to cry. First she dabbed at her eyes with a handkerchief, then she blew her nose. "God, I'm sorry, Sam," she said. "I was going to be so cool about this, but I just can't talk about it without crying."

For a moment she thought the line had gone dead. Then Sam's voice was in her ear again. "Don't ever apologize for crying, Dory," Sam said. "And keep in touch."

Part Four

22

October 16, 1960: A year has gone by, a year in which, though I had a great deal to say, I somehow lacked the desire to say it. Then, after not writing for so long, I began to feel the need to catch up, to re-live everything, and that is impossible. You never catch up. There simply isn't time.

We've all managed to adjust pretty well to life in Milwaukee. Ben stays at home now, reading and writing music; the boys have new schools and friends; to my surprise, I have received an early promotion to assistant professor, though with no raise in salary. I still have to teach introductory courses on Saturday mornings and the men in my department seem to have forgotten that I was hired to teach sculpture, but those seem like minor complaints. Predictably, Ben's health is worse, but he bears it remarkably well. Each morning he orders groceries over the phone and supervises the cooking at night, with the boys helping out. Between them they are able to get a hot meal on the table by the time I get home from work. Sometimes I feel overwhelmed by our situation—in the middle of a faculty meeting I will inexplicably feel like crying. I tell myself it is silly, that there is nothing especially tragic about my working to support the family or Ben's staying home. But then I see Ben standing in the kitchen, spatula in hand, leaning on his cane in front of the stove while the boys set the table, and I realize that courage can be expressed in the most ordinary ways.

December 1, 1960: Awake at five, walked to the lake, fresh snow and fog. Then back home for hot coffee and rolls. Now I sit in bed reading the

Ladies' Home Journal and writing. It is six-thirty and the house is quiet. I have been waking earlier since I moved down the hall; it's ironic, since the reason I moved originally was that Ben's tossing at night disturbed me. Perhaps I feel guilty for not staying with him and wake early to punish myself. On the other hand, this is the best time for me, before dawn, when no one else is up. Things seem clear at this hour, there are no distractions. It is a time when I can pretend that I have nothing more serious to worry about than my spring wardrobe.

January 8, 1961: Last night I was awakened by Charles screaming. He said that Martians had been coming in his window, that they wanted to kidnap him. I'm not sure what the Martians would want with Charles, but the episode surprised me, since he is usually so quiet. He's been acting strangely since we moved him into his own room. The boys used to fight all the time when they shared, but now they are closer than before. They seem to have regressed in some ways, putting their arms around each other and walking to school together. Michael has started touching walls, doors, corners, and tables again. He seems to leapfrog down the street, watching for cracks and telephone poles in his path; it's pathetic how aware he is of danger in the world. I don't know what to do. I don't blame Charles for worrying about Martians or Michael for fearing trees. What bothers me is the suspicion that this whole tragic experience will affect my boys in more serious ways, ways I can't possibly know.

February 16, 1961: Two A.M. Ben called just now and I went into his room to find piss on the sheets and Ben in tears. He was angry and frustrated and blamed me for not putting the bottle in the right position. He says inches make all the difference, and of course he is right. But I can't do everything. At least, not always. I work all day, come home and cook dinner, and then grade papers or do preparations for the next day. I help Ben get ready for bed, and I suppose sometimes I put the bottle in the wrong place. I can't help it.

Now I'm too jumpy to sleep, and I resent Ben. Yet I don't hate him, even when he's like this. It might be better if I did; then I could leave. But I'm cursed with understanding. I know he yells at me when he's frustrated and that it's the only defense he has. And he's got a right. Whatever problems I have, I also have a new life here—a job, friends, students. Ben has nothing, except what he can make for himself. He spends his time reading and listening to music, and he does remarkably well. It's embarrassing when he exposes his helplessness, not for me but for him. He has to maintain the image in his mind of husband, father, protector, and provider, no matter how far from the truth that is. I don't like him to yell at me, but I treasure his anger. It would be awful if suddenly he wasn't mad anymore. Anger is dignity. I wouldn't deprive Ben of it if I could.

March 22, 1961: One problem I have in my job is that the men I deal with are very different from the other men I've known. Far from having the slightest concern for me as a person—or interest in me as a woman—they seem almost afraid of me, as if I could contaminate them somehow. Although my exhibition record is as good as anyone else's, I am allowed in the sculpture studio only when the men aren't using it. This puts me in a paradoxical position: my success and promotion depend on my producing, yet every effort is made to deny me the necessary facilities. I'm scheduled to show in two group exhibitions this year, but I have no place to work or store my equipment. How can they be jealous of me when they all have tenure? I sometimes wonder what they are doing in the studio during those hours when I'm not allowed inside. I dream of breaking the door down and finding them all on their knees, pederasts, but I doubt it is really anything so interesting. In the end, I will probably have to rent a studio, but we are already in debt, and besides, why should I? This is supposed to be a university, not the Boys' Club. It makes me mad that there's nothing I can do, no one to complain to about it. Sam used to say that for the first few years you should smile at everyone and keep your mouth shut. It's hard advice to follow, but I try. It would be more satisfying if the men would try to seduce me—at least it would show they know I'm here. If I ever allude in any way to Ben, they become embarrassed and turn away, as if I had farted. Stiff upper lip and all that. The only man I like is Fred Newman, who is arrogant, flirts with everyone, and shows all over the country. Of course everyone hates him. Fred says the trouble with our department is that the women have no breasts and the men have no balls. Just my luck to land in a colony of eunuchs.

April 11, 1961: My birthday, and it looks as if it will be a lovely day. I rode my bicycle around the lake this morning and stopped to talk to an old man who was fishing along the McKinley breakfront. He offered to bait an extra line—the most gracious offer I've had lately—but I declined and rode off. Today I'm forty-two. It's odd to think that Mother and Father were both dead by this time. If I have only another two or three years of life, how best to spend it? Of course, this is only superstition. Daddy had a heart condition and was overweight. Mother died suddenly because of hardening of the arteries. I, on the other hand, am healthy, slim, and have shown no signs of congenital disease. My doctor told me that if one lives to forty with no serious problems, she is likely to make it to a ripe old age. It's comforting to think so. At least I'm glad that the pace of the last few years hasn't affected my health. God knows it's affected everything else. But today I'm not worrying about that. It's my birthday. Ben has slowed down, but he's lost none of his enthusiasm for birthdays. Later we'll go out for dinner and a movie and spend more money than we should. Then Ben will ask one of the boys to go to the hall hatrack and get out my presents, which have been sitting in the storage compartment for months. We'll sit together and eat birthday cake and laugh at old jokes. It will be very much as it always was.

April 14, 1961: I woke this morning thinking of Al Sinclair, an old radical we knew in Madison, dead for three years but still alive in my mind's eye. Remembering Al always makes me feel optimistic and selfish at the same time. He was always pursuing some faraway evil, badgering me to sign a petition or give money. The last time I saw him he had lost a lot of weight and was blind as a bat from cataracts, which he refused to have surgically removed. This did not stop him from riding his bike downtown every day to his law office. His friends used to worry that he would either get lost or be hit by a car, but Al seemed to make out all right. Now he is dead and I sit here feeling guilty for doing nothing about Indochina or Cuba or black people in Alabama. I am so involved in my own life, in our struggle, that I seem to lose energy for other people's problems. That isn't right, I know, but I have the feeling that Al wouldn't hold it against me.

May 5, 1961: Last night, when he was coming home from Chess Club, Ben fell on the sidewalk and broke a tooth. When he came into the house his mouth was streaming blood and he was swearing. But he was also ashamed, and that made me feel awful. I wanted to tell him: Raise all the hell you want. You have a right! An incredible thing has happened to you, an unjust thing. You have every right to scream it to anyone who will listen. It hurts me to see him quiet and apologetic; I would rather he be furious.

June 5, 1961: The year is over. Yesterday I turned in my grades and locked the office. Fred Newman has a Guggenheim and gave me his studio for the summer. I'll spend the days there and my nights at home with Ben. There is a lovely old natatorium across the street from Fred's studio, and I can go swimming there. Almost everyone else in the neighborhood is Negro, and when I go to the natatorium, the slap of brown bodies in the water makes me feel like I'm living in the middle of a Gauguin. I haven't seen so many Negroes since I left Kentucky. Most white people I know marvel at my courage in biking to work, but everyone has been very nice. The children stand outside my door every day, and I've found that they are content if I give them paper and felt pens and let them draw. Milwaukee is terribly conservative and the natives suspect outsiders of any color, I think. Black people not only look different but talk and dress differently. Three strikes and you're out. But having been brought up by Negroes, I find that when I'm down on Hubbard Street I slip back into a high-pitched Southern accent.

Yet it's ironic that my liberation coincides with Ben's imprisonment. Summer is the worst time of the year for him; he hardly dares go out and is only comfortable in air-conditioned rooms.

June 10, 1961: Tomorrow is Michael's birthday and I haven't done a thing about it. It makes me sad that we're apart so much now, not just Michael and I, but all of us. I'm gone all day and too tired at night to have much time with them. It's easier on the boys than Ben. I have my job; Ben only has me. I get lonely for Ben, and for our old life. Then it seems we could do it all again—all the old things. Until I see Ben in his room with his bottles of urine and the wheelchair in the corner, and I know it isn't really possible at all. He still walks, but less often now, and not as far, and hardly ever with me. I worry, about him and about the boys, too. Michael's compulsions are worse—he's developed involuntary facial tics along with the rest. Charles seems withdrawn, though at least the Martians haven't made another appearance. I suppose we'll make it through. After all, what choice do we have?

23

MOSHE EMERGED from the Milwaukee Road station and squinted into the morning light, looking for a cab. He had purchased a 45-day "See America" ticket and had been traveling relentlessly for weeks from Washington to Boston and then across the continent until he ran out of land, whereupon he traveled south to Los Angeles before backtracking to Milwaukee. From Denver he had called his son to announce his visit. "Slow down," Ben had said. "Take some time for once in your life, you'll enjoy it more." But Moshe could never escape the feeling that he might be recalled to his tailor shop, and he didn't want to miss any opportunities. Besides, he liked to get his money's worth and his ticket would soon expire.

A taxi pulled up. Moshe threw his bag in the front seat and climbed in. "Summit Street. You know Summit Street?"

"Avenue."

"What?"

"Summit Avenue. There ain't no Summit Street."

Moshe looked at the cabbie. He was a boy, maybe a college student. "Okay, professor, let's go there."

Milwaukee was an old city, a city made up of smaller cities, of Serbs, Croatians, and Poles, each with their own parks and newspapers, a melting pot, but one with specific boundaries, a place where you could raise your kids with certain knowledge that property values would be protected until time immemorial; it was a city with an accent—rather, many different accents—and that made Moshe feel at home.

Fond as he was of Milwaukee, however, Moshe's visits had been less frequent since Ben had moved. Something about being the mediator in a family crisis made him wary of getting involved again. Only when he had seen them living in a cramped four-room apartment had he intervened and insisted on putting up the down payment on a nice old house with a yard near the lake. The boys were growing up; they needed space to play. For once, Ben did not argue.

The house was white with gray shutters and a three-story cupola that ended in a peak of rusted copper. Moshe paid the cabbie and walked to the door. When he rang, there was no answer, so he walked in; as usual, the door was open, the house a mess. He could never get used to it after Sarah, but who was he to criticize his son's wife? He dropped his suitcase and walked through to the kitchen, where he heard voices, but the room was empty. Outside, in the driveway, the boys were shooting baskets. Charles at ten was two inches taller than his older brother, who was thin and blond from the sun. But the younger boy was clumsy, and Michael snaked around him repeatedly to score.

Ben leaned against the fence, his cane swinging from his arm. When the boys finished, he said, "Give me the ball a second."

Michael ignored him, dribbling between his knees, drum-popping the ball off his elbow, then hooking it toward the basket. Charles grabbed the rebound and started toward Ben, but Michael stole the ball and retreated beyond the foul line.

"Michael, give me the ball."

Michael stopped now and looked over. "You want to play?"

"Just give your crippled father the goddamned ball," Ben commanded. Michael smiled and bounced it to him. Ben aimed carefully, bent his knees and let fly. The ball landed in the garden.

"Nice shot," Michael said.

"That was practice," said Ben.

Moshe walked out into the yard. "Now we got enough for teams," he called out.

Though it was summer and she was on vacation, Moshe saw little of Dory. She left early in the morning and came home at night after they had eaten. Ben stayed in his room in the heat of the day, and while Moshe was welcome, the cool air-conditioned study seemed unhealthy to him. He had spent too many summers in the close heat of his shop to change now. Summer wasn't summer if he wasn't sweating through the back of his shirt. So Moshe took the boys to ball games and to the zoo and sometimes he went to the senior citizens' center in the park, where he played sheepshead and flirted with the widows.

After a week, he knocked on Ben's door. "I got to go," he said.

Ben was seated at his desk, a book on his lap. "Go where? You disappear for two years, then you come to stay for a week. What's your hurry?"

"I got things to do, Benjy. This ticket don't last forever, you know."

"You never stay long enough for us to talk."

"Who can talk in an icebox? We talk when you come out at night. Anyway, you're busy, I can see it. I don't want to get in the way of your work."

"Who works?" Ben said. "I sit here on my ass all day. Dory's off at her studio. The boys, God knows where they are."

"You lonely?"

"Not exactly, but it's different. I used to have an office, a job. I complained about it then, but I miss seeing people. No one expects me to be anywhere now."

"How many years has it been?"

"Time doesn't make any difference. You don't get used to it. I don't, anyway. You wait for people to come by; it's a big deal if the phone rings or the drugstore delivers some cigars."

Moshe looked around the room. The exercise mat was dusty, and now there was a wheelchair in the corner, though he hadn't seen Ben use it. "You still working out, Benjy?"

"I'm too tired," Ben said. "Anyway, the doctor says it wasn't doing any good."

Moshe nodded. "Maybe, but you felt better that way, I remember."

"I'm okay, Pop, really."

Moshe stood and put his arm around Ben. "Benjy, I don't like to see you like this, all alone in your room. Maybe you could go out sometimes, see some people."

"I go to Chess Club with Charles twice a week. I get out. I mean it, Pop, don't worry."

"How can I not worry? What kind of father would I be?" Moshe walked to the door. "From now on, I'll call you once a week, no matter where I am, on the long-distance telephone."

"I'd like that, Pop. Where are you going now, anyway?"

"Detroit. I ain't been there before. I got a friend—friend, I ain't seen him in twenty years—a landsman there."

"I was in Detroit once," Ben said. "We played a concert at the university in Ann Arbor."

"So, how was it?"

"You'll like it. It's old, like Milwaukee, falling apart, but interesting."

"We should only be so lucky," Moshe said.

Ben laughed. "I'm glad you came, Pop. It's always good to have you here."

"That's the best time to leave; then you're always welcome."

Ben nodded. "You're probably right. But keep in touch. Let me know where you are."

"I told you. Every week I'll call. You can count on me, Benjy."

24

BEN WAS ANNOYED. He'd been waiting all day for Dory. She had told him
six, and now it was eight-thirty. At five he'd gone into the kitchen and sat
on the stool next to the stove to make dinner. First he'd shelled peas, then
he had fried some chops and boiled rice. There was a salad of fresh vege-
tables Charles had picked in the garden. At six dinner was ready, but Dory
hadn't arrived. The boys ate and went out. At seven Ben went into his room
to watch television, bringing his plate with him. But he saw the blue picture
before him only intermittently.

At seven-thirty he phoned some friends, but Dory had not been by. At
eight he called the police. His wife had a studio in the inner city, he explained. Naturally, he was a little worried. No, there was no phone, and he
was an invalid. The officer on call said he'd send a squad car around to
check, but when Ben called back, the officer said the studio was dark and
there was no sign of forced entry.

Ben wasn't really worried. It was not so unusual for Dory to be late; if
she was anything, it was absentminded. She might have forgotten or assumed he meant six the next morning, for all he knew. But he had been
alone all day and he wanted company. Dory was still thin and attractive. He
liked to watch her and make her laugh. He felt almost like a widower at
times as he sat alone in his room. Where the hell was she?

At nine-fifteen Dory came in the door, smiling and happy. She threw
her arms around Ben, saying, "I'm sorry I'm late. I rode my bike, and the
sunset was so beautiful I stopped twice to look. Did you eat?"

Ben shoved his plate at her in disgust, and it slid off the table and broke at her feet.

"Ben, watch out! What are you doing?"

"What do you care? You're out all day, painting or swimming or some goddamned thing. Then you traipse in here in the middle of the night and ask if I've eaten. Why don't you come home on time some night and see?"

Without thinking, Dory knelt and started picking up the pieces of the plate. "I said I was sorry. I am here for dinner most days, but this is the only time I have to work on my sculpture. If I don't do that, I won't have a job."

Ben wasn't pacified. Dory enjoyed herself too much for him to believe it was duty that kept her so late. He'd never enjoyed practicing as much as she liked working in her studio.

"Do you know," he said, "that often I sit here for the whole day, the whole fucking day, from morning to night, and never see anyone? Never talk to anyone. Never pass the time of day with a single person. I am a god-damned prisoner in my own house. I can't go out because it's too hot, and anyway, I'd probably fall on my ass. Meanwhile, God knows where my wife is. I call your office; I call our friends; no one knows. It's a little embarrass-ing, as you can imagine. Hello, Betty, this is Ben Seidler. I'm fine, and how are you? I was wondering if you've seen Dory. No, there's no message. You get the idea? I wonder sometimes why we remain married, why we bother. Of course, there are the children, but they never see you either, or at least they'd see as much of you if we were separated. With visiting privileges, you'd be around once a week."

Dory sank onto the bed. The feeling of healthy exhaustion had been re-placed by a headache that extended down to her neck and vibrated merci-lessly. They'd had this argument before. Ben threatening divorce, she agreeing that he was right and asking forgiveness. It was a kind of ritual, necessary for Ben's self-esteem. Neither of them ever mentioned Sam Mat-thews; they didn't have to. To plead innocence when he had not accused her would be to affirm his suspicions. The best thing was just to say noth-ing, to avoid arguments.

"I'm sorry you see it that way," she said, rising. "I know you have a hard time being alone all day, but I'm very tired. I'm going to go to bed. We can talk about it in the morning."

"You'll be gone in the morning."

"Then tomorrow night."

"Why should tomorrow be any different from tonight?"

"I'll try to make it home on time."

"That's what you said this morning."

Dory looked at Ben. His face was stiff and tense. Somehow the argu-

173

ment had assumed real importance to him, as if to give in was to admit defeat. She understood this; since he had become ill, control of the minutiae of life, of the things she rarely thought about, had become an obsession with Ben. Unable to play the fiddle anymore, he had assumed command of the household, and generally she welcomed this. She had no time to order the groceries and supervise the boys; she was glad Ben took an interest in them. "Ben, what do you want me to do?"

"I can't exist in a vacuum, Dory. You know that."

"But you have the boys, you have people over here all the time."

"It isn't the same. I want you to come home at night and talk to me for a while, the way other people's wives do. Is that so unreasonable?"

It wasn't, but Dory had trouble conceding the point. "I'm not like other wives; you're certainly not like any other husband I know. When have we ever lived our lives like other people? We have an unusual situation here, Ben, you know that. We just have to make the best of it. It's certainly not very pleasant when you start yelling at me for deserting you as soon as I come home." She rose to face him, the plate in pieces in her hands. "I have a headache. I'm going to bed."

"I guess I'll have to get a divorce," Ben said.

Dory could not let it go by. She turned, livid, and faced Ben. "Good. Do it. Get a divorce, if that's what you want. But before you do, you might think about how you're going to live on your own."

"Don't concern yourself about that. I'll go to a hotel. I have my pension from the musicians' union. I'll make out."

"See you in court," Dory said.

They didn't talk in the morning. Ben had been right about that. Dory left the house before anyone else was awake. She worked in fury all morning, swam in the early afternoon, and found her anger had dissipated by four o'clock. It was silly to fight over such a simple thing. All she had to do was come home on time. She was already working ten hours a day. Another two wouldn't yield any masterpieces.

At five she got on her bike. It was almost two miles to the East Side, and it took her between a half-hour and an hour, depending on traffic. She stopped to buy a bottle of red wine and arrived at the house just before six. She parked her bike in the garage and went inside. Ben's room was empty, but she was early. Occasionally he went to the drugstore for a cup of coffee and some company. She walked into the kitchen to wait. At six-thirty Charles came in the side door. He kissed Dory and sat down. "What's for dinner?" he said.

"I don't know. Where's Daddy?"

"He went to a hotel. He said you'd make dinner." Charles was calm. He had been through this before. Perhaps his grandfather would come soon with more presents.

Dory was not scared this time, just resigned. She should have known Ben would take his threat seriously, even if she didn't. "Which hotel?"

"The Knickerbocker. I heard him tell the taxi."

Dory nodded. "I don't think he really wanted to go," the boy said. "He left a lot of stuff behind."

Dory hugged the boy to her. "I know, honey. But Daddy has a hard time. We don't always know how hard it is for him."

Charles went outside, and Dory sat staring at the unopened bottle of wine, concentrating on the label, thinking what to do next. Then she got up and went to the phone. Ben's room didn't answer. "Any message?" the operator asked.

"No, thank you," Dory said.

The Knickerbocker Hotel had once been among Milwaukee's best, but in recent years it had become little more than a retirement home, with most guests paying by the week or month. Ben was fond of it because the quartet had stayed there and he knew the bell captain and the maître d'. The hallways were always in the process of being widened or narrowed, and the lobby remodeled, though what sort of renaissance lay in store for the place was uncertain.

Dory arrived at noon and called Ben from the house phone. He had debated whether to meet her in his room or in the bar, neutral territory. Finally, he asked her up. "How unusual to see you at this hour," he said. "What brings you over this way?"

"Very funny," Dory said, and marched into the room. She thought of the Belmont and their confrontation there, but that had been much different. Then Ben had been defiant; he still was, but there was an edge of desperation to his expression. He was trying very hard, but the balance had shifted. "Sit down," he said, and collapsed onto the bed. Then they sat facing each other. Dory was depressed by the cracked wallpaper and grease-spotted furniture. It was the kind of place she avoided instinctively.

"Would you like a cup of coffee?" Ben said.

"What I want is for you to stop this nonsense."

"I don't think it's nonsensical. After all, this is the first time we've spent an afternoon together in weeks."

"You know, Ben, it seems to me that you're either ironic or melodra-

175

matic most of the time. Either way, it's hard to deal with you on a simple, human basis."

"At least I'm not simple."

"You see, you did it again. It's impossible for us just to talk; you always need that distance, the upper hand."

"No psychoanalysis, please. Anyway, what would we talk about, my irony? Your tardiness? We are limited, Dory."

"We've always had plenty of things to talk about, you know that. We still do."

"Not lately."

"All right, but if you'd just come home and stop causing trouble, we could try again."

"I didn't cause anything. I just called a cab and came down here. I don't see why that should inconvenience anyone else. My life is difficult enough without having to spend a lot of energy trying to figure out where my wife is today."

"You know where I am, at the studio, working."

"So you've said."

"Where else would I be, Ben? Say what you mean. I'm tired of innuendo."

"We've been through all that already. There's no need to mention it again."

"You're talking about Sam?"

"There, you mentioned it. No, not necessarily him."

"Who else? Ben, look at me. I'm not exactly a bathing beauty. I'm forty-two years old. I was never really pretty, even as a girl. I have varicose veins and I'm putting on weight."

"You don't do yourself justice. Actually, you've gotten better-looking with age. You used to be too thin, though you were always attractive to me."

Dory looked out the windows at the lake, blue to the horizon, where a small fishing boat made its way to port. Ben couldn't help being honest, whether he was mad at her or not. How could she turn her back on a man who thought she was beautiful, no matter how unreasonable he was? And he had a point: Ben was isolated and she was gone too much. She couldn't blame him for being unhappy.

"I'm sorry, Ben. It would be more interesting if I had a lover, but I don't. I only have you, and you have only me. I know it's frustrating, but you can't live alone."

"Why not?"

176

"You know why not. You're an invalid. I hate it as much as you do, but it's time you accepted it. In the future you'll need more help, not less. I don't want to depress you, but you've got to stop kidding yourself."

Ben's diction was precise. "I know perfectly well what my condition is, Dory," he said. "What you don't seem to understand is that I'd rather live among strangers than be taken for granted. If you don't want to spend time with me, fine. I'll stay here. If you want me to come home, I'll be happy to. But only if you agree to more regular hours. I don't see any sense in going on this way."

"Why do you always see things only from your own point of view? I have to put in long hours to succeed, to be promoted. Even then, it's not a sure thing. Only one woman in our department has tenure. Maybe because you were a prodigy you don't know how hard ordinary people have to work, but I remember sitting at home while you were away on tour. You're not the only one who ever waited."

"Maybe not, but for me it's a life sentence."

"We all have life sentences. I'm not always crazy about my job, but I have to do it anyway. You have responsibilities too, to me, to the family. The boys need a father."

"They could move in here. We could all get a suite for a few dollars more a day."

"Can't you stop joking around? Is it too threatening to look at things as they are? You've got to come home with me."

"Is that an order?"

"Would it help if it were?"

"I might feel a little more important."

Dory shook her head. "When have you ever in your life been unimportant? That's just the trouble—you've gotten too much attention. From the time you were fifteen years old, other people have fawned on you. You talk about being ignored, taken for granted, but even now you're the one making demands. It's ridiculous. It would make inspiring reading for invalids everywhere. You could do it for *Reader's Digest*. 'How to Control Your Life and Your Wife!' "

"Not bad," Ben said, and despite herself, Dory laughed.

"You are frustrating."

Ben shrugged. "Now you see how I feel. Multiple sclerosis is a very frustrating disease."

"I know," Dory said quietly. "It's amazing that you do as well as you do. I'll try to get home on time. I'll even buy a watch."

Ben was smiling. "The question is whether I could get more concessions by holding out longer. Let's discuss it over lunch. They have a decent swordfish steak here."

Ben stood and opened the door. Dory looked at him, still smiling slightly. "What I don't understand is why you don't act more like an invalid," she said.

"I don't know how," said Ben.

Dory watched her husband, standing in the doorway, waiting for her. He seemed stronger now, as if the argument had ameliorated his condition. His stance was confident, relaxed. "I hope you never learn," she said.

25

SMALL CHANGES OCCURRED in the aftermath of Ben's rebellion. Dory couldn't cure Ben's disease, but for the rest of the summer she came home faithfully at six. After school started, she called twice a day to see if Ben needed anything. She always left numbers where she could be reached. For his part, Ben took a greater interest in Dory's work, listening patiently to her explanations of the university and her department. She was right: things had been different when he was with the quartet. They never had to worry about promotions and tenure, but Dory did.

With the cooler weather, Ben's strength returned and he began exercising. His life wasn't over yet. Although now he spent a great deal of time in the wheelchair, he couldn't rule out the possibility of a spontaneous remission. According to the latest statistics from the Multiple Sclerosis Society, 60 percent of the cases arrested themselves. Moreover, he had started writing music again. Even if he couldn't play, he could use his training. He was in no mood to give up.

One morning as he worked on a new quartet, he heard the bell. Ben called out but heard no reply. Then he was aware of someone else in the room and looked up to see Heinz Ober standing in the doorway.

Ober was wearing a gray suit with vest and a patterned necktie. His shoes were shined and his hair was immaculately combed. Though he was nearly seventy, he still stood erect and projected an air of dignity. Ben wore a white smock spattered with egg over a flannel shirt. His gabardine trousers were open at the waist and he wore only maroon carpet slippers on his feet.

"May I come in?" Ober said at last.

"Why not? If you can find space, you can even sit down."

Ober scanned the room, examining the possibilities. The two chairs were piled high with books. The bed had not been made, but at least it was clear of debris. Ober pulled the bedspread over the sheet and sat. His feet did not touch the floor, so he rested them on a chair. It gave him a casual look that put Ben at ease. Still, he didn't speak. He hadn't seen Ober since the day he walked out of Music Hall after resigning from the quartet. Let him do the talking.

"I was in town on business," Ober began, "so I thought I'd drop by to see you." When Ben did not respond, Ober went on. "Of course I've been here before and often thought of you, but somehow there never seemed to be time . . ."

"Of course," Ben said. "I understand. You were busy."

"I was, but it wasn't that, not really." Ober paused for a moment; then he looked at Ben directly. "I've always felt bad about the way we parted."

Ben shifted his weight. "You have a funny way of showing it."

"I tried to call you, remember? You wouldn't come to the phone. I wrote, but got no response. Then the next thing I know, you're in Oklahoma of all places, and then you've moved out of town without even saying good-bye. I assumed you had no interest in seeing me."

"A reasonable assumption," Ben admitted. He was pleased that Heinz had come, but he was careful not to show it. He liked having Ober on the defensive for a change. "Why don't we have some coffee?" Ben suggested. "We can go into the kitchen."

"I don't want to inconvenience you," Heinz said.

"It's nothing," Ben said. "But you'll have to move out of the way and let me by."

Heinz stood aside, and Ben rolled past, maneuvering the chair skillfully around the corner into the dining room and on to the kitchen. Heinz followed and watched as Ben carried the teakettle to the sink to fill it with water. Then Ben took two cups off the drainboard and spooned instant coffee into them before stopping himself. "Maybe you'd prefer tea, Heinz?"

"Ah, no, coffee is fine, thank you."

When the water boiled, Ben poured it over the coffee and put out a plate of cookies. Then he and Heinz sat at the table, looking out over the garden, covered now with snow. At first they didn't speak, but Ben was not uncomfortable with the silence; he was glad Heinz had come to see him. He had long since forgiven his old mentor.

"You make out very well, it seems to me," Heinz said at last.

"I do all right. After a while you almost forget it was ever any other way."

"But you actually cook for yourself?"

"I'm not very ambitious, but I can do simple things. Actually, I enjoy it, and recipes are easy to follow. I just sit here and read, and every now and then I add something or stir the broth."

They sipped their coffee. Then Ben said, "I hear the new kid you got is very good."

"A slight exaggeration," Ober said, "but he is not bad. In time he may be quite good. You know how it is. He has a lot to learn."

"That's what you said to me fifteen years ago."

"Was I wrong?"

Ben laughed. "No, but I don't feel smart yet."

"That's what you have learned. The younger the musician, the more impressed with himself he is likely to be. Coming to understand and acknowledge one's weaknesses is what maturity consists of. Was it Socrates who said, 'I am the wisest man in Greece because I know I know nothing'?"

"I never went to college, remember?"

"It seemed to me you were always taking classes."

"What did it get me? I still have three credits of German before I can graduate."

"Perhaps I could be your tutor."

"I don't want the degree that badly."

They both laughed now, and Heinz seemed to relax.

"How's Ernst, and Beaulieu?"

"We all grow older. Or perhaps it is only that the new man, Barry, is so very young. You know, you were younger than any of us by ten years, but he's just a baby. Things have also deteriorated as far as the university is concerned."

"Doesn't the president's wife usher anymore?"

Ober smiled. "Let us say enthusiasm in the community has diminished. The university has grown tremendously; it is like a small city now, and we are no longer the main attraction."

"You should like that. You always complained about all the distractions, the parties, receptions, and meetings."

"That is the problem. Since we're no longer so important, our responsibilities have increased. We are no longer indulged. We have classes now, graduate students, committee meetings of all sorts. It's awful."

"Why don't you refuse to do these things?"

"We can't. As I said, we're all getting older. I'll have to retire in a year.

181

Ernst and Antoine have nowhere else to go. The School of Music has decided we should no longer be artists-in-residence. Now we're associate professors."

"Who cares?"

"It further diminishes our individuality, reduces our autonomy. Now we are only faculty members, like everyone else."

"But you still tour?"

Ober looked weary. "Yes, yes, of course. I insist on that as the minimum, but we seldom make as long a tour. It is all very difficult, really. Ernst and Antoine wanted to get tenure so as to be assured jobs in the future, and who can blame them? But this affects their loyalty to me. One can't serve two masters."

"And you? Didn't you want tenure?"

"I'm too old. For me, it doesn't matter. In another year they put me out to pasture, it is a university rule. I understand how Ernst and Antoine feel, but I'm upset at losing the quartet. I'd always hoped we could go somewhere else after my retirement, or perhaps tour. Now that's impossible."

"It looks like I got out just in time."

"Yes, I suppose so," Ober said. He spoke very softly now, his shoulders sagging. He finished his coffee and sat mulling it over, his short legs dangling free of the chair. Then, abruptly, he straightened, and resolve returned to his body. "But this isn't why I've come," he said. "What does my future matter to you?"

"I'm interested," Ben protested. "I was in the damned quartet for twelve years. How could I not be interested?"

"Of course," Heinz said. "But I wonder if you know Howard Jacoby?"

"Should I?" Ben said.

"He lives here in Milwaukee. He used to play second violin in the Chicago orchestra. He was an excellent musician, but now he is retired, like everyone else."

"What's he doing here?" Ben asked.

"His daughter and her husband live in town, so he came to live with them. But he is also director of something called Young Musicians, which organizes concerts for young people and sponsors an orchestra. Jacoby says they're quite good."

Ben was losing interest. "Since when do you follow youth orchestras?"

"As I grow older, youth becomes more and more appealing," Ober said. "But I was really thinking of you. Jacoby asked me if you might like to become involved with his organization."

"I haven't sunk that low, Heinz. Anyway, I was a lousy teacher even

182

with advanced students in Madison. How could I teach kids, and why would I want to?"

Ober looked steadily at him. "The only reason any serious artist takes students is in the hope of finding true genius," he said. "Think how your first teacher must have felt when he came upon you, and think what you owe that man for realizing the gift you had and having the sense to encourage you. Perhaps now you can give back some of what you learned to talented children who could use it."

"I've never been much of a philanthropist."

"Jacoby assures me that you will be paid well and that you will have only the best students."

"But in Milwaukee? How good could even the best be, Heinz?"

"Who knows? Plants grow in the rockiest soil, even in the desert. Is it any less likely that you'll discover a gifted musician here? This isn't exactly Antarctica, you know."

"This is very strange, you promoting a violinist from America's hinterlands. Don't you remember how all of you used to make fun of my American education?"

Ober bowed his head. "We were fools, and snobs. The truth is that the best young musicians today are American—only a fool could fail to see that. I heard a wonderful cellist at Juilliard last winter, a girl from Minnesota."

Ben thought for a moment. Though he had never liked teaching, it would give him something to do, and money too. And he might like Jacoby; he had few friends in Milwaukee. Still, he remained skeptical, in part because Ober brought the offer. "Why didn't Jacoby call me himself?" he said.

"Only because we are old friends and I was coming by."

"Are you sure you didn't call and twist his arm, ask him to do his bit for the crippled musicians of America?"

"Don't be so suspicious. What if I did suggest your name? Howard jumped at the chance. He was looking for someone and didn't know you were in town. All I did was bring you together. I'm a *shadchan*, an old, honored profession."

"Not yet you aren't. I haven't agreed to do it."

"Ben, for God's sake. You're too proud for your own good. This is something you can do, something you know better than almost anyone. There is no question of your qualifications. Go call Jacoby yourself. Believe me, no one is doing this as a favor to you."

"I don't know," Ben said. "I've actually been pretty busy. I started writing music again. Remember that crazy Frenchman who thought I was so talented? Well, who knows? Anyway, I enjoy it."

183

"Of course. It is much more satisfying than merely playing someone else's compositions. But imagine how it would be to have your own ensemble to play your creations."

"You mean these kids?"

"Why not? How old were we when we started playing professionally?"

"That was different, Heinz."

"Who says so? It could be the ultimate challenge to find the essential raw material here in Milwaukee and then fashion it into something wonderful."

"Don't you think you're getting a little carried away?"

Heinz smiled. "Perhaps, but it is an exciting idea, to me at any rate. And children are wonderfully resilient; you can push them and push them and they don't get discouraged."

Ben nodded. Though he didn't really believe he could teach schoolchildren to play his music well, the idea was appealing. He could write something easy for them, once he knew their strengths and weaknesses. "I'll think it over," Ben said.

"Good," said Heinz. "Excellent. I'm sure you will find it interesting and enjoyable." Ober stood to go and noticed a chessboard sitting on the table. "You're still playing chess?"

"Twice a week. I go to a chess club on the West Side with my kid. You'd be surprised how many good players there are in Milwaukee. My son made Expert this year, and he's not even the best in his age group."

"It's a shame we haven't time for a game. I remember when you were in Madison we used to play frequently."

"I've improved," Ben said. "You'd only have to give me a pawn now."

"On the contrary, I will give you nothing. I am an old man, I need every advantage I can get." Ober offered Ben his hand. "It is good to see you again, Ben. It bothered me to think we were no longer friends."

As Ober was leaving, Ben had an idea. "Heinz . . ." he called.

Ober turned.

"I thought we could play postal chess. You know, you mail me a postcard with a move on it, and I send one back with my reply." Ben liked to play, but he also wanted to keep in touch with Ober.

"That's a wonderful idea," Ober said. "In fact, I will not wait until I get home. I'll make my first move now." He walked over to the board, shoved aside some papers, opened the box of chessmen, and extracted a white pawn. "In deference to my age, you should at least give me the first move, yes? Well, then, in return for your generosity I will keep things simple. Pawn to King Four."

184

Ober stood back and looked at the white pawn alone on the field of black and white squares. Then he turned to Ben. "Now I must go," he said. "Call Jacoby, and don't forget, you owe me a postcard." Ober squeezed Ben's arm, and then he was gone.

26

VIOLINIST JOINS YM

Howard Jacoby, music director of Young Musicians, Inc., today announced that Benjamin Seidler, formerly second violinist of the Casa Bella Quartet at the University of Wisconsin, has joined his teaching staff.

"We are particularly pleased to have a musician of Mr. Seidler's prominence joining us," Jacoby said. "We feel his presence will be of immeasurable value, especially to youngsters in the string section who hope to attend conservatories and prepare for careers as performers."

Seidler, who held the rank of artist-in-residence at the university, has had a long and varied career. He attended the prestigious Curtis Institute in Philadelphia on a scholarship, after which he joined the famed All-American Youth Orchestra and toured the country for two years. In 1943 Seidler made his debut at Town Hall in New York. Following his debut, Seidler was principal violinist with the NBC Symphony and then joined the WOR-Mutual Network orchestra, where he played a number of nationally broadcast recitals under the baton of Alfred Wallenstein. In 1946 he joined the Casa Bella Quartet, with which he concertized until 1958 when serious illness forced his resignation.

Jacoby said Seidler's duties with Young Musicians will be restricted to private instruction and work with a newly formed quartet made up of members of the string section of the YM orchestra.

The story was accompanied by a picture taken ten years before, while Ben was still with the quartet. He wore rimless glasses and held his fiddle in

186

the crook of his arm as he studied a score. But the most striking thing about it was that he looked so serious, as if the interpretation of the piece was a matter of life or death. Ben had learned some things about mortality since then.

But the story was fine. He had read it four times. He particularly liked the résumé of his career. And he was grateful to Jacoby for making sure the story got such prominent play in the papers. It was objective proof that he was still alive and respected, and that reassured him.

Dory was delighted, and even Moshe was pleased. He had called that morning to offer congratulations.

"Pop, how did you know?" Ben said.

"This is big news, kiddo, You think you could keep it a secret?"

Dory must have called him. It was ridiculous, but he felt excited about teaching a quartet of kids from Milwaukee. He was back in music again. "When will we see you, Pop?"

"Who knows? Maybe I'll come in for your concert. I've never seen you in action."

"Who told you about that?"

"I heard it on the radio. See you soon, Boychick," and he hung up.

Ben sat back in his chair and reread the article. The work would be another matter, but Jacoby had given him almost complete freedom. He would teach at home and was allowed to refuse students he thought were unprepared or lacked talent. Still, he didn't want to promise more than he could deliver, and he was anxious to see what he would be working with.

The day after Ober's visit, Jacoby had stopped by. Ben liked him immediately. Tall and rosy-cheeked, with a fringe of white hair around a bald pate, Jacoby was both jovial and intelligent. He asked to hear some of Ben's recordings and then they had lunch. Howard had been forced to retire from his job, too, and also because of his health. Two years before, he had had a heart attack, and now, he said, the conductor was afraid he'd drop dead in the middle of a concert.

"Fortunately, it hasn't turned out that way," Jacoby said, smiling. "Though at times I'm not sure my son-in-law wouldn't prefer it. But we're not here to talk about my problems. Heinz says you might consider joining Young Musicians, and we'd love to have you."

"Then Ober must have told you about my reservations."

"He did mention something, but I'm sure we will find some students worthy of your genius."

Ben saw Jacoby was mocking him. "I didn't mean to sound pompous," he said.

"Why not? You're arrogant, you have a right to be. I wouldn't be interested if you weren't."

Ben wanted an hourly guarantee of $50, but Jacoby would only give him a contract for $150 a week. They compromised by agreeing that Ben would work only three hours a week.

When Jacoby left, Ben had the feeling he had missed something, that Howard was too agreeable, too nice. Perhaps there was a hidden clause somewhere that said he had to attend potluck suppers on alternate weekends. But nothing untoward had followed, and now there was this press release. Ben's reverie was interrupted by the phone.

"Yes?" he said, holding the receiver tight.

"Ben, how did you like the article?" It was Jacoby.

"Not bad considering all the things you left out. Why didn't you mention my triumph at my bar mitzvah, for example?"

"Space, Ben, it's a newspaper, remember? But I'm glad you liked it. The music editor of the *Journal* said he'd like to come out and interview you, if you're interested."

"Is it still Riley?"

"Yes, do you know him?"

"That schmuck can't even read music. He goes to a concert and tells you what color socks the musicians wore."

"Well, what do you expect? This isn't New York, Ben."

"Must you remind me? I was feeling so good about things."

Jacoby laughed appreciatively. "The reason I called was to say I've got some students for you. I think they might work quite well as a quartet, and one of them might even be capable of more. Can I send them around?"

"I'm working for you, aren't I? Sure, what would be the best time?"

"It would have to be after school, of course, but you can choose the day."

"How about a week from Monday at four? If there's a problem with that, have them call me and we'll work something out."

"I'll tell them. And, Ben, it's good to have you with us."

"You may not think so after I see the kids."

Jacoby laughed again and hung up.

Since Ben would now be making some money, Dory decided to hire a cleaning woman. She didn't like the idea of Ben being alone all day. What if he fell and couldn't get up? What if the house burned down? Ben did not share Dory's anxiety, but he didn't seriously object to the idea.

Dory called the state employment office and asked if they had a cleaning woman. She interviewed three applicants and chose a statuesque black woman named Lucille Plavy who had recently moved to Milwaukee from Arkansas. Lucille had heavy shoulders, well-muscled arms, and high cheekbones which gave her a malevolent look. But when they talked, Dory was surprised by her soft, deep voice and shy smile. When she introduced Lucille to Ben, Dory knew she had made the right choice. The chaotic jumble of papers and books did not faze Lucille. She took a casual look around, smiled at Ben, and said, "Looks like you need some help." From the start, they got along fine. When Lucille learned Ben's students would be coming to the house she baked cookies and insisted he wear a coat and tie in keeping with his new position. She also refused to let Ben meet the students in his room.

"What the hell's the difference?" Ben asked.

"It ain't right. Little girls coming into your bedroom."

"You come in here every day."

"That's different. They ain't never seen bottles like that."

"Well, why do I have to wear a tie? It's uncomfortable, and I don't have to impress anyone."

Lucille refused to discuss it. She could be very stubborn, and Ben had learned to pick carefully the issues he wished to fight over. He allowed her to dress him in a starched white shirt and wrap a knit tie around his neck. Then she wheeled him into the living room, where he sat next to the piano waiting for his new students.

When he heard the bell, Ben screamed, "Come in!" at the top of his voice, as usual, which brought Lucille into the room at a dead run. "What you yellin' about?" she said.

"What's the matter with you, Lucille? I just told whoever it is to come in."

"People don't like being yelled at," Lucille said. She went to the door to greet their visitor. "Jesus," Ben muttered. This new job was going to change his life.

Lucille led a short fat girl into the living room and pointed to Ben. "This here's Mr. Seidler. What's your name again, honey?"

"Sally Freeman. It's nice to meet you, Mr. Seidler."

Ben nodded. "Sit down," he said. "The others should be here shortly." Ben could see Sally was a fiddler, but asked anyway. This rudimentary exchange completed, he realized he had absolutely nothing to say to a sixteen-year-old girl. They sat in uncomfortable silence for a few minutes, avoiding each other's eyes. Finally Ben said, "You can warm up if you want."

Sally took out her violin and played some scales. Within moments Ben knew she was competent but had little potential for improvement. She would play second violin—at least, she would if the other violinist was any better. He was glad to hear the bell.

The quartet consisted of three girls and a boy, who was much better than Sally, to Ben's relief. The first session was spent getting the musicians acquainted and giving assignments. Ben listened to each of them and was surprised to find they played quite well. The cellist was a somber girl with straight brown hair named Julie Barker, who was quite competent. The violist, Shirley Farmer, was also good, if unimaginative. But the one who showed real promise was Roger Sherman, the first violinist.

After an hour Ben gave them all scores and Lucille got their coats. The girls left immediately, but Roger stayed behind, taking a long time to pack his fiddle. Ben was anxious to get back to his book, but didn't want to appear rude. Finally the boy was ready to go, but just as he was leaving, he turned. "Mr. Seidler?" he said.

"Yes, Roger? Something I can do for you?"

"Mr. Jacoby said you might accept me as a private student."

Ben looked carefully at Roger. He was tall for his age, but very skinny. His face was covered with pimples, but if he ever filled out, he'd be a handsome kid. "How old are you, Roger?"

"I'll be sixteen next month."

"Sixteen," Ben said, thinking that he had been a professional at the same age. It was too late. No matter how good the kid was, he should have started five years earlier. At the minimum. Howard knew that, he had to. But maybe Roger didn't have any grand ideas. Maybe he wanted to do what Ben was doing—teach others to play.

"Why do you want private lessons, Roger? You play very well and you're already studying with Mr. Jacoby."

"I know, but I thought—or Mr. Jacoby said—I could try out for a conservatory in a few years. He says he can't take the time to prepare me, but that maybe you could." The kid looked so hopeful Ben hated to turn him down. He didn't want to tell him the truth, that he was very good but not good enough. Not single-minded enough. Roger probably had friends, went to the movies on Friday nights, and lived a fairly normal life. He'd never make it. But Ben couldn't say that.

"It's a very hard life, Roger. Very competitive. Why do you want to do it?"

Roger looked puzzled, as if he hadn't thought about not trying. "I don't know," he said. "I like it. Mr. Jacoby says I play pretty well. I'd like to try."

"Do you know what that means?" Ben said. "If you want to audition for Juilliard or Curtis in two years, which is the minimum you'll need to prepare, you'll have to practice at least four hours a day every day, and preferably more. I'll have to see you twice a week, in addition to the lesson with the quartet, and you'll have to learn an enormous amount of music. It will affect your schoolwork and it will certainly cut into your social life."

"That doesn't matter," Roger said.

"It does matter!" Ben shouted. "It matters very much, believe me, I know. If you want to do this, you have to know what you'll be giving up."

"I understand all that," Roger said sullenly. "If you don't want me as a student, why don't you just say so?"

Ben was amazed. He was trying to do the kid a favor, and Roger thought he was brushing him off. "Roger, I don't mind at all. Why should I? In fact, I'd like to have you as my student. You're a very talented boy. What I'm trying to say is that I don't think you'll want to do it, once you realize the sacrifices you'll have to make."

"Why don't you let me worry about that?"

Ben was impressed with Roger's maturity, his toughness. Maybe his assessment had been wrong. Determination counted for something. "All right," he said at last. "You're absolutely right. I'll leave it up to you, and I won't lecture you anymore. But there is one thing—have you told your parents?"

"They're divorced. I don't know where my father is; my mother works. She wants me to go to law school."

"We have a great deal in common, Roger," Ben said. "My parents were against it too. All right, next week we'll meet after the quartet's lesson and I'll give you some scores. Now, get lost. I'm tired and the hour is up."

"Sure, Mr. Seidler." Roger moved toward the door again. He was smiling broadly now, happy to have been accepted. "See you later," he said. But Ben hardly heard him. He was thinking of his own days at Curtis. He felt sorry for Roger, even though he would do his best to prepare him. He would try to be compassionate and understanding, even encouraging. There were things he couldn't control, though. Things Roger would have to learn for himself.

Lucille came into the room, looked around, and saw Ben was alone. "Ready to go back in your room?"

"Yes, Lucille, I'm ready now." Suddenly Ben felt very tired, hardly able to hold his head up. Though he had been with the quartet for only an hour, it seemed like a very long day.

27

MARCH 11, 1962: Four A.M. and I sit in my bathrobe waiting for Michael and grading student papers. Sometimes I imagine I am grading my son or my own performance as a parent; I am afraid neither of us would do very well right now. Michael has been staying out all night recently. When he does come home, it is through his bedroom window. He locks his door from the inside, and it's as if he has his own apartment, which is what he wants, I guess. I asked why he locked the door, and he said he was afraid Ben would break in in the middle of the night and try to kill him. Ben is not much help. He says as far as he's concerned, he only has one son, two if you count Roger. I know it's natural for adolescents to fight with their parents, but Michael's whole life seems to be affected. He never dates and his schoolwork is barely acceptable in a rotten school. He wants very badly to be tough, but despite his pretensions, I know he is really terrified: of Ben, of the vision of mortality he must confront every day. It is heartbreaking to see my boy so frightened, just as it is heartbreaking to think that a son of ours should lock his door against his father at night. Yet I know he is really trying to lock out the disease, the possibility of death, and I don't blame him for that. It is as if Michael thinks staying out all night can make him indifferent to pain and insulate him from our problems. It would be wonderful to be able to anesthetize oneself to the pain and loss of those around you. Wonderful and sad. Michael is terribly angry with Ben, but also with me and with himself for hating what Ben can't help.

April 3, 1962: Roger has been spending more and more time with Ben, and this makes Michael jealous. Tonight Michael asked me if Roger has parents of his own. His jealousy was so transparent it was hard not to laugh. I said some people looked up to Ben, no matter how he felt. This made Michael furious. He said, "All he does is sit around. He doesn't work, he can't do anything for you. He's useless. Why don't you get rid of him?" And then, as if appalled by what he had said, he turned and ran out of the house. I feel I should be more upset by Michael's tantrum than I am. It is cruel, insensitive, and entirely understandable that he should feel the way he does. Ben is helpless and he doesn't go off to work or make much money. But these things aren't really important. We're not rich, but we never were. And even when Ben had a job he was home most of the time. What has changed is the fact that I am gone so much and have to work so hard just to stay even with the other members of my department. Knowing that Ben is behind me makes that easier to bear. Michael needs someone to push against, but if he pushes Ben, he will fall down. Michael knows this, and it scares him. Perhaps in time he'll come to appreciate his father more.

April 21, 1962: Last night I went into Charles's room and found him reading *The Castle*. I said, "Why, Charles, I didn't know you were reading Kafka." He said, "I liked *The Trial* better." I don't know why that should surprise me. By the time I was his age I'd read everything in my parents' library. But Charles is so mysterious, he reveals so little. It's as if he's trying to hide himself away from us, for protection. I half-expect to wake some morning and find him gone, but actually he's the model son: quiet, studious, respectful of his father. He comes home after school, fixes dinner when Ben doesn't, and takes Ben to the Chess Club on Monday nights. But he does it all in an impassive way. I wonder what he thinks, feels. If he really doesn't mind at all, and if not, why not. I want to encourage in Charles the very things that worry me about Michael. I want him to open up and express his feelings, but when I ask, he says nothing is wrong. When friends from school call, he tells them he has to stay home without even asking me. I said that he could go to the movies if he wanted to, but Charles said he'd rather read. I have no right to complain, but I don't feel I know him. I wonder if he's still worried about the Martians.

May 16, 1962: Ben spends more and more time in his wheelchair and has had a string of urinary infections, each of which leaves him weaker than before. Last night I made a steak and we sat in his room drinking wine and listening to his old records. It was warm outside, and there was a nice breeze off the lake. I felt tender and romantic. Ben took my hand and asked me to come to bed, but when I did, he was unable to move and lost his erection.

It's been months since we've slept together, but it never seemed final before. Sitting on top of him, I felt as if I had mounted a corpse, and when he went soft, Ben started to cry. I felt so sorry for him, but there was nothing I could do. We lay there holding each other for nearly an hour, but I couldn't convince him that he was only tired, that everything was all right. Perhaps because I don't believe it myself. If he asks, I'll come again, and again, no matter how ill he gets. But now I find myself wishing for the first time that sex will no longer be a part of our lives. Like most wishes, this one will probably not come true, but tonight was too painful not to wish it just the same.

June 8, 1962: Roger is a sweet boy. He comes on Mondays, Tuesdays, and Thursdays for his lessons, but often he stays around for dinner or comes by on weekends to help out. He doesn't get along with his own father, and his mother works, so he's adopted us. Now, as a sort of summer job, he's painting the kitchen while I sit and write. He is tall and lean and energetic, and he is even getting along better with Michael. Lucille told me that she overheard the boys talking the other day. Roger was praising Ben for being so demanding, such a perfectionist, all the things Michael hates. Michael said, "That's why you like him?" And Roger replied, "Sure. He wouldn't make me do all those things if he didn't believe in me. My parents don't think I can do anything. That's why I like Mr. Seidler. He expects a lot." I hope it sinks in, that Michael will begin to understand. The only thing I can't understand is why someone as nice as Roger wants to be a musician. He doesn't seem neurotic enough. Of course, that isn't fair. The boys in New York that Ben played with were wonderful, our best friends. But Roger seems different from them. Perhaps it is only that he is Midwestern, so eager to please. He has good teeth and ironed shirts and isn't Jewish. Still, Ben says Roger plays very well. Maybe he will surprise us after all.

28

BEN WAS in the kitchen having breakfast when Lucille came in to announce a visitor. "Who is it?" Ben asked.

"A short man," Lucille said. "I like the way he talks."

"It must be Ober," Ben said. "Bring him in."

Lucille left the room and came back with Ober. Ben turned to Lucille. "Lucille, I want you to meet Mr. Ober. Heinz, Lucille." Ober shook Lucille's hand and bowed, which made her laugh. "Give him something to drink," Ben said. "He likes tea, in a glass."

"Oh, that's not necessary," Ober said, embarrassed.

Lucille started water boiling and left them alone. Ben was glad to see Ober. It helped to make up for the fact that Moshe's calls had become more infrequent. Not that he had forgotten them: each winter Ben received boxes of oranges from Florida or avocadoes from California. Occasionally Moshe would call long distance to tell Ben a joke. But the closeness between them had diminished. Ben no longer felt entirely comfortable talking with his father. Moshe didn't really seem interested anymore. Heinz, on the other hand, was eager to talk, and Ben suspected that things were not going well in Madison. They'd play chess or Scrabble and talk about past concerts, past tours. It seemed to comfort both of them to retreat occasionally from the present, to remember when they were both obsessed by the same thing.

Lucille brought Ober his tea in a grape-jelly glass. Ober read the inscription on the side: "Woo woo Welch's," he said.

"Only the best, Heinz."

Ober nodded and smiled. "So, how are things with your musicians?"

"Not bad, considering. I have a boy who is really quite good. He wants to go to Juilliard—at least he thinks he does."

"And what do you think?"

Ben shrugged. "You know how it is. He has talent, but others have more; in the end it may depend on how badly he wants it."

"And the others?"

"They are all competent. You were right: they'll do whatever I tell them. They work hard."

"I spoke to Howard last week and he mentioned having a recital this year."

"What are you, his messenger?"

"Not at all, but what are you afraid of? It's been almost a year, maestro. The public is entitled to see what you have been doing."

"Go to hell," Ben said. "But before you do, let's have a game of chess."

Ben had not forgotten about the concert. In fact, he had written a new string quartet and a trio and given them to his students. But he didn't want to hurry; he wanted to make sure everything was ready, that they would not embarrass him. But perhaps Heinz was right; what would be gained by waiting longer? When he talked to Jacoby the next day, he suggested that they schedule a recital for December.

"I'm afraid that's not such a good time, Ben. Our Christmas pageant, remember?"

"What about January, then?"

"School vacations, and then we're into the second semester. February is really the earliest we can do anything, I'm afraid."

"I want to start working on some new things with Roger then. We won't have time for both. To hell with it, it was just an idea. Let's forget the concert."

"No, not at all. Why not do it in November instead?"

"But that only gives us six weeks to prepare."

"And what have you been doing since January?"

Ben thought for a moment. Did it really make so much difference, one month, or two? This was not the Casa Bella, after all. "All right, Howard. We'll do it in November. I'll give it to myself for a birthday present."

"Excellent. And what will you play?"

"I'll surprise you," Ben said, and hung up.

Ben was pleased to find that the students were excited about playing the recital and responded to his increased demands with enthusiasm. First they started meeting two times a week, then three. In the final month, Ben met with them individually, in addition to their group lesson, but no one complained about the extra work. Julie Barker, his cellist, had improved markedly over the summer, so Ben wrote a duet for violin and cello for her and Roger. To this, the quartet, and the trio, he added a Haydn quartet. The program would not be demanding, but that was just as well. Later, if they continued to improve, he could become more ambitious. The only thing that worried him was that the quartet had never performed in public before. He had no idea how they would react to an audience. Jacoby had called the newspapers to try to get them to review the recital, and there would be a reception afterward in Ben's honor. Ober was driving over for the evening, and Moshe was flying in for a visit. Now all Ben had to do was get his quartet ready to play.

The concert was being held in a small recital hall in the art center. Ben had tested the acoustics as best he could and found them adequate. Now he sat backstage in his wheelchair, listening to his students tune up. Artistically, it was a long way from New York, Chicago, or even Madison, but he felt the tension nevertheless. As he watched Roger, in shirtsleeves, fiddle held tightly between shoulder and jaw, he saw himself thirty years before. He had been smaller and broader and it had been Washington, not Milwaukee, but the vacant stare was the same. The kid was intense, Ben could see that.

"Sally," Ben called. "Come here for a minute, will you?"

The second violinist came over, carrying her fiddle and bow. Ben had misjudged her when they first met; she had worked hard and improved considerably. Now, however, she looked scared. Ben had asked the students not to wear formal clothes, but they had all dressed up anyway. Sally was wearing lipstick and her eyes were black with eye shadow. "Yes, Mr. Seidler," she said.

"What's the matter? You're not warming up like the others. The concert begins in a few minutes."

Suddenly Sally started to cry. "Oh, Mr. Seidler. I'm sorry; I'm awful. I can't play. Every time I try, my hands shake too much and the bow bounces up and down."

Ben took Sally's hand in his and held it; it was cold to the touch. "Sally," he said firmly, and she looked up at him. "Sally, you've been playing with me for almost a year, haven't you?" The girl nodded obediently. "And in that time I've listened to you play literally for hours on end, haven't I?"

Sally nodded again. She had stopped crying. "Now, Sally, do you think for one minute I would even consider putting you onstage as a member of my quartet if I didn't have confidence in you as an artist?"

Ben waited for an answer this time. "I don't know," Sally said at last.

"Well, I know. I wouldn't. I would have gone to Mr. Jacoby and told him I needed a replacement, that you weren't good enough to play with the quartet." He waited a moment for the words to sink in. "And did I ask Mr. Jacoby for a replacement, Sally?"

The girl shook her head no this time and smiled slightly.

"The reason I didn't ask Mr. Jacoby for a replacement is that I have absolute confidence in you. In fact, of all the students, I think you have improved the most. Now, let me ask you another question, Sally: Do you think there is anyone in the audience who is as critical as I am? Of course not, so what do you have to worry about? If you've played for me and I'm satisfied, what could possibly go wrong tonight?"

Now Sally was beaming. She threw her arms around Ben and kissed his cheek. "Oh, Mr. Seidler. Thank you."

"All right," Ben said gruffly. "Now, get over there and tune up. You're going onstage in a minute."

As the quartet played, Ben sat in his wheelchair, watching and thinking of his own career, of Ober, of the Casa Bella. He wondered if he had taught the kids to lean into each other as they played, to respond physically to the music, or if it was something else, something unconscious. He couldn't remember, but he was surprised at how good they sounded. Not that they were competent; that didn't surprise him. But that they could seem as professional as they did, considering how young they were. They still lacked training: there were imperfections, dropped notes, mistakes in timing. But one would expect this. As Ben listened, he felt proud of the musicians, the music, himself.

The concert seemed to go quickly. There was a short intermission, and then Roger and Julie were playing the piece Ben had written for them. Watching, Ben thought of the Brahms Double, of his lapse, of Richler's anger. It all seemed so long ago; hell, it was four years. He had forgiven Ernst; he had almost forgiven himself. And now, watching these two kids, fresh as lovers, bowing to each other in turn, Ben felt a new excitement, as if life was starting all over again.

Roger and Julie finished the duet, and the whole quartet went onstage for an encore. Applause echoed through the hall and then someone was calling for Ben. "Maestro, maestro," a single voice called. It was Ober.

Then the whole crowd took it up, like a chant at a school basketball game. It was absurd. Ober would never consent to such a thing himself; what did he mean starting this nonsense? Now Jacoby was at Ben's side. "Come, Ben, you really must, they are asking for you."

"Don't be silly, Howard. Ober's just having fun."

"Ben, the whole audience is on their feet. This is a triumph. You must go out."

Ben protested, but Howard would not hear of it. Finally Ben straightened his tie and pulled his coat around him. Then he noticed that a button on his shirt was undone. He looked at Howard, but Jacoby was talking to a stagehand. With difficulty Ben took hold of his shirtfront and tried to manipulate the small bit of plastic, but he couldn't seem to steer it into the buttonhole. He would not go onstage with his stomach showing, but then Jacoby was back. "Come, Ben, now we must go." The stagehand pushed Ben toward his students, who were standing applauding him. In the moment before he emerged into the light, Ben managed to pull his jacket down. He pushed his glasses higher on his nose and was suddenly facing his public.

Jacoby had not lied. The audience was standing and applauding. Now Julie walked over with a boutonniere. She pinned the flower on his lapel and kissed him on the forehead, her lips moist and warm. Then the audience quieted down, expectant. Ben had not prepared a speech. He did not know what to say, or whom to address. He couldn't see very well because of the stage lights, but he spotted Ober in front with Dory and Moshe. He sat in his chair, squinting into the audience for a moment. Then he said, "Thank you very much. You have honored me and my musicians. Thank you." He waved, and the applause started anew. Then he turned the chair to wheel himself backstage.

29

DECEMBER 11, 1962: It is wonderful to see how Ben has reacted to the concert; he is actually excited about music and the future again. Who would have thought of him as a teacher?—and yet he seems to be wonderful. He charms the girls, and Roger has always adored him. He is even talking of taking the quartet on a tour, not very different from the kind of thing Casa Bella used to do each winter. He is becoming more and more like Ober.

It is a good thing Ben is happy with his job, because mine has been frustrating lately. I have now been here for three years, and while I didn't expect to get tenure yet, the signs are beginning to worry me. I finally rented a small studio and have been working pretty regularly. I've just been nominated for a teaching award. But there is nothing I can do about my sex. I got a favorable rating on my three-year review, but supposedly the dean takes a dim view of all this. Shelly Barron, who just got turned down, told me the dean said, "If I give her tenure, I'll have to do it for all the other women in the university." Shelly has her share of sour grapes, but looking around, I don't see many women who are senior faculty members. Thank God I've got my teaching certificate and can always go back to high school.

January 4, 1963: A new year, but I'm not feeling optimistic. Ben had another attack and was flat on his back in bed for a week. Now he's up again, but weaker; the damned disease always leaves him weaker than before. It makes me more aware of the fragility of life than I'd like; all Ben has to do is catch a cold and he's unable to get up in the morning. I called the doctor, but he wasn't encouraging. He said most multiple sclerotics die of infections having nothing to do with the disease. How nice. Still, it hasn't discouraged Ben. Rather than letting his students take the week off, he made Lucille call them all and tell them to come to the house, where he met them in his bedroom. The man does have spirit.

February 16, 1963: This is the most brutal time of the year. Short days and endless, bitterly cold nights. No one goes outside, and the car won't start. Yet there is no togetherness, no tough pioneer spirit among my friends, just a kind of general depression. Instead of having nightly gatherings in front of the fire with popcorn and songs, we all sit in our rooms and try, unsuccessfully, to stay warm. My phone doesn't ring in February, and I dread morning, when I will either have to walk to the university or try to start the car, whose battery will surely be dead. No doubt it is only the weather, but I feel my life now is empty of any warmth or happiness. Things have improved with Ben, but work gives me little satisfaction. At first, I made a few friends at school, but I lack the energy to sustain them. It is hard to believe my days were once taken up with meetings of the League or the ward unit of the Democratic party or the Cub Scouts. That I took the boys for picnics to the beach on summer afternoons and that Ben and I had leisurely breakfasts while sitting in the dining room admiring the lilacs. Were we really so happy then, or is it only nostalgia?

February 21, 1963: I am alone so much I begin to think it is my natural state. Or perhaps it is a process of evolution—that I have grown into a more solitary person because it suits my environment. Yet it worries me. I was such a bookworm as a child—almost no friends, yet I liked thinking of myself as gregarious, a joiner, popular with the people I met. Now I am small in spirit, cramped as my cold bed on this winter night, alone in my home and in the world. I feel it is a failing in me, a concession I should not have granted so easily to Ben's illness. I should give great parties with good food and wine; I should not withdraw as I do. I sometimes get as far as planning a dinner, but when I sit down with my address book, there seem to be few people to call, and even those are not real friends. Tonight, as the wind blows outside and the storm windows rattle, I remember I have had friends; I have had lovers. I will have to be satisfied with that.

February 24, 1963: It seems to me my life has been formed by men. There was Grandfather and Daddy and Ben. There are Michael and Charles and Roger and Moshe. There was Sam. My best teachers were all men. Mother and I weren't close—she always preferred boys—but I loved her. Now there are younger women around the university who admire me and come to me for advice. I try to help, but it is they who have what I want: youth and hope. Against my best efforts, I seem to have become some kind of symbol of accomplishment, a success in a man's world. I wonder if the

201

artists I looked up to when I was young felt this way. What I want most now is compassion, intimacy, love; what I have is respect, and it is pretty thin soup.

March 1, 1963: The snow is a dirty gray border on our backyard fence, but crocuses push their way through the ice. It reminds me that for all the times I feel despairing, I lead a surprisingly happy life—something worth remembering. My students generally like me, my work pleases me much of the time, and though my colleagues are not friends, they stay out of my way and let me do as I wish. There's some comfort in knowing I don't have to add job hunting to my other chores. Beyond that, there's the simple satisfaction of knowing I've survived when there was every reason to give up. Without any preparation for the job, I have taken on the responsibility of providing for the family, and done pretty well. Today I feel hopeful for the future. I think there is a cycle to this business of suffering and loss. Perhaps it conforms to the seasons of the year. I have hit bottom, and now, slowly, like the crocuses, I am making my way back up. There is only so much crying one can do, only so much pain the body will endure. I think it was La Rochefoucauld who said one can no more look steadily at death than stare at the sun without going blind. Both Ben and I now accept the fact that he will get worse and that someday he will have to go to a nursing home. We know he will finally end up on his back in bed, unable to feed himself or control his bowels. We know this, but there is no need to talk about it or let it dominate our lives. The question is: Knowing what is in store for us, what can we do with the time that is left? For me, and for Ben too, I think, there is only one answer: Go on trying. I will try to do my sculpture, though I will never be a really fine artist; we will try to keep our family together, despite the difficulties of doing so; Ben will continue with his students and music as long as he can. Most of all, we have to keep alive our feelings for each other. Doing that seems like quite an accomplishment—at least I think so this morning.

30

THROUGH THE SUMMER, with the air conditioner for accompaniment, Ben worked with Roger. The boy took criticism well; he never complained about the hours of practice or Ben's ascerbity. He had given up his summer job and spent all his time on music. The sessions expanded from one hour to two, from two days a week to three and then four. On weekends, when he had nothing else to do, Roger would hang around to run errands. Sometimes he and Charles would go with Ben and Dory to a movie. Michael was seldom home; the more Roger came by, the less Michael was there. Ben knew that Roger's audition meant more than simple musical success for the kid. If Juilliard turned him down, Roger would have disappointed a father, Ben would have failed a son.

When school started in the fall, they cut back to twice a week. When Roger wasn't with Ben, he practiced at home. But Ben had come to think that solitary practice had its disadvantages. How did they know Roger wouldn't freeze, once he had to play in front of an audience? Just being in New York by himself would be intimidating enough, not to mention performing for the Juilliard faculty.

In October Jacoby arranged a solo recital for Roger. The critic for the *Journal* came and wrote both a favorable review and a Sunday feature on Roger's hopes of going to New York. Roger was pleased but Ben cautioned him: "It's nice, especially the first few times. But don't let it go to your head. The guy doesn't know anything about music or your chances for Juilliard.

And even if you were as wonderful as he says you are, there'd still be plenty of room for improvement."

During Roger's winter vacation they switched back to the summer schedule. Because of the weather and to save time, Roger would sometimes stay overnight. They worked on Christmas and on New Year's Day. Yet as winter turned to spring, Ben experienced a slight feeling of resignation. It was March; the auditions were in May. No one could have worked harder than Roger, but his judgment the first day had been correct: Roger was very good, but not brilliant. There was no point in fooling themselves.

Still, Ben did not rule anything out. Roger had already been admitted to Oberlin, and his improvement had been remarkable. In less than two years the kid had gone from being a talented *potzer* to a nearly professional musician. Ben had long since put aside objectivity; he suppressed the idea that what Roger was trying to do was almost impossible. It would be hard, but Ben thought he had a chance. Anyway, if he failed, Ben would have failed too. The judgment would fall equally on them.

During spring vacation Ben sent Roger to Madison to spend some time with Ober. There was little more Ben could tell him. The technical work had been done and redone. He wanted Roger to see how professional musicians lived and worked. He would stay with Ober, do household chores, and go to rehearsals. But he could only watch; he must never speak.

At first, Roger rebelled. "What's the point of wasting time in Madison?" he said. "Can't I just watch you?"

"You could if I was still playing," Ben said. "But Ober's an exceptional man. I had twelve years with him. You'll have ten days; it's not enough, but it's more than the other kids will have. It might help."

"Help what? Can't you show me what he taught you?"

"No, because I don't really know. Heinz has a peculiar attitude toward music and life. You'll see what I mean."

But when Roger returned, he said, "Actually, Mr. Ober reminds me a lot of you, Mr. Seidler."

In May, Roger went to New York. Ben tried to persuade him to stay with his old friend Jimmy Shapiro in Brooklyn, but Roger wanted to stay in a hotel. "This isn't the class trip, you know," Ben said. "You're going to New York on business, not to fool around. If you get into Juilliard, you can go on all the Gray Line tours you want."

"If I get in, there won't be time."

"What do you know about time? The first six weeks I was at Curtis, I did nothing but go to the movies and read."

"And they almost kicked you out, right?"

"What are you, a wise guy or something?"

"No, but I'm not staying in Brooklyn. What's the difference? My mother's paying for it."

"You're a stubborn little bastard. All right, but I want to make a reservation for you at the Wellington. It's two blocks from Carnegie Hall; you can practically look out your window and see Horowitz. I know the bell captain there. He'll keep an eye on you. And I want you to call Mr. Shapiro at the Philharmonic every day. You could call me too, if you have time after the UN."

Roger smiled. "Don't worry," he said. "I will, but I've never been to New York before. I want to look around."

Roger called, but he also visited the Statue of Liberty and took a tour of Wall Street. He walked from his hotel down to Greenwich Village and made a side trip to the Bowery. He never knew Manhattan was an island before, he told Ben. Did Ben know there were Indians in New York? Had he ridden the Staten Island ferry? Had he been to Chinatown?

The night before the audition, Ben spoke to Jimmy Shapiro. Jimmy had friends who taught at Juilliard, and Ben trusted his judgment. "He's a nice kid," Jimmy said. "Most of them aren't as nice as Roger."

"To hell with that," Ben said. "What about his playing? I'm out of touch. Do the others play as well as he does?"

"Who knows? I don't listen to auditions."

"Come on, Jim, you know what I mean."

"He plays pretty well, technically; I've heard better, but so what? He might make it. It depends."

"On what?"

"A lot of things. How the judges feel that day. Whether they like the way he looks, dresses, carries himself. They wouldn't say that, of course, but subconsciously it makes an impression when you see some eight-year-old kid in short pants come out with a cut-down fiddle and play like Heifetz."

"Roger's not eight."

"And he's not Japanese, but he isn't run-of-the-mill, either. He walked into Philharmonic Hall the other day in dungarees and a flannel shirt and work boots. The other guys thought he was a steeplejack. There's something appealing about a farmer who can play the fiddle."

"That kid's never been on a farm in his life."

"Nu, so how do we know? I'll call you, Benjy."

Ben sat by the phone all day, but the only one who called was Moshe.

"I can't talk, Pop," Ben said. "I'm expecting an important call."

"More important than your father?"

"No, but I've got a student trying out for Juilliard. I'm waiting to hear if he got in."

"You sound nervous, professor."

Ben laughed. "You know, Pop, it's funny, but I'm more nervous about this than I was about my own auditions."

"That's because you always won the prize. So okay, I'll let you talk to your students."

Ben hung up, but the phone did not ring. He knew the audition was scheduled for ten o'clock in the morning. At noon he started calling Roger's room. He tried Jimmy first at Lincoln Center, then at home, but with no luck. He left messages for both of them, but the phone was silent all afternoon.

At five, Jimmy called. "They've got one spot left. It's between Roger and another kid," he said. "They won't know for a few hours. They want to hear the other kid again. It might not be until tomorrow."

"Did you go to the audition?"

"They wouldn't let me in, but I've got a friend who was there. He said Roger was good, that they liked him. He'll be an alternate for sure."

"That's no good. He's got to tell Oberlin this week."

"I can't help that. I'm not even supposed to tell you this."

Roger was subdued when he called. "I don't think I made it," he said. "But I played as well as I can. You should have heard some of the kids, Mr. Seidler. There was this little boy, an Israeli, who was better than anyone I've ever seen."

"You'd be as good if you started when you were four."

"Anyway, I got to see New York. I think I'll go to the Metropolitan Museum before I leave."

Jimmy called the next day with the word of Roger's failure, but Ben was more downcast than his student. Roger immediately wrote Oberlin that he was coming and went out to look for a summer job. Ben sat in his room thinking about the last two years and the work he'd put into Roger's musical education. Then he wrote Howard Jacoby a letter of resignation.

Jacoby called to protest. "Don't blame yourself," he said. "Who says you failed anyway? We've never had a student from our program get into Juilliard, or even Oberlin for that matter. You knew it was a long shot to begin with, so why should you feel suicidal because Roger didn't make it?"

"It's not only that. It was possible. I could have gotten the kid ready, and I didn't."

"Maybe, but I doubt it," Jacoby said. "If that boy had worked any harder, he would have had a nervous breakdown. No one could have gotten more out of him than you did, Ben. Christ, Roger was sleeping at your house at the end. How can you expect any more than that?"

"He's a good boy," Ben said. "I'm not criticizing Roger. I'm the one that failed."

"How? How did you fail? What did you do that was so awful?"

"I don't know," Ben said. "That's what bothers me. I don't know what else to do."

"That should tell you something. It would be nice to think that all we have to do is work hard and things will fall in place."

"They did for me, Howard."

"Sure, and for me, and for Heinz and Richler and Beaulieu, too. That's your problem, Ben. You assume everyone is as gifted as you were, as we all were, and they just aren't. Roger did his best, so did you. To fail under those circumstances is no disgrace, forget it."

To hear Jacoby say so made Ben feel better. "I don't know," he said.

"Sure, I'm right. And anyway, you've got other students. What about Julie? She's a very talented kid, and I've got another boy, a little younger but very good, I think. He can take Roger's place. You've got a public now, Ben. We're planning another concert for the fall."

Ben had never thought of himself as a teacher. He had taken Roger on because he was gifted; the quartet was a sideline. To his surprise, however, he had gotten involved with the other students, and now he realized he didn't want to let them go. Through Roger, he had relived his early years in music. He had experienced again the sick feeling of anticipation, greed, and fear with which he had always approached auditions. The only difference, as Howard said, was that he had always succeeded and Roger had failed. Maybe he should take his cue from Roger: the boy was working as flagman on a construction crew for the summer, eager to get to Oberlin in the fall, undismayed by what had happened in New York. There were other things in life besides playing classical music for a living, and Roger would find out what they were. In a way, Ben envied him.

"So what do you say?" Jacoby interrupted. "Will you forget this *mishegass* and stay with Young Musicians?"

"It depends," Ben said. "I was going to ask for a raise."

"Is that what this is all about?" Jacoby laughed. "I expected more, Benjy."

"You expect too much."

Jacoby laughed again. "All right, but I never negotiate over the phone. We'll have to have lunch. In the meantime, can I send the new boy over?"

"As long as he's as good as Roger," Ben said. But he knew none of his students would replace Roger, at least not for a while.

31

APRIL 12. 1967: Yesterday was my birthday. I am forty-eight, impossibly old, and yet I feel fine, even optimistic. It seems as if I have gotten by something in life, as if a psychic boulder has been rolled away, and now I can see the road ahead. Last night I came home to find the house empty and dark. I stood for a moment, feeling neglected, then suddenly Ben appeared in the kitchen doorway and walked toward me carrying a cake with three candles on it. He hasn't walked much for years, and I was touched. Then, just as he was about to hand me the cake, he tripped and the damned thing fell on the floor. I got down on my knees and tried to repair it, but it was impossible. I looked up and saw that Ben was smiling. "What the hell," he said, "it'll probably improve the taste, I made it myself." Then he made me get my presents from his room. They were exquisite, entirely atypical of Ben: an expensive edition of Picasso drawings; a silk scarf; violet soap; and a dozen pink roses. I was so touched I cried. I expect jokes from him or something functional and boring. I wasn't aware he even knew about perfumed soap. Ben had Lucille make duck and told the boys to go to the movies. For one night it was as if we were on a date; it reminded me of the summer he courted me at Alfred, and again I felt special, desired. What a lovely man he is. Whatever happens to us now, I feel fortunate. I am lucky to have found great love in my life; luckier still to have been able to hold on to it.

April 15, 1967: As quickly as it appeared, Michael's rebellion seems to have passed. He gave me flowers on my birthday too, and the next day we all went out for dinner at Mader's. Then Michael told me he made the honor roll and that he has applied to the university. He and Ben still fight, but now Michael stays home in the evenings and he's started reading everything in the house. I wish I knew why these changes take place, but when I asked, Michael seemed embarrassed that I had noticed.

May 12, 1967: Just back from the lakefront, where I walked with the boys and collected driftwood. I am so pleased with them. It seems amazing that I ever worried. Charles is now the tallest in the family. Though he is only fifteen, he is very handsome, with jet-black hair and clear blue eyes. Girls call the house asking for him, but when I mentioned this to a colleague, who is a homosexual, he replied, "Charles is attractive to both men and women, Dory." It's old-fashioned, I know, but I hope he limits himself to women.

Michael is much quieter and more introspective now. He rarely goes out and has become attentive to my every need. He takes me to movies and is not ashamed to be seen having coffee with me in public. If he weren't going to college in the fall, I'd be worried. A boy shouldn't be too devoted to his mother. Maybe he feels he's making up for the last two years, but I hope not. Everyone is entitled to rebel against his parents. He seems to be gathering his strength for something, but I don't know what. I doubt if he does either. He asks about my days in art school and Ben's life in New York as if he can use our lives to fashion his own. I don't mind reminiscing, but of course he'll have to do it himself, as we did.

June 6, 1967: Michael graduated tonight. He bought a new suit and had his hair cut in a Princeton for the occasion. Though he's still short and slight, he's grown a few inches this year and is as tall as Ben, which is enough to make him look more like a man and less like a boy. He's very serious about things. He told me solemnly that he thought the graduation exercises were foolish, but I know he was pleased that Ben and I were there. Afterward a girl came up to him in tears and said, "Michael, I'll probably never see you again, but I wish you every best . . ." She couldn't finish and threw her arms around him. I was touched and asked Michael who the girl was, but he said he didn't know her name and looked disgusted. In his suit and tie he looked like a fraternity boy or a junior executive, and I wondered what he would become. I suppose I shouldn't care, as long as he's happy, but I do. I know I should only want him to do what pleases him in life— God knows that's hard enough. But that wouldn't satisfy me. I would be crushed if he became an insurance salesman. I don't tell him this, of course, but he knows. Michael pretends things don't matter to him, and when I cry he is embarrassed for me, but he wouldn't deny his feelings if they were unimportant to him. I think he's afraid of what he feels, afraid that he'll reveal too much and be destroyed.

At the reception I met Michael's college adviser. Stone-faced and fat, she told me Michael had been accepted at the university, despite his low grades. She seemed disappointed, and I was glad to rub in his intelligence. No wonder he remains uninspired with slugs like her teaching him. It suddenly seemed miraculous to me that he did as well as he did. After graduation, we came home and ate cheesecake with Ben and Charles. Ben was proud, but of course he didn't say anything about it to Michael. Not for the first time I realize it is not easy to be his son.

JULY 15, 1967: Five A.M. The sun hasn't risen yet, but there is an orange tinge to the sky. I got up to make breakfast for Michael, who has a summer job at a construction site in West Allis and has to be at work at six. Since he is small for his age, we were surprised he got the job. He must be stronger than he looks. Apparently the test involved carrying bags of cement up and down flights of stairs, and somehow Michael passed. He is deeply tanned and his hair is bleached blond. When I pass the bathroom I occasionally catch glimpses of him flexing his muscles in the mirror. Moshe bought him a used Chevy as a graduation present, which makes Michael feel very independent and mature. We don't have much time to talk in the morning, but I know he appreciates my getting up. I enjoy it too. We sit and drink coffee and look out into the dim backyard and share the morning. I am so glad he is a man at last; I find it interesting to be with him, and there is no tension between us. I feel special satisfaction in Michael because I produced him first; he is mine in a different way. I want to brag about him to my friends and put a stamp on his forehead to claim credit. Then all the girls he meets would know who is responsible. He doesn't have girlfriends yet, or if he does, he doesn't tell me about them. But he will, and I am already curious about them, and jealous.

September 8, 1967: Just back from Madison, where I went to take Michael to school. We drove over in the van, filled to the top with his things, but we didn't talk much. I felt teary, as one might expect, and Michael, while trying to be nice, was anxious to be rid of me. His dormitory is small, with a red Spanish-tile roof, and right next to the lake. His roommate wasn't in yet, so Michael and I took a short walk. After that, I got in the van to leave. He turned to go back to his room; then at the last moment he came to the van and held me tight. I cried on the way home, but now I feel an enormous sense of relief. I'm sad too, desolate that my firstborn has left the nest. But there is great satisfaction in the knowledge that I made it this far;

that I didn't collapse, give in, fail to raise my boys and give them what they needed. There is still Charles to shepherd through another two years of high school, and Ben gets worse. But five years ago I doubted I could make it this far. I have a terrific feeling of pride. Michael has gone off to college and he's not noticeably scarred by this whole thing. Perhaps now he can take care of me.

October 2, 1967: In this morning's mail I received a letter from the dean informing me that I have been given tenure. "Given" does not seem right, for I have fought for it over the last eight years and watched men hired after me move on before I have. Yet this morning I felt no rancor; after all this time, tenure does seem like a gift, completely unexpected, from an adoring father. So my immediate impulse is to call my department chairman and thank him and then work my way down through the executive committe to the junior faculty and finally to the graduate students. I am really very happy and proud—I am the first woman to get tenure since I arrived here—but mostly relieved. Now I know we won't starve to death. It is a brilliant fall day and the colors are nearly at their peak. On such days I think the beauty of nature should be enough, and it very nearly is enough. Still, it's nice to have tenure, too.

October 26, 1967: Ben went to the doctor today and came back with good news. Apparently there is a theory that at some point the disease can "burn itself out"—that the patient will simply stop deteriorating. I am wary of theories—I still remember all the early talk we got about spontaneous remissions from doctors who didn't want us to worry. But it has been almost three years since Ben's last serious attack, and now there is at least the possibility that the worst is over. I am happy, of course, but that is tempered by Ben's condition. It would be wonderful if the disease mercifully stopped, but it has taken a great deal away already. It is ten years since Ben fell down in Chicago and eight since he was forced out of the quartet. He was a young man then, vigorous, involved with life. He is still reasonably young, and more optimistic than anyone has a right to expect. He is as demanding and intolerant as ever; he is still Ben, and I still love him. But it hurts me to see how he has changed: he almost never gets out of his chair; he has put on weight and has trouble straightening out his hands, arms, and legs; because his hands are stiff, he stopped shaving, and his beard came in white, which makes him look much older than forty-nine. But perhaps this is too pessimistic. The doctor says Ben's muscles have not atrophied completely, and that physical therapy can help him. Furthermore, Ben has his own life: he has his students and he is writing new things all the time. He enjoys chess and books and has friends. Most important, Ben has adjusted to the fact that he is no longer a concert artist and that he can never be one again. I have to remind myself: we are not yet fifty; we may have twenty more years together. They won't be like the first twenty, but they can be good years just the same. At last Ben's health seems to be improving, and I have tenure. Things could really be much worse than that.

Part Five

32

DORY FILLED the sterling coffeepot from the urn in the corner, then returned to the serving table. There was a full plate of cookies, but she piled more on to hide her irritation. A tenured professor and still pouring at receptions. It was the price she paid for working in a department dominated by men. When she looked up, the guest of honor was beaming at her.

"Ah, Mrs. Seidler," Hoyt Andrews said. "How nice of you to take care of all of us. The cookies are wonderful."

"I didn't make them," Dory said. "Cream with your coffee?" Dory felt like pouring the coffee onto Andrews' pink dome, but instead she smiled. It wasn't really his fault. Andrews had been visiting artist several years before, and when the university announced a competition to select a new piece of sculpture for the library mall, he had applied.

"Thank you," Andrews said, accepting the cup. Dory wished the man would leave, but after looking around the room, Andrews turned back to her. "It is so delightful to come to Milwaukee," he said. "Things are so peaceful here, so . . ." He searched for the word.

"We're kind of a backwater," Dory said helpfully.

"Now, that isn't what I meant at all," Andrews said. "It's just that I travel so very much and am so busy that it's nice to come here and see people who are content just to live and work in one place."

"Have you been traveling a lot?"

Andrews seemed to swell with the question. Dory noticed that he had grown silver muttonchop sideburns, which now blocked her view of the room. "A show in Alaska, one in Seattle, another in South Dakota, and now this commission for the library. Sometimes I long for the simple life I had years ago, when no one knew my name and I could bury myself in art."

Dory felt herself begin to laugh and concentrated on the cookies. Talk about backwaters. And the commission had been the result of three months of determined ass-kissing coupled with the fact that the committee's first two choices had been involved with other things. Bury himself in art indeed.

"And you, Mrs. Seidler?"

Dory looked up now. Why couldn't the man take a hint and go away? She disliked Andrews' work only slightly less than his manner. "Oh, pretty much the same," she said.

Andrews nodded his head vigorously. "I complain," he said. "But I wouldn't want to see the day when I wasn't too busy. Art is my life, you see." Then Andrews saw the dean enter the room. His head swiveled as purposefully as a pointer's in a duck blind. It was as if Dory no longer existed. Andrews started across the room; then, as if he had forgotten something, he turned back. His face was now heavy with pity. "Perhaps someday for you, Mrs. Seidler."

"Perhaps someday for you too," Dory replied. But Andrews was walking, arms outstretched, toward the dean and did not hear.

After talking to Andrews, Dory was glad to have the coffee table to attend to; she was too angry to mix with her colleagues. She cleared off the dirty cups and set them to soak; then she made another pot of coffee and put out still more cookies. When she looked up again, Sam Matthews was standing before her like an apparition, his red hair flecked with white, his face lined. He looked now like a university professor, all gray and tweedy; he had lost his dangerous quality, but he was still attractive. Sam smiled. "It's been a long time, Dory."

In spite of herself, Dory felt a flush spread across her face. She had imagined their meeting again hundreds of times, but never with her pouring coffee. It would have been better in Paris or New York, or even in Madison. For all the times she had been back over the years, she had never seen Sam. He had gone on and become successful with galleries in Rome and London. *Time* magazine had even done a story on him with reproductions of his lithographs a few years ago. She had never called him, in part because she was afraid they would resume what they had broken off before. Yet now she could think of nothing more to say than "It *has* been a long time. Would you like some coffee?"

"I was hoping they'd have something stronger," Sam said.

"Sorry, there's some rule that we can't have any liquor on campus except light beer. The chairman thought that would be inelegant."

"He's right about that," Sam said. "But maybe we could go somewhere and have a drink. Can you get away?"

Dory felt herself blushing again. This was ridiculous. They were no longer lovers. There was nothing wrong with having a drink with an old friend. She put her apron aside. "Let's go," she said.

Sam drove to a dark tavern on the east side of the river, where the walls were papered with fake antique beer signs. He ordered martinis for both of them. He seemed to inhale his before Dory had even started, then ordered another, after which he seemed to relax.

"I didn't know you were an admirer of Hoyt Andrews'," Dory said.

Sam made a face. "God, I hope you don't think I came over to see that bastard. I was in town and dropped by. Actually, I thought I might get a chance to see you."

"You can see me anytime," Dory said.

"I haven't, not in all these years."

"You're gone a lot," Dory said. "I read in *Time* that you spent a year in Rome."

"You never called, Dory. You never wrote. I couldn't phone you, even though I wanted to, but you could have called me."

Dory shifted uncomfortably in her chair and looked down into her drink. "What for, Sam?"

"Because we meant something to each other, that's why." He was speaking louder now, and Dory wondered if it was only the martini. "Because I was in love with you and I think if you had been honest with yourself, you would have left Ben, that's why."

Now Dory looked up. "That's a long time ago, Sam, and I'm not even sure you're right. You meant a lot to me; you still do. But I love Ben and I've never regretted staying with him. You can always talk about what you might have done, but what good does it do? All you can do is live as best you can with what you have. There's really no point in talking about the past."

For a moment Sam looked hurt; then he shrugged. "You're right. I didn't mean to grill you. The truth is, I'm just happy to be able to see you again." Now he smiled. "Will you forgive me?"

"There's nothing to forgive," Dory said.

"At least have another drink."

"I haven't finished this one, but go ahead."

Sam signaled the waiter, and Dory decided to leave after the next round. She didn't want to sit and watch while Sam got drunk. But his manner changed and he sipped the new drink, quiet and thoughtful in the dark room. "How is Ben?" he said at last.

"Actually, he's doing pretty well, but if you saw him you'd be shocked. It's an odd disease; it moves like a glacier, and when you look back, something you loved is gone."

"You've lost a lot, Dory. I don't see how you do it."

Dory knew he was sincere, but looking at Sam, she did not feel sorry for herself. He was well-known as an artist, secure in his job, but alone and middle-aged. "We're really doing fine, Sam."

"I see Michael around campus sometimes," said Sam. "I took him to dinner once, and he cleaned me out."

"He mentioned that in a letter. It meant a lot to him, I think, that you remembered him."

"It doesn't seem that long ago that I was taking him and Charles to the scout dinner," Sam said. "And now he's a man."

"Not quite a man."

"Maybe not to his mother, but he seems very mature to me, serious and polite in a way I wouldn't have expected. I mean, he was one of the most unrestrained kids I ever saw."

Dory was glad to hear it. She still worried about Michael flunking out of college. "Tell me about you, Sam. What have you been doing with your life that hasn't been written up in the newspapers?"

Sam laughed. "A lot, I guess, but it seems like nothing very important. I almost got married, to one of my students, then decided against it. I realized I didn't want to be an old man when she was only forty."

"What difference does it make, if you love each other?"

"None, I suppose. It's probably just vanity. It's the trouble with teaching. You have these bright young kids looking up to you all the time, expecting you to tell them how to live. Sometimes it's hard not to think you're as wise as they think you are. You start speaking in aphorisms and you forget the whole world isn't eighteen years old and that you're not as impressive as they think. I thought I'd be reminded of that every day as this girl got older, that she'd see me as I am."

"You don't give yourself enough credit, Sam. Why shouldn't they be impressed with you? Why shouldn't anyone? You've done a lot."

Sam waved his hand in front of his face. "Thank you, thank you. I shouldn't have started talking, Dory. You know all that; you're a teacher yourself. And you don't have to worry about my feelings. I know what I am and what I'm not. My work sells well, and I'm not ashamed of commercial success. But I feel less satisfied than when I was thirty."

218

"You're not a young radical anymore."

"I never was, really. But in another couple of years I'll be wearing a straw hat and selling at outdoor art fairs."

"Would that be so bad?"

Sam smiled again. "I don't mean to sound vainglorious. I've been luckier than a lot of people."

"People with talent tend to get lucky," Dory said. "I've got to be going, Sam. Ben expects me for dinner."

Sam paid the check and they walked to the car. He was quiet driving home, but when Dory was about to open the door, Sam held her arm. "Dory, it was good to see you," he said.

"I've enjoyed it, Sam." She wondered if he would kiss her.

"I'm sorry I waited this long. I imagined you would hold it against me, not coming before, and then with each year it seemed more impossible, as if there was too much to make up."

"You shouldn't have worried about that. I never blamed you for anything, and neither did Ben after a while. I'll never forget what you did for us that winter."

Sam nodded, looking out at the empty street. Dory opened the car door now, but Sam called her back. "Dory, do you think we could do this again? Just to talk, I mean."

Dory looked at her former lover. He seemed so hopeful that she felt sorry for him. "Sure, Sam. Give me a call sometime."

"I'd like to see Ben, too," Sam said wistfully. "There's no one like him left in Madison."

There had never been anyone like Ben in Madison, Dory thought. "Well, give him a call, too," she said. Then she got out of the car.

Dory went in the house, hung up her coat, and turned the heat on under the stew. Ben was taking a nap. She went in the living room and picked up the newspaper. As she did, she happened to glance out the window. Sam had not driven away. His car still stood idling in the street, and he was staring down the block like a sentry in the growing dusk.

33

November 20, 1970: Six A.M. and still dark. I have a chest cold, complete with sore throat and cough, but no fever. I am just sick enough to spend the day in bed reading women's magazines and sipping herb tea without feeling too self-indulgent. It has happened many times that I collapse the moment school vacation begins, but somehow I can't ever manage to become seriously ill during the year. I've decided the cause is arrogance: I think I secretly fear that if I were to miss a week, the diligent barbarians I teach would never learn anything about the baroque period—Rembrandt, Rubens, Velázquez—and I couldn't allow that. Does it really matter? Not in Kenosha, I suppose, and probably not to my students either. But it matters to me, to my idea of myself and my responsibility to pass on something to the next generation. All anyone can really teach is the accumulation of her experiences. The fact remains that one of the most wonderful things that happened to me as a young artist was just being allowed to sit in the Corcoran Gallery at lunchtime and look at pictures uninterrupted for an hour. That is what I teach—and Rubens and Velázquez too.

November 22, 1970: I'm getting great satisfaction from my yoga class these days. Since taking it up, I've accomplished many miracles, the latest of which is a shoulder stand I can hold for five minutes. My teacher is a beautiful young boy of twenty-three, and whenever I plead the excuse of my aging body, he scoffs and insists I try something impossible. I may someday achieve the headstand—I like the idea of viewing the world upside-down—and who knows what else. If the body is flexible, can the mind be static?

November 24, 1970: I've been thinking about Sam since seeing him last week. It had never seemed to me before that good-looking men suffer the onset of age as much as women. He's still handsome, but it's hard to think of him breaking up anyone's marriage anymore. It makes me feel grateful that I've always been rather plain. Actually, I think I've improved with age—I've lost the pallor of youth, and my body has filled out; people don't find me unattractive. What was poignant about Sam, though, is that I knew he wanted to impress me, wanted me somehow to regret my choice to stay with Ben. I don't know if I made it clear that I am impressed with him, with his art and what he's done certainly, but more with the kind of man he is. Nothing he could do as an artist would impress me more than what he did the morning he came over and built a fire and made breakfast for the boys and me. Sam knows he did something right once, and now he tries to figure out what it was. It's sad to see old boyfriends. They can't help but disappoint you. I wonder if I disappointed Sam too.

November 26, 1970: Thanksgiving and no trace of the flu, so I'll get up and make turkey and cranberry sauce. I don't really like turkey, but Michael has this idea of me as Donna Reed—incongruous as that is—and our home as something out of a television situation comedy. I always let him down with reality, but must try anyway. It is little enough for him to ask that I spend a few days before he comes home baking and cleaning. Michael informed us the other day that he is bringing a girl home for the first time. Her name is Ricky, which immediately makes me suspicious. Why does he choose a girl with a boy's name? Is he a latent homosexual and this the only way he can act out? Or is Ricky simply a diminutive of some perfectly nice girl's name, like Erica? I know I'm acting in classic mother-in-law fashion. He does seem happier lately, and more mature. She's probably nice, with many good qualities. Michael says she's very smart and pretty. Still, Ricky?

November 29, 1970: Thanksgiving came and passed uneventfully, though I don't like Michael's girl. She's extremely polite, too much so for my taste. She continued to call me Mrs. Seidler even though I asked that she call me Dory. Very middle-class and prissy. Not our type at all. Oh, well. Today is Ben's birthday and I have gotten him mixed nuts, chocolates, and a rich red corduroy shirt that I like very much. We'll sit and eat Chinese food in his bedroom and listen to records. Seeing Sam last week made me think more about the last few years and whether I've done the right thing. I'm convinced I have. Life with Sam would have been exciting, but I would have felt guilty leaving Ben. More than that, with all his problems, Ben remains a more interesting man than Sam. He is alive in a way few other people are; he surprises me still, even after twenty-two years of marriage. My friends tend to idealize me for not deserting Ben and the boys. But what

221

would my life have been without them? I really think Sam Matthews is worse off than I.

December 2, 1970: I complain often about my colleagues, but they are not really a bad lot, just different, as I must appear very different to them. Steve Herman had a party at his house—a post-Thanksgiving pre-Xmas party, as he explained—and I realized looking around the room that I had come to care for these people, or at least some of them. Steve is large and pleasant and German. He is courtly too. Once when I mentioned that I had to get the storm windows up, he appeared the next Saturday with his sons and an enormous ladder to do the job. Moreover, the neglect I often feel is not directed at me personally. Would my co-workers be more friendly and helpful if I worked in a foundry or was a secretary in an office? Or is it, as I suspect, that we are alone when it comes to sickness and death, except for our families and closest friends?

December 10, 1970: One of the hazards of gaining tenure is that I'm among a select few such women on campus. What this means is that whenever there is a particularly visible committee that must represent the university, I'm likely to be chosen for it. Right now I'm chairman of the student-conduct committee and we are having hearings on last fall's draft protests. I try to be impartial and forget my own days at George Washington thirty—God!—years ago. I was always fairly cautious. But I admired the radicals then, and now I sympathize with the students whose cases we hear. Is this liberal guilt accumulated over three decades? One boy who is in my painting class comes before us today for writing "Fuck the Army" on the library wall in red paint. I suppose the boy must be disciplined, but the red paint was an improvement over those plain white walls. The university lawyer thinks we should expel the boy, which means he'd get drafted. That seems a bit extreme to me. I suppose we'll compromise eventually—maybe a limited suspension. Or we could make the boy wash the wall. Meanwhile, I sit and listen while the students excoriate the establishment, realizing only slowly, and with some amazement, that this time I *am* the establishment. To hear these kids talk, you'd think Lyndon Johnson and I planned the whole thing. My own sons remain quite conservative, on the whole. Not that I want them to go around breaking windows or bombing buildings, but I wish they were more unconventional. When I saw my student this morning, we talked about his work, which he's neglected this term. Then, as he was about to leave, he turned and said, "Until tonight." It's going to be hard to be impartial.

December 15, 1970: I've seen little outside the four walls of my office this week. With my classes, committee work, and the ever-increasing mound of papers on my desk which must be graded before Christmas, I have little choice about how to spend my time. Ben offers to grade the papers for me. But he's always so shocked by the students' grammar that he spends most of the time talking about the failure of education in America and we get little done. In a week, vacation will start and I'll be able to spend more time with him. The boys will be home together for the first time in a year, and I'm looking forward to having my family around me. For now, things seem pretty much under control at home. I get older and Ben is weaker, but we have reliable help and the boys are on their own. Now it is on to the real challenges of life—getting my grades in and trimming a tree before Christmas Day.

34

Ben watched as Julie Barker struggled through the last few bars of the Schubert lieder he had transcribed for her. She was a wiry, muscular girl and the cello thrust between her legs seemed slightly erotic to Ben. As Julie played, the tip of her tongue was visible and there was a glow of sweat on her forehead. At last she finished and turned to Ben.

"I'm sorry, Julie," he said. "It still seems too slow to me, almost sluggish. This is romantic, a song of love. You've got to make it sound that way somehow."

The girl slumped in her chair. She had been working on the piece for weeks and was to play it at the recital in January. Ben had hoped Julie would turn out as well as Roger, but he had been overly optimistic. "Maybe I should just quit," Julie said.

"Don't be ridiculous," Ben replied, but he understood how she felt. He tried again. "Look, Julie. Do you remember how it was back in September, when we started working on your program for the recital?"

The girl looked down at her instrument.

"Well, you've improved enormously since then. You've memorized this and the other pieces the quartet is going to play. All I'm asking is that you try to work more on the interpretation of the piece and play with greater feeling. Can't you do that?"

The girl looked up now, hope showing in her eyes. "Do you really think it's better, Mr. Seidler?"

"Julie, there's no question about it. But you still have to practice some more, that's all. The concert is only a month away."

She smiled and nodded her head. "And after the concert I can start practicing for my audition at Juilliard, right?"

Ben smiled slowly. This would be more difficult. "Right now I don't want you to worry about that," he said. "That's a year away and we'll have plenty of time to talk about it." He looked at his watch. "Okay, that's all we have time for today. But I'll see you next week?"

"Next week is Christmas."

He thought of Heinz Ober's attitude toward holidays. But these were kids, not professionals. "All right. No lesson next week. But the week after that, we'll go for an hour and a half."

Julie nodded and began to pack her cello in the large black case. Ben looked around the room. He had managed to persuade Lucille to let him hold lessons there, now that it was harder for him to get around, and he was more comfortable surrounded by the clutter of books and paper. He had continued writing, but lately his compositions had lacked energy.

Julie rose to leave. "See you in two weeks, Mr. Seidler. Merry Christmas."

"Merry Christmas to you," Ben said. "Ask Lucille to come in, will you?"

The girl nodded and was gone. Ben waited, chin in hand. He had lost the angularity of youth. His shoulders were rounded now, and his lips full. The hair that ringed his bald head was gray and his beard was cut so close to his face that it gave the impression of not being a beard at all, but simply the accumulation of several days's growth. He wore Dory's red corduroy shirt and his paunch was held in check by a white canvas belt, which was fastened to the back of his wheelchair. He shook his head like a horse bothered by flies. He felt sleepy and he still had to make it through Sally Freeman's lesson that afternoon. "Goddammit, Lucille. Come in here, will you?"

The black woman appeared in the doorway. "What you yellin' about?" she said. "I told the little girl I'd be a minute. I was all the way down in the basement."

"I'm sorry," Ben said. "She didn't tell me. But I have to eat my lunch. I have another student at one."

"You ain't going to starve to death," Lucille said, looking at Ben's stomach.

"Obesity can sometimes be a sign of malnutrition," Ben said, and laughed.

Lucille smiled now. "So what you want to eat?"

It was not a simple question. He made elaborate plans for meals to be eaten three days hence. To him, a meal was like a symphony. He made Lucille scour the city for various delicacies. He was particularly fond of seafood. Recently, though, he had been put on a diet by the doctor. "I guess I'll just have a salad." Then, brightening, "Of course, you could put some of that leftover salmon in it."

After lunch Lucille cleared the dishes. When she reappeared, she was wearing her coat. "I'm fixin' to go," she said. "You need anything else?"

"I don't think so. Wait, there is something. Will you fill that water glass? My doctor says I should drink plenty of water or else I'll get another urinary infection."

Lucille poured the water, then turned to him. "You all right?"

"Sure," Ben said. "I'm fine, just tired, that's all."

Lucille smiled and patted Ben's head, smoothing the few strands of hair that remained. "I'll see you tomorrow, hear?"

Ben felt better after talking with Lucille. He knew he didn't suffer terribly from the disease. After all, he wasn't in pain. He had no sensation at all below the waist. He had plenty of time to work, and no serious financial problems. That was the important thing. He disliked his isolation, but he had never enjoyed playing with the quartet. The traveling, the fights, the running battles with the music faculty. Good riddance to all that.

Of course, there had been moments when music was the most wonderful thing in the world, times when he felt capable of anything, and now he could do almost nothing. He looked again at the fiddle. It seemed enormous. How had he ever handled the damned thing? How had he controlled it? It seemed remarkable to him that the same hands that had once played the most difficult Paganini etudes were now unable to hold on to a piece of paper. As far as the fiddle was concerned, "Come to Jesus" in C minor was beyond him.

Still, Ben had few regrets. He remembered a concert somewhere up north when the audience had interrupted with sustained applause between movements of one of the Beethoven quartets. Even Ober had lost his composure and started laughing. Then there had been the soirees after the concerts. The parties always made Ben feel like a whore hired to entertain the rich, and of course it was true. Musicians existed at the whim of the wealthy, and always had. Who supported Mozart, Beethoven, and Haydn? Who supported the arts in America? Thank God he was through with that.

What was worst was simply being limited to the house, now mostly to his room. As a young man he had always liked to walk, simply for the exercise. Often he would leave home with a headache after practicing, and walk for miles, returning refreshed and ready to work. Now he was often unable to sleep until two or three A.M. He remembered long tours of Manhattan with Dory, and afternoon journeys to Mickies. Now he couldn't make the distance of his horizontal bars without stopping to rest.

Yet Ben knew he was lucky. His friend Tony Jacuzi, who had contracted the disease only five years before, was flat on his back. Tony was only thirty-five, and his wife had taken a lover. Then there was Isidore Lasky, who had been born with deformed hands and feet. Isidore came to play chess with Ben, and at first Ben had been repelled by him. Isidore would go to great efforts to light his pipe, his crablike hands grasping the bowl; then the damned thing would go out. He spent half the night lighting and relighting the pipe, refusing to settle for a cigarette instead.

At one o'clock Sally Freeman called to say she couldn't make her lesson. "What's the matter, Sally?" Ben said.

"I don't know, Mr. Seidler. I have a fever. Mom doesn't want me to go outside in the cold."

Ben looked at the ceiling. First Julie, now this. Maybe they should just cancel the damned concert. "When do you think you'll be able to come, Sally?"

The girl sounded scared. "I'm sorry, Mr. Seidler. I'm really sick."

"It's all right, Sally. It's just that we have a concert next month and we have to get ready. What about Friday instead?"

"Okay, I'll be there." The girl hung up.

Suddenly Ben had the afternoon before him. He called Dory, but her secretary said she was in class and had a meeting after that. Could she take a message? Ben thanked the woman and told her it wasn't important. He would speak to his wife when she got home.

Perhaps he could chance a cigar. He looked at the box of kitchen matches on the television set and remembered the time he lost control of a burning match and dropped it on the floor, igniting some papers. The firemen had arrived in five minutes, but a part of the floor had been irremediably charred, and it remained a blackened reminder of the incident.

Dory had been upset, and though he didn't admit it, Ben was frightened too. "You might have killed yourself," she said.

"That would have been an improvement."

"Can't you see that this isn't a joke? It's not funny, Ben."

"The whole thing is funny; it's funny that I'm alive under these conditions." When the firemen asked how the blaze started, Ben told them he came from a long line of self-immolating Buddhist monks. He had done it for religious reasons, he said.

Despite the jokes, however, he was unnerved by the fire. It would be

227

an unpleasant way to die. Painful. Yet during his last physical the doctor had stuck two long needles into his legs and Ben felt nothing. Perhaps fire wouldn't be so bad; it would be warm. Still, he did not want to lose his legs. They were large and sturdy, so much so it seemed remarkable at times that they were incapable of supporting him. Moreover, they sheltered his penis, which still miraculously came to life occasionally. A green shoot in a petrified forest. Sometimes he felt evanescent, as if his mind existed in a realm independent of his ruined body and floated free in spiritual partnership with his genitals.

Ben had always been attracted to the myth of the phoenix, and now he wondered if perhaps the key to rejuvenation lay within himself. When the smoke from his cigar curled around his head, causing his eyes to tear, he imagined himself enthroned upon a funeral pyre, presiding over his own rebirth. This was why he felt most like smoking when he was alone; alone he could preserve the illusion of freedom. The cigar was company, the match excitement, drama, possibility. Wreathed in smoke, the world became an abstraction; he felt temporarily euphoric, in control, alive perhaps.

There was also simple pride in accomplishment. After all, it took dexterity to light the damned match. It gave him comfort to think he could still do some things for himself.

Still he hesitated. Once, because his circulation was so bad, the smoke caused an oxygen shortage. He had first become pale and sweaty; then he lost consciousness. If Dory hadn't been home, he might have died. She had come into the room to find Ben semiconscious, the cigar butt smoldering in his crotch. The phoenix was attractive; suffocation was not.

Michael had made a special trip home to ask Ben to stop smoking. He was only concerned for Ben's safety, but they all acted as if he couldn't blow his own nose. Hadn't he gone out and gotten a job in the middle of the Depression to support his family? Hadn't he supported them for years?

Yet Ben was fond of Michael too. He loved both his sons, but he thought of Michael more often, for it was Michael who had rebelled against him. Charles indulged Ben by playing chess, and they never argued. But Charles didn't get home very often anymore, and when he did, he seemed like a stranger. Charles was tall and dark and didn't look like anyone in the family. He and Ben were more like acquaintances than father and son. It was too bad, but that was the way it was. They had history in common, but they were uncomfortable with each other.

History. It was ironic, but for all the days he spent daydreaming about the past, Ben's memory was spotty. Grocery lists were useless; he forgot to give Dory her messages. His mind wandered free of all restraints. What he

228

remembered was so personal that there was no point in repeating it: the way winter sunlight looked on the red brick of Science Hall from his office window; the golden sheen of a stage in Philadelphia; Dory's smile, expectant and sad, viewed from a train window when he returned from tour. Sometimes he would remember something and wonder if it had really happened at all.

The telephone rang, and Ben moved forward as quickly as possible. He used his left hand to form the right into a prehensile claw and wrapped it around the earpiece. Usually the phone rang six times before Ben could get it off the cradle. Often the other party hung up. This time, though, it was Michael, and he knew enough to let the phone ring.

"Yes?" Ben said.

"Pop?"

"Who did you think it would be, Edmund Wilson?"

"Funny. How are you, anyway?"

"I could complain, but I don't want to ruin your day. No one ever listens to me anyway."

Michael laughed. His voice was warm; he sounded, people said, like his father. "What I meant was, how are you relatively? Not in cosmic terms. Just day-to-day."

"In day-to-day terms I'm like I always am," Ben said. "Lousy. It doesn't change much, you know. I'm a very sick man. I can't move my legs, and it took me six rings to pick up the goddamned phone because my fingers aren't strong enough to hold on to anything. Sooner or later this fucking disease will affect my mind. Then when you ask how I am I'll recite the Gettysburg Address or give you the Sermon on the Mount. But if I'm lucky, I'll die before that. Sometimes you ask stupid questions."

"Well, Charlie's the genius in the family," Michael said. "But I'm sorry. I thought you were getting better."

"It's all relative," Ben said. "What can I do for you, kid?"

"I was wondering if you sent my check yet. It's the fifteenth, and I'm pretty low."

"I thought you were working."

"I am, but it's only part time. I'm a scholar, remember?"

"When I was your age I'd been sending money home for five years."

"You were a good son, a fine man. I admire you. But where's my allowance?"

"Let's see," Ben said. "I sent the check the day before yesterday, so it should be there by now. But the Christmas mail might hold it up. Do you need the money to get home?"

229

"Not really, but I'd like to know it's there."

"Good. Don't cash the check right away. Hold on to it until after your vacation."

"Is it good?"

"It will be, trust me."

"Just don't buy any marginal stocks with my allowance."

Ben was genuinely shocked. "I wouldn't dream of such a thing, Michael."

"Great. Listen, what do you want for Christmas?"

"What do I care for these pagan holidays? But you'd better get something for your mother."

"I already did. Anything else?"

"Did you hear the one about the cross-eyed seamstress?"

"I don't think so."

"She couldn't menstruate."

"I think I'll hang up on that."

"What do you expect? My brain cells are dying off daily."

"See you tomorrow, Pop."

Ben hung up. He appreciated Michael's keeping in touch, even though it was about money. When Michael was in Europe, he wrote home every week despite Ben's refusal to answer after one of his letters had been lost. What was the sense of writing, he reasoned, if the French post office was going to lose his letters? But he was pleased with Michael's loyalty. Most kids wouldn't bother. Hell, Charles was only in California, and they never heard from him.

Ben remembered a night when Michael took him to a Garbo festival on the West Side. It had been an awful evening, snowing like hell; it was ridiculous to make the trip, but they went anyway. It was an adventure, Michael said, and he almost made it more of one. As he was taking Ben down the icy stairs, Michael slipped and nearly dumped Ben on his ass before recovering and depositing him in the dark well of the truck. Then Ben nearly froze to death with only a lap robe over him on the ride to the theater. But it was worth it. They saw *Mata Hari* and Michael indulged Ben's taste for treats. When he spilled popcorn all over himself, Michael bought another box. When he dropped that, Michael bought a third. Ben had been busy picking kernels of popcorn out of his pants for days, but he appreciated the kid's efforts. Now he regretted their quarrels.

The problem, he knew, was that he couldn't take any back talk; wouldn't, shouldn't. And Michael couldn't keep his mouth shut. They were always getting into arguments that neither cared about, halfhearted bragging

230

matches that counted on the other's ignorance to win the day. Tony Jacuzi said things were different now, that kids were smarter, knew more. To hear Tony talk, you'd think Michael spent all his time doing differential equations. Ben knew better. A son had to respect his father. That was all. Simple. But it never was.

He wondered how Moshe would have handled Michael. He couldn't imagine his son making deliveries on the train to the relatives in Baltimore or working in the shop after school. Still less could he see Michael in the *shul* or taking violin lessons. He would have gotten out of it somehow; there would have been some excuse. Charles had always ended up doing everything around the house while Michael was out somewhere. Maybe that was why Charles never came home. He had served his time.

Ben sighed and rested his head in his hands. Images flickered on the television screen to his right, and though there was no sound, a soothing electronic susurrus comforted Ben. He thought again of smoking. He liked to hold the cigar in his teeth. It gave him a feeling of solidity, like a captain of industry who had just completed some multimillion-dollar deal. It reminded him of evenings on the road, when he and Ober would sit together smoking after a good meal. Heinz had appreciated a fine cigar. You could say that for him.

Ben reached for the cigar box. With some difficulty he extracted one, and then swore. He had forgotten they were encased in metal tubes, which were practically impossible to open. Ben gripped the pull string in his teeth, but the aluminum slipped in his grasp. He tried again, and by some miracle the cork came loose. Ben caught the cigar as it slid out. He was pleased with himself. Then he took a match and braced the box against the chair with his leg. Holding tightly, Ben dragged the match slowly against the striking surface. Nothing happened. He swore and considered waiting for Dory. Then he shook his head and tried again. This time he managed to generate more force, but it was not enough. The match made a harsh, grating noise, but it did not ignite.

Maybe he should forget about it. The cigar had gone from Cuba to Davidoff's and from Geneva to Milwaukee already. It might have gone stale on the way. Ben selected a new match, and this time, to his surprise, it ignited, the flame burning in his fist. He let the fire caress the cigar until the heat became uncomfortable. Then he flipped the match at the ashtray.

The stick balanced for a moment on the edge of the ceramic dish, then fell to the floor. Ben's reaction was instinctive. He rolled back in his chair, holding the cigar in his teeth. The match was beginning to burn through some letters. He turned his chair sideways and grabbed the water glass. Because of the angle, Ben succeeded only in upending the glass, however. The water dripped from the table, partially extinguishing the fire, but the letters continued to burn. Now the flames began to spread.

Ben pushed a pile of letters off the table and momentarily smothered the fire. But then the flames rose again. Ben's heart was pounding, but his head was clear. Fire blocked his path to the door, and it would be hard to maneuver between his desk and the table. There was only one thing to do. Slowly, careful not to drop it, Ben curled his fingers around the telephone and put it to his ear. Then he dialed the operator.

35

ST. MARY'S HOSPITAL stood on a hill overlooking Lake Michigan, across the street from an old stone water tower that was nonfunctional but served as a landmark. Dory climbed the steps and made her way through the lobby to the elevator. She pushed the button marked Up and leaned against the wall to wait as the box made its descent through the elevator shaft. She was tired. The first she had known of Ben's accident was when her secretary pulled her out of an executive committee meeting. The call had come from the police, and Dory had telephoned around for an hour before locating the officer who found Ben.

When she had arrived at the hospital the night before, Ben was sedated. The doctor needed her permission to transfer him to St. Mary's. Ben's burns weren't critical, he said, and were confined to his legs, but he should be at a burn center. Dory agreed. She wanted the best for Ben, and St. Mary's was near the house. Then Dory was allowed to see Ben. He lay swathed in white, like a child, his high forehead almost translucent, with tiny blue veins running vertically through it. She sat beside his bed for half an hour, but Ben did not awaken. Then, when Dory felt herself dropping off, she had gone back to the university. She had work to do.

The elevator arrived, and Dory entered, along with two nuns in habits and butterfly hats and a man dressed in a dark suit. A funeral director, Dory thought. When they reached the fifth floor, only Dory and the funeral director remained. The man stood aside as the door opened. "After you," he said, and smiled.

The man was only being polite, but Dory didn't want Death behind her. "That's all right," she said.

"Please, I insist," the man said.

Dory looked at him. He was standing with one arm blocking the door, the other outstretched. "Thank you," she said finally, and walked through the man's arms.

A nurse directed her to room 518, and Dory walked down the wide white corridor looking at room numbers. Patients sat quietly in the hall watching television. On the walls were Christmas decorations and signs imploring everyone to be of good cheer. Everything was white except the floor, which was the color of butter. Dory looked at the floor.

Room 518 was a four-bed ward, and for a moment Dory thought she had the wrong room. Then she saw Ben against the far wall, washed with light, his beard blending with the white sheets. Dory was reassured; he looked better than he had the night before.

"I told them not to call you," Ben said.

In spite of herself, Dory laughed. "How could they keep it a secret? I'm your wife, Ben."

"I didn't want to worry you," he said. "I'm perfectly all right. I'll be home in a few days."

Dory nodded. Then: "Why did you smoke when no one else was home? I've asked you not to a dozen times."

"I wanted a cigar. I've got little enough satisfaction in my life, don't I?"

Dory recognized guilt in his stubbornness. "You're old enough to make your own decisions, but it wasn't a very smart thing to do."

"Well, you're the professor."

Dory smiled. "So were you, for ten years. But I didn't come here to lecture you. I was worried, scared." She leaned over the bed and hugged him, brushing his forehead with her lips. "I don't want to lose you, Ben, that's all."

Ben reached and pulled her down to him. They embraced for a moment before he released her. "I was scared too," he said. "I still can't figure out what happened. I've smoked hundreds of cigars with no problem. The only time I drop one is when I'm alone."

"I called the boys, and Moshe," Dory said. "He was ready to get on a plane and come out, but I told him it wasn't that serious. He said he'd call you tonight. Michael's coming in on the bus this afternoon. Charles will get here as soon as he can."

"Well, at least we'll get to see him," Ben said. He looked off into space. Then he said, "Sit down, honey. There, on the bed."

The bed next to Ben's was empty, and piled up on it were candy, books, and records. The man in the bed against the opposite wall looked normal except that where his right hand should have been, his fist expanded into an angry red ball. Next to the windows a black man lay propped up with pillows pushed into his back to lift him off the mattress. His wife sat next to him. She fed him macaroons, lit his cigarettes, fixed his sheets every few minutes, and at times spoke in a soft, deep voice.

"It looks like you made out pretty well compared to your roommates," Dory said. Ben looked exactly as he always did. His legs were beneath the sheets.

"I suppose so," he said. Then he turned to Dory and said in a conspiratorial whisper, "Do you know that the woman over there threw a pot of boiling water on her husband?"

"The man in bed?"

"Yes, the colored man."

Dory looked at the couple with new interest. The woman tucked in the sheets again, but the man looked impassive.

"She seems quite attentive now," Dory said.

"She feels guilty. She came home and found him in bed with another woman and let him have it."

"Did she have the water boiling just in case?"

"God knows. The funny thing is, she didn't mean to hit him. She was aiming for the woman, but she moved at the last minute. You know, they always blame the other woman; you'd think the man was raped."

Dory nodded. Just as Ben had blamed Sam, she thought. "I suppose it happens," she said.

"Anyway, now the wife feels terribly guilty. She's here all the time, morning to night, taking care of her husband, but the man will never speak to her. Before she leaves, she always gets down on her knees next to the bed and prays that he won't die, that he'll be there when she gets back the next day."

Dory was moved by the story. No one should have to go through life feeling guilty. "How is your leg?"

"Take a look if you want," Ben said.

Dory lifted the sheet and peered underneath. Ben's foot rested in a lime-green plastic boot. White gauze was wrapped around the leg to his knee. "Go on," Ben said. "You can unwrap the bandage a little."

Dory held her breath and pushed back the gauze. Yet except for the area around the heel, which was cracked and black as charcoal, it looked surprisingly good. The hair was burned off and there was a long brown scab running the length of the calf, but she had expected worse. "It looks fine," she said. "You'll be home for Christmas."

"Jesus, I hope so. The trouble with being here is that I have so god-damned much work to do. The kids are all skipping their lessons this week, and we've got a concert next month."

A nurse interrupted them. "This must be your wife, Ben?"

Dory turned to greet the woman. It irritated her that a twenty-year-old girl should call Ben by his first name. "Nice to meet you," she said.

"Should we take a look at your leg, Ben?"

"Look all you want, but don't touch."

The nurse giggled. "Your husband's got such a wonderful sense of hu-mor," she said. Then she turned back the sheet and stripped the leg clean of bandage in one motion. She chipped away at the scab with a small metal pick, and pink spots of flesh began to appear. Dory winced as the nurse dug into the scab, mining it first, then scraping the area. The nurse noticed her reaction. "It looks awful, I know," she said. "But the burn heals faster this way, so we pick off the scab as soon as we can. It doesn't hurt much, does it, Ben?"

Ben uttered a mock scream that caused the other patients to sit up with interest. "What about the heel?" Dory said. "It looks like it would come off in a hunk if you picked at that."

"We'll leave it alone," the nurse said. "I think he'll need a graft there anyway."

"But the rest isn't bad?"

"Bad enough, but we get a lot worse. Nothing to worry about."

Dory's stomach turned as the nurse picked at a thick piece of dried blood. "I think I'll take a walk," she said.

"This shouldn't take more than a half-hour," the nurse said.

Dory patted Ben's shoulder and put on her coat. She smiled at the black couple, but the man avoided Dory's eyes as she passed his bed. The man with no hand raised his fist in greeting, so Dory stopped in front of him. "How are you?" she said.

"Can't complain. You?"

"Oh, I'm fine," Dory said. "It just seems funny not to know the people my husband shares a room with."

The man shook his head. "Cranky sumbitch, your old man. Just sits there all day reading some magazine, and if we turn on the TV, he calls a nurse."

"He's very sensitive to noise," Dory said.

"It ain't noise," the man said. "It's the Green Bay Packers." Then he smiled. "I'm Vern Haubrich and I got a farm in Baraboo. Usually I'm a nice-enough guy."

Dory laughed. "I'm sure you are. My name is Dory and my husband is Ben. If you give him a chance, he'll be all right."

"He's got a pretty wife anyway."

"Well, it was nice to meet you, Vern," Dory said.

Haubrich extended his good hand, and Dory shook it. "Maybe we can whip your old man into shape," the farmer said.

Dory laughed. "I doubt it, Vern," she said. "But you're welcome to try."

36

THE SKELETON of a capon lay on a stainless-steel platter on the dining-room table as Dory passed through carrying a tray with coffeecups, on her way to the living room. Something about the capon made her hesitate. Its exposed and naked ribs both repelled and intrigued her.

As she entered the room, she had the sense that she had interrupted an argument. Charles was standing in mid-gesture, arm thrust out, while Michael slumped against the far windows. Charles had grown from a good-looking adolescent into a handsome man, but Dory no longer felt she knew her younger son. Now she crossed to him. "I brought some coffee," she said.

Charles hesitated, as if he was going to say something, then accepted the cup.

"Would you like some, Michael?"

Michael nodded and took coffee, too. Then Dory sat next to the fireplace and faced her sons. "Now, what were you boys fighting about?"

Charles ducked his head, looking guilty.

"Charlie thinks we should put Pop away," Michael said.

"That isn't it at all," Charles said. "I didn't mean that."

"What did you have in mind, Charles?" Dory asked.

Charles drank his coffee, then put down the cup carefully, like an after-dinner speaker at a political meeting. "It's true that I think it's too dangerous to have Pop at home anymore," he said. "But I certainly don't think that we should just throw him out into the snow, like Mike said."

Dory was silent. She had the feeling she was watching a performance, that she was outside it all, and that these earnest young men were no relation to her. "Okay, Charles. What's your idea, then?"

"I don't know," he said. "But the point is, we don't really have a choice anymore. And we shouldn't blame ourselves, because it isn't our fault."

"What exactly, Charles? Can you get to the point?"

Now Charles turned to Dory. "This society doesn't give us the option of a decent family life together. We've got to accept that. If we were rich, we could hire full-time help, but we're not. The only way to get state aid is to commit him. You've done your best, Mom. God, you've done more than anyone could expect you to do. The problem is that now he needs more than any one of us can give him."

"But I can't just put him somewhere, even if it is for his own protection. You see that, don't you, Charles? I have to know he'll be all right, that someone will care for him, love him. I've been to these homes. The old people just sit around in wheelchairs watching television, staring off into space, waiting to die. Ben's still a relatively young man. Do you know what the average age is in the Jewish Home? I've checked, it's eighty. Who could he talk to there? Who would laugh at his jokes?"

Charles was reassuring. "I know how you feel, Mom. All we can do is try to find the best place possible, the most humane place. There have got to be some homes for younger people, people like Pop. And consider the alternative. I mean, if we go on this way, he's going to burn the house down someday."

Michael stood looking out the big front windows into the street. They were leaded, and Dory had lined their sills with colored glass bottles, which caught the afternoon light with dazzling effect. But now they were lifeless, dull.

The house had a different feel with Ben gone. It was more subdued, darker. Michael thought he wouldn't want to live there without Ben. Losing him would rob it of some essential element. He had visited the burn ward earlier. Even there his father had managed to dominate. It seemed to Michael that Ben had lost little of his personality despite the effects of the disease. And lately they had gotten along better. They had talked for two hours that afternoon without fighting.

Michael looked out the window again, but now he saw his mother's reflection. "It's all so unfair," she said quietly, as if to herself. Then she began to cry. Michael turned away from the window and put his arms around her.

She was shorter than he, and he felt her tears on his neck as he smoothed her hair. "I know, Mom," he said. "I know." After a few minutes Dory patted Michael's arm, and he released her. She blew her nose and left the room for a moment.

When she returned, she seemed to have made a decision. Her voice was firm, her manner purposeful. "Charles, could you go down to the Jewish Home tomorrow and see for yourself how it is? Maybe we should put Ben there. At least they have a Yiddish table in the cafeteria."

"What if we got full-time help?" Michael asked.

"What if I had a million dollars?" Dory said. "I can't afford Lucille as it is."

"What if it didn't cost you anything?"

"Come on, Mike," Charles said. "What is this, twenty questions?"

"How about if I stay home with Pop?"

"You can't do that," Charles said. "What's the point of sacrificing yourself anyway?"

"It's no big sacrifice. I just don't want Pop in some nursing home smelling like piss all the time."

"He smells like piss now, what's the difference?"

"It's his own, and he's in his own home. He has a phone and he gets mail and he has a bank account and friends stop by. But I'm really doing it for myself. I like him; I like being with him, and I feel like I've missed out on something. So I'm going to stay home with him, at least for a while."

"What about school?" Dory said.

"What about it? It's no great loss, to me or the university. They won't miss me. I can go back later if I want. Or I could go to the extension."

"This is crazy," Charles said. "Forget about school. What about your life, your career?"

"What career? I'm a bartender. There's not much room for advancement where I work. It's a family business. I might do better here. Anyway, I could even get a job and work my schedule around Lucille's. The main thing is that Pop could stay home, and we all agree that's best for him, so why are we arguing?"

"I think what you're offering to do is wonderful, Michael," Dory said. "But think about it first. Are you sure this is what you want?"

"I'm sure I don't want Pop in a home, and I'm sure I'd like to spend more time with my father. Anyway, I'm still young; what difference does a year or so make? If I decide later on it's a mistake, I can go back to Madison, and we can put him somewhere like Charlie says. At least we would have delayed it for a while, and who knows what will happen in the future?"

240

"You mean he might die?" Charles said.

"People do," said Michael. "But all I'm saying is that especially with Pop, a year can make a big difference. He's recuperating from a bad burn. It's better that he do it at home."

"I think we should all think it over some more," said Dory. "But if Michael is willing to stay with Ben, it seems to me that's the best thing to do." She rose and looked at the room. "I'm exhausted. I think I'll go to bed."

Charles left too, but Michael stayed at the window, looking out through the forest of house plants. Occasionally cars drove by, snow showing in their headlights, slush rising in their wake like steam.

He was a little stunned by his offer. He would have to quit his job and break his lease. And what would he tell Ricky? For the first time he realized that she was important to him in the abstract, as an idea, as well as in person, in bed. He felt a twinge of regret, but it was not strong enough to make him change his mind. He thought of Ben in the burn ward, and he was confident he had made the right decision.

Michael waited impatiently for Charles to bring his suitcase out to the car. What had begun as a week's visit had shrunk to five days, and now Charles had remembered some pressing business that had to be taken care of after the weekend. Dory smiled, but she was disappointed; Michael was annoyed.

Finally Charles walked out the door. His suitcase was sprung in one corner, and his overcoat dragged on the ground. Michael took the suitcase and threw it in the back of the van. "Let's go," he said.

Dory had purchased the van in 1961, and Michael hated driving it. The body was rusted out, and he practically put his foot through the floor just trying to start the damned thing. The truck could do only forty miles an hour, so they had to take the old route, weaving along the lake through the worn Polish neighborhoods. Michael thought Dory kept the truck to torment him, bringing it out of the garage only when he was visiting. Now Michael wheeled the van onto Howard Avenue and headed south. Charles sat upright, staring ahead. Finally Michael said, "We've been honored by your presence."

Charles tensed for a moment, then relaxed. "My pleasure."

"Why did you stay so long? I mean, I know you're busy."

"Look, Mike. You know why I came, and since you bring it up, I didn't especially want to come. We had a decision to make, and now we've made it, so I'm leaving."

His tone angered Michael. "Well, I'm sorry to say it isn't that easy,

241

Charlie. Things might change tomorrow, or next month, or next year. Pop's situation isn't that predictable. But we don't want to inconvenience you. Go on back to lotus-land whenever you're ready."

"Don't give me the martyr act, Mike. You didn't have to offer to stay home, and you know it."

"I'm not talking about me," Michael said. "How do you think Mother feels when you split after three fucking days? How do you think Pop feels, or don't you care about that either?"

"Tell the truth. You'd like to get away, but you can't," Charles said. "I can, and I'm going to, no matter what you think."

Michael waited for the rush of anger, but it didn't come. The words seemed to hover above him in the cab, but they had no effect. He couldn't think of anything clever to say, and he knew it was because Charles had hit on a partial truth. The idea of staying with Ben comforted him, but he didn't really know why. The airport came into view, and Charles gripped Michael's arm. "Let's not end it like this," he said.

Michael wanted to feel mad, but something had gone soft inside him. "It's just that when Mom called me in Madison, she was pretty upset. I've never heard her like that before. She was crying, talking about Pop's burning the house down, killing himself, all that. She doesn't call you, Charlie."

"She calls sometimes."

"Sure, but it's not the same."

"No, it's not the same."

Charles offered his hand now. Michael took it and held on as he made the final turn for the airport terminal.

37

MICHAEL DROVE over to Madison the next day, cleaned out his room, and brought his things back in the truck. Since school was out, Ricky had gone home to St. Louis, so Michael didn't have to face her. When he took his clothes to the van, he returned to look around the room. It was amazing to him that Ricky had left nothing of hers behind; there were no posters or books with funny inscriptions; no joke ties or undershorts with hearts on them. He couldn't even smell her perfume, because the room was drafty. It was hard to feel nostalgic, but they had had something, and now he regretted leaving it behind. Wherever it was.

Ben came home early in January, still wearing his red shirt. His burn had healed remarkably well, but he was unable to sit up for more than a few hours at a time, and Lucille was worried about a bedsore he'd acquired in the hospital. The staff had taken care of more seriously burned patients first and seldom cleaned Ben's bed until noon. The wound had become infected, but the doctors assured Dory it would heal in time. Lucille was not sanguine. Ben never had bedsores when she took care of him. The hospital had given Ben the infection. Why should she trust them about its going away?

In the morning Michael and Ben sat together in the kitchen, Michael on a high stool, Ben in his wheelchair with a large white bib wrapped around his neck. The room was bright with sunlight, and Michael felt ebullient. Ben was reading *Rousseau and Revolution* by Will and Ariel Durant. He was on page 156 and had been reading for months.

"Doesn't it get a little static?" Michael asked. "I mean, at that pace I'm not sure I could stay interested."

Ben looked up, surprised. "But, Michael, this is fascinating stuff. And they're big pages. I just read a little each morning, like some people read the Bible. It gives me time to digest it, like a large meal. You should try it."

"When you're finished."

"I'll leave it to you in my will."

They were silent as Ben read. Then Michael said, "Do you ever think about that?"

"My will? Hardly ever. Is there something you want?"

"No, not really. I was just wondering."

"I've already promised my desk to Charles."

"He gets right in there, doesn't he?"

"An enterprising young man. He'll go far." Ben resumed his book.

"Do you ever worry about dying, Pop?"

Ben sighed and marked his place. "Not much. I'll be reincarnated, I hope, and besides, I've learned not to worry too much about things I can't help. With my situation, there isn't much choice about that."

"What are you coming back as?"

"I haven't decided yet. I'm still thinking about it."

"Is it up to you?"

"Oh, not entirely, but I believe very strongly in the power of individual will."

"Seriously, doesn't it bother you, being sick?"

"I'm nuts about it, Michael, you know that."

Michael smiled, unsure how to talk intimately with his father. "You've got reason to kvetch, and you do," he said. "Still, I don't remember ever seeing you really depressed."

"You know, Michael, you're right, and it's remarkable, considering my condition. It's very frustrating not to be able to move, but I'm not depressed. I don't suppose I can take credit for it, though. Probably it's all chemical. I'm just lucky."

"Amazing."

"Of course. Life is amazing, all of it. The thing to remember is that things could always be worse. I could have cancer."

"You could be dead, so what?"

"My boy, there is a profound difference between life and death, spiritual or otherwise. That's the trouble with young people, they think they'll never die. But as long as you insist on talking about this dreary subject, I do have a request."

Michael waited.

"When I die," Ben said, "I don't want a funeral. I don't even want a memorial service."

"What do you want?"

"First, I want you to play all my old records from the quartet on the phonograph. After that, take those tapes from my Town Hall recital and my national radio broadcasts and play them."

Michael thought of the family gathered around a table, eating and drinking together, but Ben wouldn't be there. In the sunny morning, he felt a sudden chill, but tried to make light of it. "I'll invite your friends," he said.

"Invite the whole town. Put an advertisement in the Milwaukee *Journal*. No flowers, but your presence is requested at the wake. Maybe you could even get the damned thing reviewed. What do you think?"

"A performer to the end. Is there anything else, as long as I'm taking instructions?"

"Yes. I want to be cremated. Ever since I read *Premature Burial* when I was thirteen years old, I've dreaded the idea of spending eternity in a box in the ground. At least if they burn me up there will be no question about my being dead. But afterward I don't want you to put me in one of those 'dignity-of-burial-aboveground' dives or in some 'perpetual-care' crypt. Instead, I'd like you to take my ashes and put them in one of those vases Mother made when she was at Alfred. The yellow one in the living room maybe, the one with the flowers in it. Then put the vase on the mantelpiece, just below the Picasso print."

"Distinguished company."

"Why not?"

"Are you serious?"

"I take death very seriously, Michael. Life, too. It's odd. I was terribly anxious about dying when I was your age. Now that it is much more likely, it doesn't bother me nearly as much. When you're young, you have this phony reverence about it."

"You sound like you're looking forward to dying."

"Don't be silly, but I'm not terrified by it. I suppose I'm curious. What if it turned out that Dante was right? That there actually were all those circles of hell and each of us was consigned to one or the other depending on what heinous sins we had committed?"

As Ben spoke he raised his chin and seemed to project to an unseen audience. Michael sat quietly watching him. This was Ben's way, he knew, of talking about intimate things, things he feared. He needed that distance, that protection. But Michael wished they had found a way to talk to each other, if not long ago, at least now. He had a sense that time was getting away from him.

"You know, Pop," he said, "all the time I was growing up, I didn't know what you did, that you worked at the university, had an office and students. I knew you played the violin, but I didn't think of that as a job, like selling insurance or real estate. Once the teacher went around the room asking all of us what our fathers did for a living, and I didn't know what to say, so I told her you didn't do anything."

Ben seemed hurt. "You mean you really didn't know? Were you ashamed of me?"

"A little . . . not exactly. I was more confused. I felt like we were different, and that made me uncomfortable. The only time I got a real sense of who you were was when Roger started hanging around."

"Roger?"

"Sure. For a while he was here all the time. I hated him until I saw it wasn't just because he needed a father, but because he really thought you were a wonderful musician. Once his audition was over, he was gone."

For a moment Ben seemed genuinely moved, but then he cut Michael short. "Well, of course, Michael. He just came for lessons; the work he did around the house was to help pay for them."

"But it was more than that, at least I thought so. He seemed to worship you; you were his mentor, like Mr. Ober was for you. He said something about it to me once."

"He did?" Then: "Well, that's nice, Michael, but that was years ago."

Ben seemed subdued. He rested his head on his hand, the effervescence gone, the speech over. In a softer voice he said, "Nothing lasts. Everything dies, Michael. That's all. Plants, birds, animals, you, me. There's really nothing extraordinary about it."

Michael reached over and put his hand on Ben's arm, glad that they could at last confide in one another. They sat quietly together, and then Ben's eyelids seemed to close as if in slow motion, and his breathing became more regular. Suddenly Michael realized he had fallen asleep.

38

As soon as she entered the house, Dory sensed something was wrong. The breakfast dishes stood on the kitchen table, and Lucille was staring out the window. Ordinarily she'd be busy either here or in one of the bedrooms but the black woman sat immobile, slumped in her chair. For a moment Dory hesitated, not wanting to know what had happened. The bottles on the windowsill glowed in the morning light, and the room was bright and cheerful. Outside, the fruit trees were tied to supporting posts, a few cornstalks from last summer's garden waved forlornly in the winter wind.

"Lucille, what's wrong?" Dory said.

Lucille turned and put her arms around Dory. "Oh, Dory, they just took him away. Michael went with him. I don't know what to do."

"Who took him, where?" Dory said.

"The ambulance took him to the hospital. First the doctor come, just to check on him, but there was maggots in his bedsore, and I—"

"Maggots?" Dory imagined an army of primeval creatures, numberless and inexorable, advancing steadily, staking out advance positions, beachheads, on Ben's unprotected pink flank. Then she felt her breakfast coming up and ran to the bathroom. When she returned, her head was clearer. "Lucille, what are we going to do?" she said.

The first operation was exploratory. The doctors wanted to determine the extent of the damage to Ben's hip and to clean out the bedsore. But after

247

a week, the bedsore, which looked like a small crater, showed no signs of healing. In addition, Ben suffered from persistent pain in his hip and was running a fever which caused his forehead to bead with sweat. In the evenings, when his temperature rose, Dory sat with Ben and bathed his face with cold washcloths. Often he was delirious, but there were moments of lucidity. Once, when Dory was sitting with him, she became aware of Ben's gaze. "You know, dear," he said, "you're still a very attractive woman. You've spent too much of your life in hospitals."

"Why don't you let me worry about that?" Dory said.

"The doctors decided radical surgery was necessary when antibiotics failed to bring down Ben's temperature. A part of his hip and thigh bone was removed, and they restructured his anus. The bedsore remained, but without the infection in Ben's hip, the doctor thought it would clear up eventually. He told Dory the operation was a success.

Yet Ben seemed smaller now, not only his body, which in fact had shrunk a few inches due to the removal of bone, but even his head and hands, which were curled tight, useless to him. Ben's beard was cut close, as always, and now he seemed, as he lay asleep, his mouth agape, almost childlike.

Because of the large open wound on his behind, Ben could lie on his back for only a few hours at a time, when he was able to read or watch television. But day and night, at three-hour intervals, an orderly came in to turn him on his side or on his stomach. His bed was on a circular track, surrounded by aluminum bars. In the middle of a conversation or chess game, a nurse would come in the room, rotate the bed, and help the aide flip Ben on his stomach. Always, Ben protested, saying he would rather die than spend what was left of his life staring at a linoleum floor, but they paid no attention. Doctor's orders. They didn't make the rules. Dory thought of the bed as a modern rack. It disturbed her to see Ben hanging lifelessly from it, his arms depending toward the floor. When she lifted the sheet to look at Ben's wound, she could discern little improvement.

Now the days and nights became a blur. Dory was on a dogged track between home, university, and hospital, unable to distinguish between her personal and professional life. Everything seemed to run together, and nowhere did she see signs of hope. Ben lay beside her, asleep, snoring lightly, and she knew that death was preferable to the life he had before him, but she couldn't bear to think of living alone. The blue vein in his forehead pulsed, a threnody of their life together, and now she began to cry silently, holding her handkerchief to her mouth so as not to wake Ben. When she looked up, however, she saw Ben was awake, watching her, his eyes sad.

"I'm sorry," he said. "Sometimes I think it's harder for you than for me."

"Oh, Ben . . ." Dory said, then was unable to continue.

With great effort Ben lifted his right hand and placed it on her back and pulled her to him. "It's all right, darling," he said. "It's all right."

Often when Dory was in class, Michael would visit Ben. They watched television and played Scrabble to while away the afternoons. In time, Michael became more openly affectionate. Now he would make a point of kissing his father on entering and leaving the room. Once, when he came in to find Ben crying, Michael put his arms around him and held him like a small child awakened by lightning. There was a mutual desire to make up for past enmity.

It was midwinter and a basketball game was on television. Ben said, "You like this stuff, Michael?"

"I thought you were asleep."

"Asleep, awake, with all these drugs, what's the difference anymore? I just woke up, I think, or else I'm asleep. Tell me something."

"Sure, what?"

"Those basketball players, how come they're always patting each other on the ass?"

"You want to watch something else?"

"Nah, to hell with it. I don't care."

"Michael switched the set off. "You were dreaming."

"Really, how could you tell?"

"You talked in your sleep; you seemed upset about something."

"I was dreaming about a concert I played a long time ago. You were just a kid, you wouldn't remember."

"What about it?"

"It was just about the time I started to get really sick, had trouble walking and everything. We were on tour and I played a duet with Richler and missed some notes." Ben shook his head. "Well, it's more than ten years now."

"So what, so you missed a few notes? Who cares?"

Ben shrugged. "Richler cared, I'll tell you that. He didn't speak to me again for weeks, and I don't think he ever forgot it or forgave me." He hesitated for a moment, thinking. "And I cared. I cared a lot. It was humiliating." Ben shook his head again. "Those fucking five notes," he said softly.

"Now they're all old men on the verge of retirement and you're still dreaming about it, feeling guilty."

Ben nodded. "Do you know, Michael, that we used to play our entire repertoire, ninety-five string quartets, from memory? We never used a score in concert, never had any music in front of us when we played."

"Why not? It seems like a lot of trouble."

"You have no idea how much trouble it was to memorize all that music. Trouble isn't the word. Torture, agony, that comes closer. But Ober had some crazy ideas, and there was no arguing with him about it. I wouldn't have missed those notes if I had a score in front of me, that's for sure."

They sat silently for a moment, the past floating between them. Michael spoke at last. "You've never talked much about music before, not to me anyway. I was only nine or ten when you stopped playing, and I can only remember going to one of your concerts, and then I fell asleep. But you never made us take lessons, never taught us anything we couldn't learn in school."

"What was there to teach? Like you said, I stopped playing years ago."

"Sure, but before that you played professionally for twenty-five years. I remember when I was a kid you used to say you were the greatest fiddler in the world. I told my friends that."

"You really said that?" Ben laughed, pleased.

"Sure, I thought you were. Weren't you?"

Now they laughed together. Then Michael continued. "But the funny thing, I mean thinking of it now, is how little music ever touched our lives, how little either Charlie or I know about it. I feel like a whole section of your life is just closed off to me. When we were kids, all our teachers thought Charlie and I were cultured as hell, because you were a musician and Mom was an artist. The truth is, my friends know more about those things than I do. Why did you keep it to yourself, Pop? Why didn't you teach us?"

Ben was on his back in the bed, but now he turned with some difficulty to look at his son. "You sound angry, Michael. I thought I was doing you a favor."

Immediately Michael felt guilty. What difference did it make? He bowed his head, looking at the spotless floor, vaguely aware of the whiteness of Ben's sheets. He could hear his father breathing heavily, and his own chest felt tight. The room seemed full of medical apparatus closing in on him, though in reality it was bare as death. "I'm sorry," Michael said, his voice soft, choked. "I just don't understand it."

When he looked up, Ben was smiling. He reached over and put his arm on Michael's shoulder. "It doesn't matter," he said. "If either of you had shown special interest in music, I would have gotten you the best instruction there was. But the same went for anything else: science, medicine, whatever you wanted, I would have tried to do for you. The important thing was I wanted you to feel free. To have a choice in life."

Ben lay back, as if his speech had exhausted him, and looked at the ceiling. Michael thought about what he had said. "Choice" and "freedom" were words he didn't associate with Ben. "Pop," Michael said, "how good were you really? At your best, I mean, how did you compare to the others?"

Ben said nothing for a moment, and Michael wondered if he had heard or if he was insulted. Then Ben spoke, softly but clearly. "I suppose I was just as good as I had to be, which was always good enough. And I loved to perform: other people freeze up during a concert, but I never played better. Conductors knew this and tolerated my laziness because of it."

"Even Mr. Ober?"

Ben laughed. "No, not Heinz. He tolerated nothing; he was the most demanding man I ever met, but he was wonderful to me. And I was pretty damned good. At a time when very few musicians could make a living playing chamber music, I was second violinist with one of the best string quartets in the world. I was never a soloist. I never toured by myself. But in part that was because I left New York to come to Wisconsin. Still, I don't regret any of it. The Casa Bella was a terrific opportunity; not many kids got a chance to play with someone like Ober."

Ben lay back on the pillow again, but he seemed only to be resting. Michael said nothing. "The best in the world," Ben said quietly, almost to himself. "It was a joke, but not a very funny one. In some crazy way I had to convince myself I actually was the best, even though I knew the whole thing was absurd. I had to think in those terms in order to play as well as Ober demanded. It was a goad to myself, and maybe in the end it was the thing that made me fail." He shook his head and sighed.

Now Michael thought he had pushed too far. "You convinced me," he said.

"That was easy. You wanted to believe it. But if I hadn't gotten sick? Well, who knows! Some of my friends made it big. Isaac Stern used to come over to the apartment and ask my advice about things. Even now he calls when he's in town, and you know something, Michael, Isaac still listens to me."

"Isaac Stern used to come to our apartment?"

"Sure, he bounced you on his knee."

"I don't remember."

"Of course not. There are a lot things you don't remember, kid. You were too young. But they happened. The amazing thing is that they really happened."

39

MARCH 5, 1971: I am tired; it seems now I'm always tired. I can't remember the time I was anxious for new challenges, full of enthusiasm for life. I am like a sleepwalker at school; I no longer bother to be pleasant to my colleagues. None of them have offered to take my classes, so to hell with them. Tonight, when I was sitting with Ben, I passed out watching television, but now I am so wide-awake I can't sleep. The house seems cold and empty and there is nothing interesting to eat or drink. God knows where Michael is; I seem to see less of him than when he was in Madison. The strain of spending so much time with Ben is beginning to show. He has lost weight and has new wrinkles in his forehead. He knows more about death than someone his age should.

March 8, 1971: The worst thing about this situation is the isolation— I never see my friends, never talk to anyone, and Ben hardly responds anymore. Yet while I'm lonely, I'm surrounded by people all day long. I supervise students, sit on committees, teach, and the phone never stops ringing. Still, there is very little human contact. None of the boys in my department even ask about Ben, except Lou Meisner, who is an unctuous fairy and wants me to vote for his tenure.

March 12, 1971: I just spoke to Charles on the phone and feel frustrated. Not that it is entirely his fault, but I am inhibited talking to him and never get to what I really feel. I think I'm afraid that if I let him know how anxious I really am, he will reject me and go away forever. I never worry

about that with Michael. Charles is different, cooler, more remote. I sometimes think he has no inner life, no perception. He seems utterly insensitive
to what we are going through here, relentlessly cheerful, talking about his
projects. Maybe I expect a lot, I know I do, but dammit, I deserve more
than he gives me. Perhaps I should spell it out, write him a letter, call in
my maternal IOU's. But I feel that shouldn't be necessary. He should know
what I want, goddammit, he should know, and he should do something. He
should come and be with us now, when we need him, and to hell with his
classes and his California life. We are his family, after all, and this is not too
much to demand of him. But when he asks if it's serious enough for him to
come, I don't know what to say. I tell him it would be nice if he got here
while Ben can still enjoy seeing him. But Charles doesn't take the hint.
What do I mean? he wants to know. What the hell could I mean? What is
so ambiguous about saying his father is still conscious, but might not be
much longer? How can I have produced a child who is so insensitive? Yet
when Charles asked whether or not Ben was dying, I backed down and
couldn't bring myself to say yes, so perhaps I'm to blame after all. He probably thinks I'm exaggerating. God only knows what he thinks. Everything I
see tells me Ben is dying, but somehow I always think he will improve because he always has before. I imagine there will be another remission, that
the infection will miraculously clear up, and we'll go back to living as we always have.

March 15, 1971: Last night Ben was out of his head and didn't recognize me. He had a fever of 103 and the nurse told me it was because of the
infection. They've started him on a new antibiotic and the doctor thinks this
should bring the fever down. When I wiped Ben's forehead with a wet towel
he said, "Mother?" It occured to me that in a way I have become his mother. Still, I doubt Sarah would be flattered by the comparison.

March 16, 1971: The fever has gone and Ben recognizes me again, but
now he has sores on the roof of his mouth. It's hard for him to talk and he
can't eat anything but soup, which is the worst torture of all, since he loves
food. The doctor says the sores may have been brought on by the antibiotics
they gave him to bring down the fever. Is Ben like Job, being tested for reasons that remain unclear and therefore absurd? What strikes me often is how
courageous he is in the face of all this. The sheer anonymity of the hospital
is so demoralizing, not to mention the endless operations, the IV needles in
his arms, the pills, and the recurring infections. Often he is in a daze and
can't know what is being done to him. He is besieged by clergymen, rabbis,
faith healers, and candy-stripers, all of whom claim to have an
interest in him, but who really don't care at all. And he bears up amazingly

well. I am a malcontent, a bitter scold, compared to him, and I have an awful reputation with the nursing staff. Ben flirts with the girls and asks about their boyfriends. Tonight, when I learned of the sores in his mouth, I started to cry and Ben comforted me. "It doesn't do any good to worry about it, dear," he said. "I'm all right."

40

When Moshe appeared at his bedside, Ben thought he was dreaming. It had happened before. He had learned not to say anything for fear of rousing Dory, who would then lean over the bed and ask anxiously, "Is anything wrong, Ben?" embarrassing him and making him doubt his sanity. So this time he closed his eyes and tried to go back to sleep. But he heard the vision breathe, and the fabric of his knit pants brushed the aluminum side bars of the bed. Ben opened his eyes again. "Pop?" he said.

"Who else? I'm sorry I didn't get here sooner. Your wife didn't tell nobody you was sick. A big secret."

Moshe looked terrific. He was wearing a gray suit, yellow shirt open at the collar, and his jaw had been given shape by a new set of dentures. In addition, he was tan and wore a silver toupee. Ben thought Moshe looked a little like George Burns.

"I'm always sick. Where's Michael?"

"I sent him home to rest, that boy was exhausted. He told me he quit school to come and be with you."

"He's a wonderful kid. He comes here every day to see me. Sometimes he sneaks in pizza and beer."

"At his age it ain't so wonderful that he spends all his life in a hospital. Why didn't you call me? How many times I got to tell you to let me know if you need help? I could hire a nurse. You're too stubborn for your own good, Benjy."

"How many nurses do I need? Why don't you just sit down so we can talk? You're like a doctor walking around the room. You even look like one, for Christ's sake."

Moshe sat, but both of them were uncomfortable because they couldn't acknowledge the obvious: Moshe had come because he knew Ben was dying.

"So tell me about yourself," Ben said. "It's been a long time. Did you ever make it to China?"

"Not quite, but I been around the world twice already. I ain't traveling so much anymore. I'm getting old."

"How's Ma?"

"That's the other thing. Remember when I told you sometimes I missed her? Even if she was a kvetch, after fifty years you get habits."

"So you're back together? I'm glad to hear it."

"We bought a condominium. It ain't so bad. Every day I go for a walk, check the stocks, sometimes watch the baseball. We got friends. It seems like everyone down there is Jewish now. They even talk Yiddish with a Southern accent."

"When I get out of here, I'll come visit."

"Your mother would love it. She still won't come, but she worries about you all the time, wants to know if you're in pain."

"I don't feel a thing, especially with the drugs. But what I hate is that they make me lie on my stomach for hours, and then I can't do anything. That's the worst thing about this damned disease, Pop. It bores you to death."

"You got your thoughts, your memories, a man like you."

"Sure," Ben said. "I've got Michael, too, and Dory. Things could be worse, I guess." It was a strain talking to Moshe. With Dory he didn't have to pretend he didn't know about his condition. He was grateful that his father had come, but now it was too much.

"Pop," he said, "I'm feeling kind of tired and I think I'd like to take a nap. Could you come back later, maybe with Michael and Dory? I'd like to talk, but I'm exhausted."

"Sure, Benjy. The nurse told me, but I forgot. I'll go back to the house. I told the boy I'd buy him a coat. But we'll be back. Don't worry, Benjy. We'll be back."

"That's great," Ben said, but his eyes closed before the old man got to the door. He was dreaming again.

41

MARCH 18, 1971: I feel as if I'm running a boardinghouse. Moshe's suitcases are spread around the living room, and he sleeps on the couch. Even Lucille can't keep up with the clutter of two men and me. I asked Moshe why he didn't just take Ben's room, since it's vacant now, but he looked at me as if I'd committed a sacrilege. Moshe is a dear and it is selfish of me I know, but I wish, with all the other demands, the house could somehow be neater. If I can't have order in the world, I would like some at home. Still, Moshe makes life more bearable. The refrigerator is loaded with Jewish food, and when that fails he takes us out to a Chinese restaurant. That is worth a little clutter, I suppose.

March 20, 1971: Michael and I have worked out a system. Lucille goes to the hospital in the morning to make sure Ben is cleaned and fed. Michael visits in the afternoon, and I go at night. Michael offered to double up some days so I wouldn't have to go, but I want to be there every night. Sometimes I can't get to the hospital before the end of visiting hours, so I use the emergency entrance. The nurses on Ben's floor know me now and let me come and go as I please. I used to wonder what good it did to sit there with him, since often we only watch television and he falls asleep. But whenever I get up to leave, he awakes and asks where I'm going. In some way, it's still important to him that I be there. If he feels that way, I won't desert him.

March 22, 1971: Michael is off visiting his girlfriend, who has a birthday, so I visited both in the afternoon and at night today. As I sat there, I realized that part of the reason I find it calming to be with Ben, even now, is that I've been sitting with the dying all my life. When I was a girl, I was with my grandmother during her last months. When Daddy died, I was the only one free to sit with him. I was with Mother the last month of her life, though she was out of her head most of the time. I remember coming once to visit her and she gave me a mousse because she knew I was fond of them. Even the Jewish custom of sitting *shiva* has always appealed to me. So now I sit *shiva* for Ben, and perhaps I will again after he's gone. It seems intolerable to me that one should have to go through the agony of death alone, though most of the people in the hospital do. As I walk down the halls, I am escorted by the most incredible wails and moans. People call out for help. They think I am their wife or sister or mother. It is all very sad. I wish I could be with all of them. So I go and sit with my husband, who seems to suffer literal and continual crucifixion. He hangs upside down in his bed, his bleeding ass exposed to the world, his hands clenched tight, his mouth and lips puffy, his teeth slowly decaying. Yet he wants to live. Much of the time our talk is mundane; he asks about the boys, the weather, baseball. We sit together holding hands and enjoy each other. Today he told me I was beautiful, and though I know better, when Ben looks at me he sees me not as I am—gray and tired, my face more lines than flesh—but as I was years ago, when we met. Of all the things we've lost and will lose, that is the hardest for me—my youth. Ben is the only one left who knew me when I was slim and pretty, and so to him I will always be an attractive young girl and we will always be in love.

March 26, 1971: At last it is sunny and warm and there is movement in the garden. Squirrels race along the porch railing and I feel bad that Ben isn't here, since the only aspect of nature he ever cared about was the squirrels on the back porch. This morning Moshe and I ate breakfast together. I feel sorry for him. He's come to be with Ben, but there is really nothing he can do, and he can't bear to see Ben this way. I told Michael he should show his grandfather around town, but Michael is already giving enough. This morning we ate bagels and cream cheese and enjoyed the sunshine. Moshe told me about Sarah and their pleasure palace in Florida, but didn't ask me to visit. Odd that it's been so long and still I remain a nonperson to her. Afterward we just sat together for a long time without talking. I wondered what he thought now about my affair with Sam, if he had forgiven me, but I didn't have the nerve to ask. Finally, when I got up to leave, Moshe said, "It ain't right for a man to bury his son."

March 29, 1971: I'm afraid Ben is dying at last. He has been running a temperature for three days and often doesn't know me. The doctor says the infection in his hip has returned and spread, and that Ben should have another operation. I doubt that he can take it. Ben is now unbearably thin and weak—his legs are like matchsticks and he has lost thirty-five pounds. He refuses to eat hospital food and yesterday he tore the IV needle out of his arm. I try to tempt him: I bring Chinese food, pizza, corned beef. But he shows no interest. At first I thought his mind had snapped, but he seems lucid much of the time, despite the fever. I think he's just tired of the whole thing, and who can blame him for that? Tonight I got him to eat some applesauce; I nurse him like a child or a wounded animal. When I left, he held my arm firmly and asked me not to go. Tomorrow I'll see if they can set a cot up for me in his room. I have classes, but the university will have to understand. I want to spend the rest of the time he has left with Ben.

42

THERE WAS a spare bed in the nurses' dormitory, and Dory moved in immediately. Ben's mood improved, and when she started having her meals with him, he was willing to eat. Dory knew that canceling classes for a week was frowned upon, but she was relieved to be able to devote all her time to Ben. If he improved further, she could resume her teaching schedule. Perhaps she could even stay on in the dormitory; it was convenient to the university and she could be called to Ben's room at a moment's notice.

Except for the fact that Ben was critically ill, now their life together was much as it had been in Madison. Dory would sleep late and come over for breakfast. Then they would sit together over coffee, talking or watching television. Sometimes Dory would read aloud to Ben, and occasionally they would listen to the radio. When Ben complained about the distortion in the speaker, Michael brought a portable stereo to the hospital, along with some of his old recordings. The room began to seem more like Ben's study at home. There were family pictures and books and magazines scattered around. Dory brought in a bottle of Scotch and every night they would have a drink together before dinner. The hospital staff ignored her trespasses on the rules. There was no question that Ben was happier and less trouble to them with his wife in residence.

The infection did not respond similarly to Dory. Ben was weaker than ever, and while his appetite had improved, he had lost a great deal of strength. It seemed worst in the evening, when the fever would return and

Ben would sleep fitfully, awaking suddenly with a cry of anger. Then Dory would go to the bed and bathe him in cold wet towels, and he would subside into a drugged somnolence. The doctor came daily but said little; the medication continued as before, but the infection would not go away. Finally Dory cornered the doctor as he was leaving one day.

"What are you going to do?" Dory said. "He's getting weaker all the time."

The doctor was a tall man with white hair and gray eyes. He seemed kind but distant. "We're doing what we can, Mrs. Seidler," he said.

"Isn't there something else you could give him, some other antibiotic?"

"We have him on a combination now; we've changed it twice. If this one doesn't work to bring down the fever, we'll try something else. It takes time."

"He doesn't have enough strength for experiments, doctor."

The doctor said nothing. He understood how she felt. He gave Dory his home phone number in case of emergency and left.

Dory had been reading *Great Expectations* aloud, but Ben had fallen asleep, and now she sat looking out the window at the park across the street, the book closed on her finger. In a burst of optimism Ben had decided he should make a project of reading the Victorians. He called the library and ordered *Middlemarch, Vanity Fair,* and several novels by Dickens. Now the books sat on his bedside table, and each afternoon Dory would read until he fell asleep. She decided to go for a walk, but when she rose from her chair, Ben said, "Don't leave me, dear."

"I'm sorry," Dory said. "I thought you were sleeping."

"I was. Now I'm awake, though."

"Would you like me to read some more?"

"Not right now."

Dory sat and took Ben's hand in hers. His fingers were twisted, and she straightened them out and held them, as if this could halt the progress of the disease.

"Where's Michael?"

"He'll be over later. He's working part-time at Hafeman's, driving their truck."

Ben looked surprised and a little annoyed. "What for? Don't we give him money?"

"He was restless," Dory said. "He wanted something of his own, too, I guess."

"He's a good kid." Ben paused. "Of course, it makes sense, he's got a wonderful mother."

261

"And father," Dory added. Now she put a fresh towel on his forehead and straightened his sheets.

"Not bad," Ben agreed. "But you—you come every day, even when you're teaching at the university."

"I want to be with you, Ben. That's why I do it."

"I know, but a lot of wives wouldn't, and no one could blame them."

"You'd do the same for me."

Ben nodded. "Maybe, I hope so. But that isn't the point. Before this happened, you were supporting the family."

"The family supported me too."

"Sure, that's true." Ben was silent for a moment. Then he looked at her seriously. "You know, I was thinking about Sam Matthews the other day," he said. "I wanted to thank you for that, too," he said.

"There's nothing to thank me for."

"Yes, there is," Ben insisted. "I was too damned stubborn to realize how hard it was for you, but I'm grateful that you came up to the Belmont and convinced me to come home. You've given up a lot for me; you were a young woman when it happened."

It was the speech of a dying man anxious to clear his accounts, but Dory was grateful for it. She felt her eyes fill and was unable to speak.

As if he understood, Ben changed his tone, his voice taking on some excitement. "Do you remember when we met, dear, and before that, when I was courting you through the mail?"

"How could I forget?"

"It was my second year in Wisconsin and I had the whole summer to convince you, but when you wouldn't even meet me, I started to get a little discouraged."

"You? I never got that impression."

"Sure," Ben said, smiling. "Do you have any idea how much I spent on flowers and candy that year?"

Dory laughed. "It's a good thing you were making a lot of money."

"I'll say. And do you remember when we actually did meet, in the restaurant, and I told the maître d' to send the piano player home?"

"It was the most outrageous thing I'd ever seen. Of course, I was very young."

Ben laughed. "It's a curious thing," he said. "Meeting you was just confirmation. I knew from the time I started writing that I wanted to marry you."

"You've always said that, but how could you really?"

"I don't know. I just did."

262

"What if I hadn't agreed to meet you?"

"That wouldn't have changed it. I just would have had an unhappy life."

"Hasn't your life been unhappy, Ben?"

Ben was silent, thinking. Then he spoke, his voice quiet, his expression serious. "I know it seems as if it must have been. But I don't think of it that way. Not that I'm pleased to be sick, but I've been able to do most of the things I wanted to do. I had a career. I had a family. Most of the healthy guys I knew in New York didn't manage as well."

"Nobody manages as well as you," Dory said.

Ben smiled and closed his eyes. Dory thought he would sleep, but she didn't leave. She sat silently by Ben's side, thinking of her life, their life together. Now she saw Ben was looking at her.

"You know, dear," he said, "the only trouble with my dying is that it means we won't be able to be together anymore."

43

THE MORNING of Ben's funeral was sunny and cold. Though it was April, the cars still had snow tires. The service was held in an interdenominational chapel on the campus in Madison. Dory had considered having it in Milwaukee, but Ben had been at his best when he was in Madison, with the Casa Bella. A young rabbi who knew Ben only by reputation presided, and to Dory's surprise, the sanctuary was nearly full of friends and former students.

Dory did not really know what to expect. She had been unable to bring herself to do anything, so Michael had made the arrangements, called the rabbi, reserved the chapel. Now he sat next to her as Roger Sherman led the renamed Seidler Quartet through Schubert's "Death and the Maiden." Dory smiled in spite of herself. Ben would have approved the choice: it was a beautiful piece and easy enough for almost anyone to play. And she was proud of Michael for calling Roger in Ohio and asking him to come.

A young cantor sang the kaddish, and the rabbi read from the Torah. Then the rabbi stepped aside, and Heinz Ober, lean and white in a charcoal-gray suit, stood behind the lectern to give the eulogy. Dory was surprised to see that Heinz seemed uncomfortable. After all these years of performing, he still felt nervous, or perhaps it was the imminence of death that did it. Now Heinz cleared his throat and began to speak.

"It is odd to think of Ben Seidler being gone already," he said. "He was a young man, and while I knew of course that Ben was very ill, I somehow always expected a miraculous recovery, that one day I would see him standing in the door of my office asking again for an audition. For it was not in Ben's nature to give up; it was both his great charm and the most irritating thing about him that he could never conceive of failure. It is easy of course to say now that he was a great man, a proud father, a loving husband, the things one says at occasions like this. I don't know if these things are true, but I think they are. But my relationship with Ben was essentially professional. Ben's whole manner was musical, in tune to the inner dynamics of life and personality. In those musical terms, then, I can say with certainty that he was among the most brilliant players I've heard or been associated with in over fifty years on the concert stage. He was my student, my colleague, my friend, and in some ways, finally, my master. I shall miss him the rest of my life."

Dory wondered how much longer that would be. Heinz looked smaller, older, slightly slumped. She was surprised and moved by his talk. It was nice to hear after all these years.

The rest of the service was brief. The rabbi read from Ecclesiastes, and the quartet played again, though this time an elegy Ben had written for them. Dory watched as Roger led them into the last movement, leaning first to Sally, then to Julie, just as Heinz had done, as Ben had instructed them. It was a chain, a long procession from old to young, and if the result was not entirely artful, she knew Ben would have been happy with it. With all their limitations, this quartet was his creation; he had made them up, and the music they played.

Afterward there was a reception. Michael had arranged to have Ben's records played, and various friends wandered through the music. Dory and Michael and Charles stood in a kind of receiving line greeting guests. Moshe had refused to come, both because he was not yet through sitting *shiva* and because a reform rabbi was officiating. Lucille was having another service at her own church the following day.

Now Howard Jacoby was holding Dory and shaking Michael's hand; then Beaulieu and Richler, whom she hadn't seen for years. Former students she couldn't remember, and some she could. Sally Freeman, red face in tears, stammered, "Oh, Mrs. Seidler, I just can't believe he's gone." And Dory comforted them, thanked them, reassured them all, until finally exhaustion descended upon her. She had been up since six and hadn't been sleeping well lately. She touched Michael's arm: "Can you handle this, honey?" and without waiting to hear his answer, she walked out the back door and stood alone in the parking lot.

In the distance were trees and water. In Madison you were never far from a lake; she had forgotten. Her forehead was pounding, so she closed her eyes and felt the cold air on her skin. Then she heard the door open again, and without turning knew it was Sam. She stood waiting for him to approach, to feel his hand on her shoulder, his breath on her neck. But Sam kept his distance, and when she turned, he looked hesitant, unsure of himself.

"It's all right," she said. "I'm just tired."

Sam was wearing a beautiful brown tweed jacket and a tie. Yet his aspect was somber. "It was a nice service," Sam said. "The music was a good touch."

"Michael's idea. Ben told him what he wanted, so we did it that way. The quartet was really quite good, I thought."

Sam nodded. "How are you, Dory?"

"Oh, Sam, I don't know. I'm all right, I guess. I can't sleep and I can't sit down and I can't remember whether I'm wearing underwear or not, but otherwise I think I'm all right. I feel I should be in mourning, but I'm too restless. My father-in-law is at home saying prayers. I ought to be doing that too, but somehow I don't think Ben would mind."

"Perhaps you've already done your crying."

"Maybe. I've cried a lot, I know that. I cried this morning, and then again when they played the Schubert. I've always cried easily; Ben used to tease me about it. But don't worry about me. I'll survive."

"I never really worried about you," Sam said. "It was something else."

"Better or worse?"

"Better, at least I think so. Deeper, anyway."

Dory smiled. "Crisis seems to bring out the best in you, Sam. Maybe it was that Boy Scout training."

"Could be. But that wasn't the only reason I came. Ben was my friend. I wanted to be at his funeral."

"I know." Dory was looking at Sam's shoes. They were brown suede, English, she thought. It was hard to think of what they had been talking about. "I'm sorry . . ." she said.

"I asked what you'll do now."

"Oh, I don't know. The same, I guess. Teach, maybe even some artwork. Now that I have tenure, there's not much else to look forward to, except retirement."

"You're too young to spend your time clipping coupons."

"I don't feel young, Sam. I feel old and tired. It was awful to lose Ben, but I wondered toward the end how much longer I could go on. He was in pain and I was exhausted. It would have been a double funeral if he had lasted another month."

266

"Before, you said you couldn't sit down."

"That's right. I don't understand it, all this energy. I expected the whole thing to hit me at the service. I thought I'd start keening and that you would have to stand with me to make sure I didn't collapse. God, this is ridiculous. I don't mean to sound like such a fool."

"You don't."

Dory smiled, but she felt uncomfortable standing outside with Sam. "Excuse me," she said. "I should go relieve Michael."

Sam seemed disappointed, but he nodded and stood aside to let Dory back into the chapel.

44

APRIL 3, 1971: It is seven A.M. but I've been up for over an hour. I went for a walk on the beach and watched the sun coming up over the lake. Now I'm back in my room, as usual, sitting in bed, drinking coffee, and reading. Though I know it won't happen, I still wait for Ben to call out for me in the morning. When he doesn't I go into his room to make sure everything is all right. Somehow I still don't really believe he's gone. I miss his mannerisms: the way he would tilt his head to the side when he was thinking; the sound of his laugh echoing through the house; his smile when I came home from work at night. He always seemed surprised to see me, surprised and delight-ed, as if he had expected me to run off. Yet, at least those last few years, there was no reproof: he was just pleased to have me home. I miss little things: his long, delicate fingers; the whiteness of his beard; his pink skin; the way he ended sentences by calling me "dear." I remember how he would be indignant at parties if anyone had the nerve to interrupt me. He would look imperiously at the interloper, then turn to me: "What were you saying, dear?" he'd say. Then I was embarrassed; now I know better. I remember his clothes, the food he liked, the music he played. I see him in my mind's eye onstage, in a full-dress suit, seeming seven feet tall, his fiddle a proud ap-pendage of his body. Ben is gone, but these images remain; the real trouble is, I remember all these things too well.

I wonder sometimes, watching couples around me split and come to-gether and then part again, if there was something about the trouble we had that made us closer than we would have been. What would we have been like if Ben had remained healthy and reached his peak as a musician, if we had raised our children in a more normal environment? Would we have grown bored with each other and looked for diversion? Would Ben have taken up with a student, would I have gone with Sam? What bothers and warms me is the suspicion that, horrible as the disease was, in some way it sustained us and allowed us to love each other more. I'm alone now and lonely, but I can't find it in myself to seriously regret what has happened.

April 11, 1971: It is my birthday and I am sitting in Ben's room with a bottle of white wine and some Gouda cheese. I am fifty-two today, and it seems appropriate to be here, surrounded by Ben's things, for he always loved birthdays. Of course, my modest celebration would not be enough for him. He would have insisted we go out to a restaurant and a show. It always pained him that there was so little to do in Milwaukee. Only New York could afford his sense of what a birthday should be. Michael has gone off to see his girl, and Moshe has returned to Florida. Now he wants to be with Sarah, which I find touching. Lucille went through and cleaned out what she could—the medical equipment is gone, and the bed is stripped—but Ben's room remains magnificently cluttered. It is still Ben, all that I have left. I have an idea that I will sift through the papers and books and organize things. Someday I will use the room as a study, not that I have anything in particular to study. I want to compile an inventory eventually, to know what is here, but for the moment I read letters, pay old bills, drink wine, and think about Ben. There are a thousand magazines, and all the articles seem fascinating.

I am like an anthropologist, but I am excavating my husband, discovering the rituals that governed my own life. I ask questions: Why did Ben have savings accounts at four banks, when none of the accounts contained more than one hundred dollars at the time of his death? Why did he continue to subscribe to the yearbook of the musicians' union, even after he had been gone from New York for over twenty years? Why did he go to the trouble of ordering by mail a pamphlet titled "Investment Banking," when he never held a stock in his life? I go through the rubble of his room looking for answers to these and other questions, and yet I know I am merely delaying, putting off the final and irrevocable closing of the tomb, in part because I am afraid of what lies ahead. I work hard and I have succeeded modestly, but the focus of my life for the past twenty-three years has been Ben.

It seems unnecessarily cruel that he should have died such a short time before my birthday, since he enjoyed these things so much. Even at the end he was capable of joy; even at the end he made me feel loved. It is now nearly two weeks, and Moshe has finally gotten up from his *shiva*. I should get up too, but somehow I feel content here, in this room, with Ben. I come in each night, after work, and look in before leaving in the morning. I listen to hear him call out when I walk in the door, and I still anticipate his outrageous compliments. I eat dinner here, in front of the television, and watch the situation comedies Ben liked. I laugh at stupid jokes, and sometimes I cry for my husband. My friends call to ask me for lunch or dinner, but it seems disloyal to go out, as if nothing has happened. A great deal has happened. I am less than I was. There is a hole inside me that only time can fill. Ten years ago I might have doubted my ability to live without Ben, alone. But his life, our life, has taught me this much: I will survive, and even prosper. The time when I will leave this room, this house, and reenter the world, may be weeks or even months away. But deep inside myself, I know that time will come.